Highly Recommended

New Edition

OSWAAL BOOKS®
LEARNING MADE SIMPLE

AF660899

NCERT TEXTBOOK SOLUTIONS

CLASS 11

BIOLOGY

Strictly based on Latest NCERT Textbook

Your Path to Academic Excellence:

1
100% Updated
with Latest NCERT Textbook 2023-24

2
Comprehensive Coverage
with All Concepts & Topics Covered

3
Visual Learning Tools
with Concept Videos

4
Extensive Revision Tools
with Crisp Revision Notes, Mind Maps & Mnemonics

5
Complete Question Coverage
All Questions Fully Solved

1st EDITION

ISBN "9789359589305"

SYLLABUS COVERED

CENTRAL BOARD OF SECONDARY EDUCATION DELHI

PUBLISHED BY

OSWAAL BOOKS & LEARNING PVT. LTD.

1/11, Sahitya Kunj, M.G. Road,
Agra - 282002, (UP) India

1010, Cambourne Business Centre
Cambridge, Cambridgeshire
CB 236DP, United kingdom

0562-2857671

contact@oswaalbooks.com

www.OswaalBooks.com

DISCLAIMER

This book is published by Oswaal Books and Learning Pvt Ltd ("Publisher") and is intended solely for educational use, to enable students to practice for examinations/tests and reference. The contents of this book primarily comprise a collection of questions that have been sourced from previous examination papers. Any practice questions and/or notes included by the Publisher are formulated by placing reliance on previous question papers and are in keeping with the format/pattern/guidelines applicable to such papers.

The Publisher expressly disclaims any liability for the use of, or references to, any terms or terminology in the book, which may not be considered appropriate or may be considered offensive, in light of societal changes. Further, the contents of this book, including references to any persons, corporations, brands, political parties, incidents, historical events and/or terminology within the book, if any, are not intended to be offensive, and/or to hurt, insult or defame any person (whether living or dead), entity, gender, caste, religion, race, etc. and any interpretation to this effect is unintended and purely incidental. While we try to keep our publications as updated and accurate as possible, human error may creep in. We expressly disclaim liability for errors and/or omissions in the content, if any, and further disclaim any liability for any loss or damages in connection with the use of the book and reference to its contents".

Printed at Sahitya Bhawan C-17 Industrial Area, Agra

Contents

PREFACE

"*Education is the passport to the future, for tomorrow belongs to those who prepare for it today.*" – Malcolm X

In the pursuit of academic excellence, the journey often begins with curiosity. As students embark on the path to success in the exams, the Oswaal NCERT Textbook Solutions Book for the academic year 2024-25 stands as an invaluable companion, illuminating the way forward.

Success in any exam goes beyond memorization; it involves developing a deep understanding of every concept. The NCERT textbooks provide the essential foundation. Introducing the Oswaal NCERT Textbook Solutions Book, a vital tool to unlock the full potential of every student.

Let's uncover what this book covers for you:

1) **Updated for 2024-25** – The books are 100% updated for the academic year 2024-25, adhering strictly to the latest NCERT guidelines.
2) **Comprehensive Coverage -** We cover all concepts and topics outlined in the most recent NCERT textbooks.
3) **Visual Learning Aids -** Explore theoretical concepts and concept videos that offer a brief description of the topic and help visualize complex concepts.
4) **Effective Revision Tools -** Benefit from crisp Revision Notes, Mind Maps, and Mnemonics designed to facilitate efficient and effective review.
5) **Complete Question Coverage -** All questions from the NCERT textbooks are covered in our solutions, providing a thorough grasp of the subject matter.

What sets this book apart is the expertise behind its creation. The solutions within are the result of the meticulous efforts of expert faculty, individuals with a profound understanding of the curriculum, and the dedication to maintaining the highest quality standards.

May this book be your guide, encouraging you to not just study but to explore and understand.

Wishing you a fulfilling and successful academic journey.

Team,

Oswaal Books

Positive Affirmations

An affirmation is a positive statement or phrase that individuals repeat to themselves with the intention of fostering a positive mindset, self-confidence, or personal development. The practice involves affirming desired beliefs or qualities, often in the present tense, to reinforce a positive self-image and encourage a more optimistic outlook.

" EMBRACE YOUR UNIQUENESS, NOURISH SELF-CARE, AND PRESS FORWARD RELENTLESSLY. TO ACHIEVE FLIGHT, UNLOAD THE BAGGAGE THAT SLOWS YOUR ASCENT."

I strongly trust in my vision and work deligently towards making it a reality.

I am capable of learning and growing everyday.

I am not defined by grades & test scores. My true worth lies in my character, compassion and positive impact I have on others.

I celebrate my quirks, for they make me beautifully unique.

I embrace my mistakes, learn from them and use them to fuel my growth & resilience.

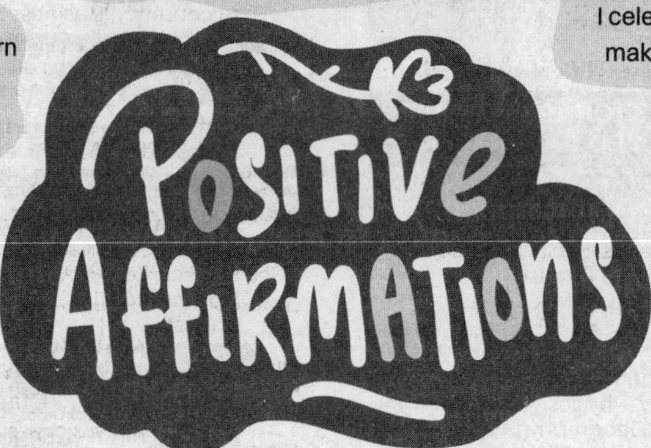

CHANGE

I am not the product of circumstances, I am the product of my own choices.

My voice matters and I believe in the power of my words to shape the world around me.

I face challenges with courage and determination.

I celebrate the achievements of others without diminishning my journey.

I believe that the twists & turns of my life lead me to an extraordinary destinations.

Exclusive School Books Suppliers

	ANDHRA PRADESH
VIJAYAWADA	Sri Vikas Book Centre, 9848571114, 9440715700,
	ASSAM
WEST KAMENG	Dutta Book Stall, 8729948473
	KARNATAKA
BANGLORE	Satish Agencies, 8861630123
	GUJRAT
RAJKOT	Royal Stationers, 9824207514
	MAHARASHTRA
PUNE	Madhusheela Books & Stationery, 7875899892
JALNA	Anil Paper Mart, 9422722522, (02482) 230733
	TAMIL NADU
CHENNAI	Bookmark-IT, 7305151653
	TELANGANA
HYDERABAD	Sri Balaji Book Depot , 9676996199, (040) 27613300
	WEST BENGAL
KOLKATA	United Book House, 9831344622

Our Distributors

	ANDHRA PRADESH
VISAKHAPATHAM	JBD Educational, 9246632691, 9246633693, Sri Rajeshwari Book Link, 9848036014
VIJAYAWADA	Akshaya Books Corner, 9666155555
	ANDAMAN & NICOBAR ISLAND
PORTBLAIR	Krishna Book Centre, 9474205570, Kumar Book Depot, 9932082455, Kumar Book Depot, 9932082455, Sree aditya Book Centre, 8332972720, 7013300914
	ASSAM
GUWAHATI	Book Emporium, 9675972993, 6000763186, Ashok Publication, 7896141127, Kayaan Enterprises, (0361) 2630443, Orchid Book house, 9864624209, Newco, 9864178188
	BIHAR
PATNA	Nova Publisher & Distributors, (0612) 2666404, Shri Durga Pustak Mandir, 9334477386, Sharda Pustak Bhandar, 9334259293, Vikas Book Depot, 9504780402, Alka Book Agency, 9835655005, Metro Book(E&C), Ishu Pustak Bhandar, 8294576789, Gyan Ganga Limited, 6203900312, Ishu Pustak Bhandar, (E & C), 9334186300/8294576789
MUZAFFARPUR	Pustak Bhandar, 7870834225
	CHATTISGARH
AMBIKAPUR	Saini Brothers, 9425582561, M.P Department Stores, 9425254264
BOKARO	Bokaro Student Friends Pvt. Ltd, Bokaro, 7277931285
BHILAI	Anil Book Depot, 9425234260
DURG	Bhagwati Bhawani Book Depot, 0788-2327620, 9827473100
KORBA	Kitab Ghar, Korba (E & C), 9425226528
RAIPUR	Shri Ramdev Traders, 9981761797, Gupta Pustak Mandir, 7974220323, Anil Publication, 9691618258/7999078802
RAIGARH	Sindhu Book Deopt, 9981935763
	DELHI
DELHI	Mittal Books, (011) 23288887, 9899037390, Singhania Book & Stationer, 9212028238, AoneBooks, New Delhi, 8800497047, Radhey Book Depot, 9818314141, Batheja Super Store, 9871833924, Lov Dev & Sons, Delhi (E & C), 9811182352, Zombozone, 9871274082, LDS Marketing, 9811182352/9999353491
	GUJARAT
AHMEDABAD	Patel Book, 9898184248, 9824386112, 9825900335, Zaveri Agency, 9979897312, 9979890330, Hardik Book Agency, (ISC) 079-24110043, 9904659821
BHAVNAGAR	Samir Book Stall, Bhavnagar (ISC) 9586305305
DAHOD	Collegian Book Corner, 9925501981
VAPI	Goutam Book Sellers, 9081790813
VALSAD	Mahavir Stationers, 9429474177
NAVSARI	College Store, (ISC) NO CALL 02637-258642, 9825099121
SURAT	Shopping Point, 9824108663
VADODARA	Umakant Book Sellers & Stationer, 9624920709
	HARYANA
ROHTAK	Manish Traders, 9812556687, Swami Kitab Ghar, 9355611088, Babu Ram Pradeep Kumar, 9813214692
REWARI	Sanjay book depot, 9255447231
BALLABGARH	Kashi Ram Kishan lal, 9289504004, 8920567245
HISAR	Natraj Book Distributors, 7988917452
BHUNA	Khurana Book Store, 9896572520
	JAMMU
	Sahitya Sangam, 9419190177
	JHARKHAND
BOKARO	Bokaro Student Friends, (0654) 2233094, 7360021503, Bharati Bhawan Agencies, 9431740797
RANCHI	Crown Book Distributor & Publishers, (0651) 2213735, 9431173904, Pustak Mandir, 9431115138,
DUMKA	Vidyarthi Pustak Bhandar, 9431310228
	KARNATAKA
HUBLI	Renuka Book Distributor, (0836) 2244124, Vidyamandir Book Distributors, 9980773976
BANGLORE	Krishna book house, 9739847334, Hema Book Stores, 9986767000, Sapna Book House Pvt. Ltd., 9980513242, Hema Book World, (Chamrajpet) (ISC) 080-40905110, 9945731121
BELLERI	Chatinya book centre, 9886064731
	KERALA
ERNAKULAM	Academic Book House, (0484) 2376613, H & C Store, 9864196344, Surya Book House, 9847124217, 9847238314
KOTTAYAM	Book Centre, (0481) 2566992
TRIVANDRUM	Academic Book House, (0471) 2333349, 9447063349, Ponni Book Stall, 9037591721
CALICUT	Aman Book Stall, (0495) 2721282,
	MADHYA PRADESH
CHHINDWARA	Pustak Bhawan, (E & C), 8982150100
GWALIOR	Agarwal Book Depot, 9425116210
INDORE	Bhaiya Industries, 9893326853, Sushil Prakashan,(0731) 2503333, 2535892, 9425322330, Bhaiya Store, 9425318103, Arun Prakashan, 9424890785,
	Bhaiya Book Centre, 9424081874, Seva Suppliers, 9826451052
JABALPUR	Vinay Pustak Sadan, 8962362667, Anand Books and Stationers, 9425323508
SAGAR	Princi Book Depot, Sagar, 9977277011
KATNI	Shri Mahavir Agency, 9425363412
UJJAIN	Shreenath Book Depot, 9827544045
BHOPAL	Gupta Brother, 9644482444
	MAHARASHTRA
PUNE	Natraj Book Depot, (020) 24485054, 9890054092, Vikas Book House, 9921331187, Pravin Sales, 9890683475, New Saraswati Granth Bhandar, 9422323859, Akshar Books & Stationary, 7385089789, Vardhaman Educational, 9860574354, Yash Book Centre, 9890156763, Pragati Book Centre, (ISC), 9850039311, Praveen Sales, Pragati Book Centre, Pune (E & C), 9850039311
AURANGABAD	Shree Sainath Agencies, 7350294089, Maya Book Centre, (ISC), 9372360150
MUMBAI	Vidyarthi Sales Agencies, 9819776110, New Student Agencies, 7045065799, Shivam Books & Stationery, 8619805332
JALGAON	Sharma Book Depot & Stat. (ISC), 9421393040
LATUR	Yash Book House, 9637936999, Shri Ganesh Pustakalay, 9730172188
KOLHAPUR	Granth the Book World, 9922295522
NAGPUR	Laxmi Pustakalay and Stationers, (0712) 2727354, Vijay Book Depot, 9860122094
	Renuka Book distributor, 9765406133, Novelty Book Depot, 9657690220, Karamveer Book Depot, 9923966466, Arun Book & Stationers, 9423110953
NANDED	Abhang Pustakalaya, 9823470756/9175940756
NASHIK	Rahul Book Centre, 9970849681, New India Book House, 9623123458
DHULE	Navjeevan Book Stall, 7020525561
YAVATMAL	Shri Ganesh Pustkalaya, 9423131275
VASAI	Prime Book Centre, Vasai, 9890293662
	ODISHA
CUTTACK	A. K. Mishra Agencies, 9437025991, 9437081319
BHUBANESHWAR	M/s Pragnya, 8847888616, 9437943777, Padmalaya, 9437026922, Bidyashree, 9937017070, Books Godown, 7894281110
BARIPADA	Trimurti Book World, 9437034735
KEONJHAR	Students corner, 7008435418
	PUNJAB
AMBALA	Bharat Book Depot, 7988455354
PATIALA	Goel Sons, 9463619978, Adarsh Enterprises, 9814347613
JALANDHAR	Cheap Book Store, 9872223458, 9878258592, City Book Shop, 9417440753, Subhash Book Depot, 9876453625, Paramvir Enterprises, 9878626248
FEROZPUR	Sita Ram book Depot, 9463039199, 7696141911
LUDHIANA	Amit Book, 9815807871, Gupta Brothers, 9888200206, Bhatia Book Centre, 9815277131
CHANDIGARH	Mohindra Book Depot, 9814920226
	RAJASTHAN
AJMER	Laxmi General Store, Ajmer, 0145- 2428942 9460652197
KOTA	Vardhman Book Depot, 9571365020, 8003221190 Raj Traders, 9309232829
BHILWARA	Nakoda Book Depot, (01482) 243653, 9214983594, Alankar Book Depot, 9414707462
JAIPUR	Ravi Enterprises, 9829060694, Saraswati Book House, (0141) 2610823, 9829811155, Goyal Book Distt., 9460983939, 9414782130
UDAIPUR	Sunil Book Store, 9828682260
JODHPUR	Second Hand Book Stall, 9460004745
	TRIPURA
AGARTALA	Book Corner, 8794894165, 8984657146, Book Emporium, 9089230412
	TAMIL NADU
COIMBATORE	Majestic Book House, (0422) 2384333, CBSC Book Shop, 9585979752
CHENNAI	Arraba Book Traders, (044) 25387868, 9841459105, M.R. Book Store (044) 25364596, Kalaimagal Store, (044) 5544072, 9940619404, Vijaya Stores, 9381037417, Bookmark It-Books & Stat. Store, 7305151653, M.K. Store, 9840030099, Tiger Books Pvt. Ltd., 9710447000, New Mylai Stationers, 9841313062, Prince Book House, Chennai, 0444-2053926, 9952068491, S K Publishers & Distributors, 9789865544, Dharma Book Shop, 8667227171
PUDUCHERRY	Sri Lakshmi Book Seller, 7871555145
SALEM	Pattu book centre, 9894816280
TRICHY	P.R.Sons Book Seller, 9443370597, Rasi Publication, 9894816280
THENI	Maya Book Centre, 9443929274
MADURAI	Selvi Book Shoppe, 9843057435, Jayam Book Centre, 9894658036
VELLORE	G.K book centre and collections, 9894517994
	TELANGANA
HYDERABAD	Sri Balaji Book Depot, (040) 27613300, 9866355473, Shah Book House, 9849564564
	Vishal Book Distributors, 9246333166, Himalaya Book World, 7032578527

0808

Exclusive School Books Suppliers

UTTARAKHAND

DEHRADUN	Inder Book Agencies, 9634045280, Amar Book Depot , 8130491477, Goyal Book Store, 9897318047, New National Book House, 9897830283/9720590054
MUSSORIE	Ram Saran Dass Chanda kiran, 0135-2632785, 9761344588

UTTAR PRADESH

AGRA	Sparsh Book Agency, 9412257817, Om Pustak Mandir, (0562) 2464014, 9319117771, Sanjay Publication, 8126699922 Arti book centre, 8630128856, Panchsheel Books, 9412257962, Bhagwati Book Store, (E & C), 9149081912
ALLAHABAD	Mehrotra Book Agency, (0532) 2266865, 9415636890
AZAMGARH	Sasta Sahitya Bhandar, 9450029674
ALIGARH	K.B.C.L. Agarwal, 9897124960, Shaligram Agencies, 9412317800, New Vimal Books, 9997398868, T.I.C Book centre, 9808039570
BULANDSHAHAR	Rastogi Book Depot, 9837053462/9368978202
BALRAMPUR	Universal Book Center, 8933826726
BAREILLY	Siksha Prakashan, 9837829284
HARDOI	Mittal Pustak Kendra, 9838201466
DEORIA	Kanodia Book Depot, 9415277835
VARANASI	Gupta Books, 8707225564, Bookman & Company,9935194495/7668899901
MATHURA	Sapra Traders, 9410076716, Vijay Book House , 9897254292
FARRUKHABAD	Anurag Book Agencies, 8844007575
NAJIBABAD	Gupta News Agency, 8868932500, Gupta News Agency, (E & C), 8868932500
DHAMPUR	Ramkumar Mahaveer Prasad, 9411942550
GORAKHPUR	Central Book House, 9935454590, Friends & Co., 9450277154, Dinesh book depot, 9125818274, Friends & Co., 9450277154
JHANSI	Bhanu Book Depot, 9415031340
KANPUR	Radha News Agency, 8957247427, Raj Book Dist., 9235616506, H K Book Distributors, 9935146730, H K Book Distributors, 9506033137/9935146730
LUCKNOW	Vyapar Sadan, 7607102462, Om Book Depot, 7705871398, Azad Book Depot Pvt. Ltd., 7317000250, Book Sadan, 9839487327, Rama Book Depot(Retail), 7355078254, Ashirwad Book Depot, 9235501197, Book.com, 7458922755, Universal Books, 9450302161, Sheetla Book Agency, 9235832418, Vidyarthi Kendra Publisher & Distributor Pvt Ltd, (Gold), 9554967415, Tripathi Book House, 9415425943
MEERUT	Ideal Book Depot, (0121) 4059252, 9837066307
NOIDA	Prozo (Global Edu4 Share Pvt. Ltd), 9318395520, Goyal Books Overseas Pvt.Ltd., 1204655555 9873387003
PRAYAGRAJ	Kanhaiya Pustak Bhawan, 9415317109
MAWANA	Subhash Book Depot, 9760262264

WEST BENGAL

KOLKATA	Oriental Publishers & Distributor (033) 40628367, Katha 'O' Kahini, (033) 22196313, 22419071, Saha Book House, (033), 22193671, 9333416484, United Book House, 9831344622, Bijay Pustak Bhandar, 8961260603, Shawan Books Distributors, 8336820363, Krishna Book House, 9123083874
RENUKOOT	Om Stationers, 7007326732
COOCH BEHAR	S.B. Book Distributor, Cooch behar, 9002670771
KHARAGPUR	Subhani Book Store, 9046891334
SILIGURI	Agarwal Book House, 9832038727, Modern Book Agency, 8145578772
DINAJPUR	Krishna Book House, 7031748945
MURSHIDABAD	New Book House, 8944876176

Entrance & Competition Distributors

BIHAR

PATNA	Metro Books Corner, 9431647013, Alka Book Agency, 9835655005, Vikas Book Depot, 9504780402

CHATTISGARH

KORBA	Kitab Ghar, 9425226528, Shri Ramdev Traders, 9981761797

DELHI

DELHI	Singhania Book & Stationer, 9212028238, Radhey Book depot, 9818314141, The Book Shop, 9310262701, Mittal Books, 9899037390, Lov Dev & Sons, 9999353491
NEW DELHI	Anupam Sales, 9560504617, A ONE BOOKS, 8800497047

HARYANA

AMBALA	Bharat Book Depot, 7988455354

JHARKHAND

BOKARO	Bokaro Student Friends Pvt. Ltd, 7360021503

MADHYA PRADESH

INDORE	Bhaiya Industries, 9109120101
CHHINDWARA	Pustak Bhawan, 9827255997

MAHARASHTRA

NAGPUR	Laxmi Pustakalay and Stationers, (0712) 2727354
PUNE	Pragati Book Centre, 9850039311
MUMBAI	New Student Agencies LLP, 7045065799

ODISHA

BARIPADA	Trimurti Book World, 9437034735
CUTTAK	A.K.Mishra Agencies, 9437025991
BHUBANESHWAR	M/s Pragnya, 9437943777

PUNJAB

JALANDHAR	Cheap Book Store, 9872223458, 9878258592

RAJASTHAN

KOTA	Vardhman Book Depot, 9571365020, Raj Traders, 9309232829
JAIPUR	Goyal Book Distributors, 9414782130

UTTAR PRADESH

AGRA	BHAGWATI BOOK STORE, 9149081912, Sparsh Book Agency, 9412257817, Sanjay Publication, 8126699922
ALIGARH	New Vimal Books, 9997398868
ALLAHABAD	Mehrotra Book Agency, (532) 2266865, 9415636890
GORAKHPUR	Central Book House, 9935454590
KANPUR	Raj Book Dist, 9235616506
LUCKNOW	Azad Book Depot PVT LTD, 7317000250, Rama Book Depot(Retail), 7355078254 Ashirwad Book Depot , 9235501197, Book Sadan, 8318643277, Book.com , 7458922755, Sheetla Book Agency, 9235832418
PRAYAGRAJ	Format Center, 9335115561, Garg Brothers Trading & Services Pvt. Ltd., 7388100499

UTTAR PRADESH

DEHRADUN	Inder Book Agancies, 9634045280

WEST BENGAL

KOLKATA	Bijay Pustak Bhandar Pvt. Ltd., 8961260603, Saha Book House, 9674827254 United Book House, 9831344622, Techno World, 9830168159

CHAPTER 1

THE LIVING WORLD

Diversity in the Living World

- The number of species that are known and described range between 1.7-1.8 million. This refers to biodiversity. Biodiversity can be defined as the number and types of organisms present on earth.
- **Nomenclature**:
  - Name of an organism in local language of a region is called common name or vernacular name. The use of common name has some problems. For example, in different countries different languages are spoken and hence, common name of an organism will be different in different countries.
  - It is difficult to learn all common or regional names of an organism that it has all over the world. Therefore, biologists assign standard names which are used all over the world. The process of assigning a standard name or scientific name to an organism is called nomenclature.
  - For assigning scientific names to plants, principles and criteria are provided in International Code for Botanical Nomenclature (ICBN) and for assigning scientific names to animals, principles and criteria are provided in International Code of Zoological Nomenclature (ICZN).
  - Each scientific name has two components: the generic name and the specific name or specific epithet. The generic name is always placed first followed by specific name. For example, the scientific name of mango is *Mangifera indica*. In this name, the first component that is, *Mangifera* represents the generic name while second component that is *indica* is the specific name. This system of providing a name with two components is called Binomial nomenclature. This was given by **Carolus Linnaeus**.
- **Rules for Writing Scientific Names:**
  - Biological names are generally in Latin or Latinised.
  - The first word in a scientific name denotes the generic name while the second word represents the specific epithet.
  - The first word representing the generic name starts with a capital letter while the specific name is written with a small letter. It can be illustrated with the example of *Mangifera indica*.

Scan to know more about this topic

Biodiversity, Nomenclature, Identifier

  - Both the words in a scientific name when handwritten are separately underlined or printed in italics.
  - At the end of the biological name, i.e., after the specific epithet, name of the author is written in an abbreviated form, e.g., *Mangifera indica* Linn.
  - It indicates that this species was first described by Linnaeus.
- **Classification:**
  - To study a vast number of different organisms found on the earth, scientists on the basis of similar characteristics systematically categorised all organisms into various groups and classes. This process is called **classification.**
  - The earliest classifications were based on the 'uses' of various organisms.
  - Classification helps in identification of an organism, study of fossils and finding evolutionary pathways. It also helps in knowing features of a group if we know features of any organism belonging to this group.

Scan to know more about this topic

Classification and its need

- **Three domains of life: (Bacteria, Archaea and Eukarya)**

The three-domain system is a biological classification given by Carl Woese in 1990 that shows the division of cellular life forms into archaea, bacteria, and eukarya. The key difference from earlier classifications is the splitting of archaea from bacteria due to changes in the structure of their cell wall.

THREE DOMAINS (Carl Woese, 1990)

ARCHAEA	BACTERIA	EUKARYA
(Extremophiles) Methanogens, Halophiles, Thermoacidophiles	Cyanobacteria, Eubacteria, beneficial and pathogenic	(Eukaryotes) Protists, Fungi, Plants and Animals

Mnemonics

Concept: Three Domains of Classification
Mnemonics: Eat All Bananas
Interpretation: **E**ukarya, **A**rchaea, **B**acteria

- **Archaebacteria**

These bacteria are special since they live in some of the harshest habitats such as extreme salty areas (halophiles), hot springs (thermoacidophiles) and

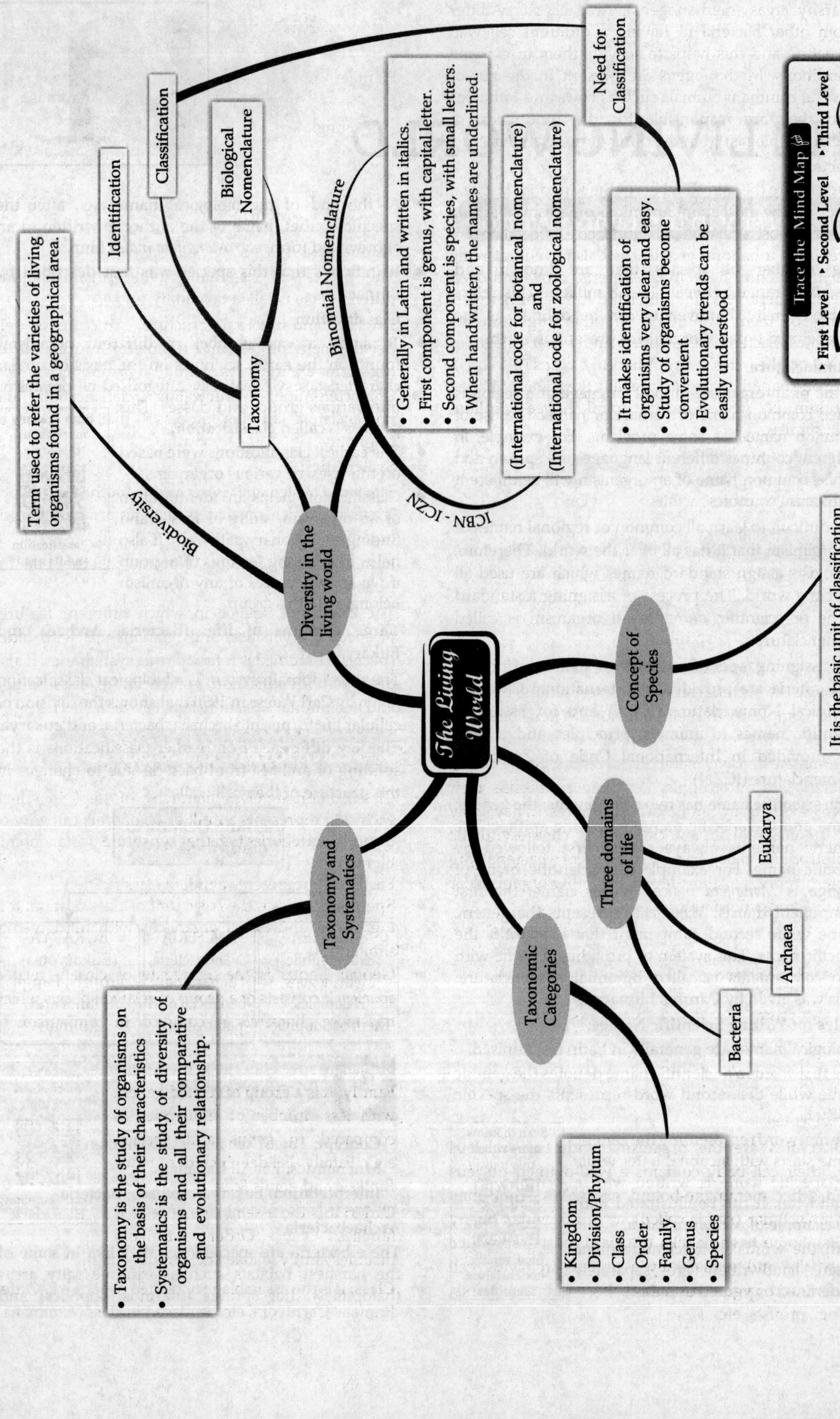

The Living World
Diversity in the living world
Biodiversity
Term used to refer the varieties of living organisms found in a geographical area.
Taxonomy
Identification
Classification
Biological Nomenclature
Binomial Nomenclature
• Generally in Latin and written in italics.
• First component is genus, with capital letter.
• Second component is species, with small letters.
• When handwritten, the names are underlined.
ICBN - ICZN
(International code for botanical nomenclature) and (International code for zoological nomenclature)
Need for Classification
• It makes identification of organisms very clear and easy.
• Study of organisms become convenient
• Evolutionary trends can be easily understood
Concept of Species
It is the basic unit of classification
Three domains of life
Eukarya
Archaea
Bacteria
Taxonomic Categories
• Kingdom
• Division/Phylum
• Class
• Order
• Family
• Genus
• Species
Taxonomy and Systematics
• Taxonomy is the study of organisms on the basis of their characteristics
• Systematics is the study of diversity of organisms and all their comparative and evolutionary relationship.
Trace the Mind Map
First Level
Second Level
Third Level

marshy areas (methanogens). Archaebacteria differ from other bacteria in having a different cell wall structure and this helps to survive them in extreme conditions. Methanogens are present in the gut of several ruminant animals such as cows and buffaloes and they are responsible for the production of methane (biogas) from the dung of these animals.

- **Bacteria**

Bacteria are the sole members of the Kingdom Monera. They are the most abundant micro-organisms. Bacteria occur almost everywhere. Hundreds of bacteria are present in a handful of soil. They also live in extreme habitats such as hot springs, deserts, snow and deep oceans where very few other life forms can survive. Many of them live in or on other organisms as parasites. Bacteria are grouped under four categories based on their shape: the spherical Coccus (pl.: cocci), the rod-shaped Bacillus (pl.: bacilli), the comma-shaped Vibrium (pl.: vibrio) and the spiral shaped Spirillum (pl.: spirilla).

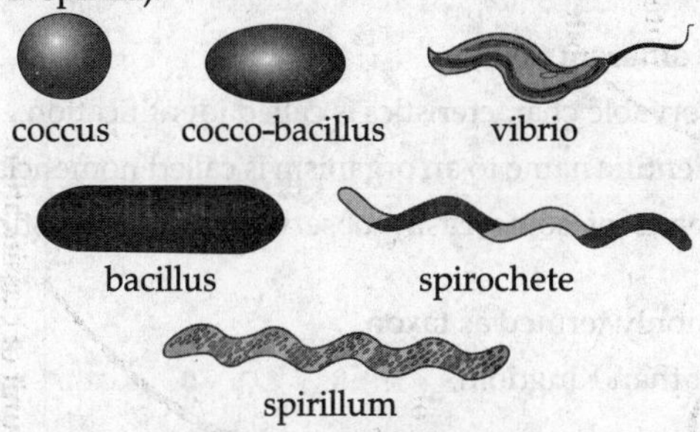

Classification of Bacteria

Though the bacterial structure is very simple but they show complexity in their behaviour. When compared to many other organisms, bacteria as a group show the most extensive metabolic diversity. Some of the bacteria are autotrophic, i.e., they synthesise their own food from inorganic substrates. They may be photosynthetic autotrophic or chemosynthetic autotrophic. The vast majority of bacteria are heterotrophs, i.e., they depend on other organisms or on dead organic matter for food.

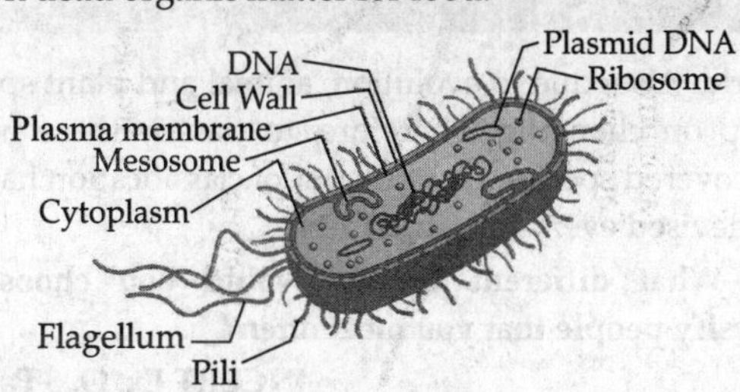

- **Eukaryotes**

Eukaryotes are the organisms with true nucleus i.e., their cell body contains a well-defined nucleus and other membrane-bound organelles. They may be unicellular (single-celled) or multicellular (many cells). Some have flagella or cilia. Protists reproduce asexually and sexually by a process involving cell fusion and zygote formation. E.g., animals, plants, fungi, protists, etc.

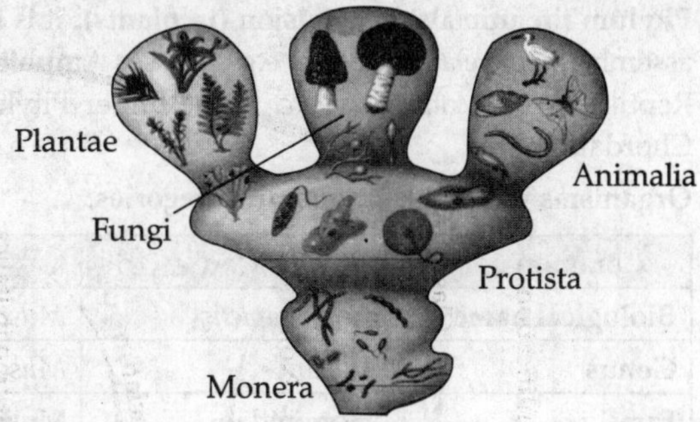

- **Taxonomy:**
  - The process of classifying living organisms into different taxa is called **taxonomy.**
  - External and internal structure, structure of cell, development process and ecological information of organisms are the basis of modern taxonomic studies.
  - Characterisation, identification, classification and nomenclature are the processes that are basic to taxonomy.
- **Systematics:**
  - The word systematics is derived from the Latin word 'systema' which means 'systematic arrangement of organisms'.
  - Linnaeus used 'Systema Naturae' as the title for publication.
  - The branch of science in which different features of species, diversities, and relationships with other species are studied is referred to as **systematics**. It also deals with identification, nomenclature, classification and evolutionary relationships between species.

Taxonomic Categories

- Classification involves hierarchy of steps in which each step represents a rank or taxonomic category or taxon. All categories together constitute the taxonomic hierarchy.
- Each taxon represents a unit of classification.
- **Species:** Species is the basic unit of classification. It is a group of individual organisms with fundamental similarities.
- **Genus:** Genus is the aggregate of closely related species. It consists of a group of related species which has more characters in common in comparison to species of other genera. e.g., potato, tomato and brinjal are species of the genus *Solanum*.
- **Family:** It is a group of related genera with less number of similarities as compared to genus and species. e.g., Family Felidae includes genus *Panthera* and genus *Felis*.
- **Order:** It is the assemblage of related families. e.g., Order carnivora includes family felidae and canidae (dog).
- **Class:** It is the assemblage of related orders. e.g.,Order Primata, Carnivora, etc., is placed in class Mammalia.

Scan to know more about this topic

Taxa, Taxonomy, Hierarchical

- **Phylum (in animals) or Division (in plants):** It is the assemblage of related classes. e.g., Classes Amphibia, Reptilia, Aves, Mammalia, etc., come under Phylum Chordata.
- **Kingdom:** It is the assemblage of various phyla. It is the highest category. e.g., Kingdom Plantae, Kingdom Animalia, etc.
- **Organisms with their taxonomic categories:**

Common name	Man	Housefly	Mango	Wheat
Biological name	*Homo sapiens*	*Musca domestica*	*Mangifera indica*	*Triticum aestivum*
Genus	*Homo*	*Musca*	*Mangifera*	*Triticum*
Family	Hominidae	Muscidae	Anacardiaceae	Poaceae
Order	Primata	Diptera	Sapindales	Poales
Class	Mammalia	Insecta	Dicotyledonae	Monocotyledonae
Phylum/Division	Chordata	Arthropoda	Angiospermae	Angiospermae

Key Words

- **Systematics:** The branch of science which deals with different features of species, their diversities, and relationships with other species is referred to as systematics.
- **Taxonomy:** It is the process of classifying living organisms into different taxa.
- **Identification:** Recognition of a species, by studying easily observable characteristics is called identification.
- **Nomenclature:** The process of assigning a standard name or scientific name to an organism is called nomenclature.
- **Classification:** It is a method by which organisms on the basis of some easily observable characteristics are categorised into different groups and classes.
- **Taxon:** The unit of classification or taxonomic category is commonly termed as taxon.
- **Phylum:** It is a taxonomic category higher than class and lower than Kingdom.
- **Class:** It is a taxonomic category which includes related orders.
- **Order:** It is a taxonomic category which includes related families.
- **Family:** It is a taxonomic category which includes related genera.
- **Genus:** It is an aggregate of related species.
- **Species:** It is the lowest category of biological classification which comprises of related organisms or populations potentially capable of interbreeding.

NCERT CORNER

Q. 1. Why are living organisms classified? **[NCERT Ex. Q. 1 Page 9]**

Ans. There are millions of living organisms on earth. All these living organisms differ in shape, size, color, habitat and many other characteristics. To understand their origin, diversity, distribution and inter relationship, the scientists have devised mechanisms to classify all of them. Classification of living organisms help in revealing the relationship between various organisms. It also helps in making study of organisms easy and organised.

Q. 2. Why are the classification systems changing every now and then? **[NCERT Ex. Q. 2 Page 9]**

Ans. There is a vast variety of living organisms on earth. Many of them have been identified by the scientists while many new species are still being discovered around the world. Also, due to evolution, animal and plant species keep on changing. Therefore, to classify these newly discovered species, new systems of classification have to be devised every now and then.

Q. 3. What different criteria would you choose to classify people that you meet often? **[NCERT Ex. Q. 3 Page 9]**

Ans. Criteria to classify people that you often meet are:

(i) Sex **(ii)** External features
(iii) Height and skin colour **(iv)** Level of education
(v) Profession **(vi)** Economic status
(vii) Nature

Q. 4. What do we learn from identification of individuals and populations? **[NCERT Ex. Q. 4 Page 9]**

Ans. Identification of individuals and populations helps the scientists to classify organisms in various categories.

It helps to determine their exact place or position in the set plan of classification.

Q. 5. Given below is the scientific name of Mango. Identify the correctly written name:

Mangifera Indica

Mangifera indica **[NCERT Ex. Q. 5 Page 9]**

Ans. The correctly written scientific name of Mango is *Mangifera indica*, where *Mangifera* is the generic name and *indica* is species name.

Q. 6. Define taxon. Give some examples of taxa at different hierarchical levels. [NCERT Ex. Q. 6 Page 9]

Ans. Each unit or category of classification is termed as a taxon.

The different hierarchical levels starting from the basic level is species, followed by genus, family, order, class, phylum or division and kingdom.

Examples include,

(i) Insects represent a category of phylum-Arthropoda.
(ii) Taxon of bacteria is Monera.
(iii) Sponges form the taxon Porifera.

Q. 7. Can you identify the correct sequence of taxonomical categories? [NCERT Ex. Q. 7 Page 9]

(i) Species → Order → Phylum → Kingdom
(ii) Genus → Species → Order → Kingdom
(iii) Species → Genus → Order → Phylum

Ans. The correct sequence of taxonomical categories is:

Species → Genus → Family → Order → Class → Phylum → Kingdom

Therefore, both (i) and (iii) represent correct sequence of taxonomic categories.

Q. 8. Try to collect all the currently accepted meanings for the word 'species'. Discuss with your teacher the meaning of species in case of higher plants and animals on one hand, and bacteria on the other hand.

[NCERT Ex. Q. 8 Page 9]

Ans. Species is one of the basic unit of classification. It is often defined as, "a group of similar organisms that are capable of interbreeding to produce fertile offspring".

In case of higher plants and animals, one genus may have one or more than one species, e.g., *Panthera leo* (lion) and *Panthera tigris* (tiger). Here, *Panthera* is genus which includes *leo* (lion) and *tigris* (tiger) as species.

But, bacteria are grouped under five different categories based on their shapes- spherical, coccus, rod-shaped, comma and spiral-shaped.

Thus, the meaning of species in higher organism and bacteria are different.

Q. 9. Define and understand the following terms:

(i) Phylum (iii) Order (v) Genus
(ii) Class (iv) Family

[NCERT Ex. Q. 9 Page 9]

Ans. (i) Phylum: A group of closely related classes having certain common characters.

(ii) Class: A group of closely related orders having certain common characters.

(iii) Order: A group of closely related families having certain common characters.

(iv) Family: A group of closely related genera having certain common characters.

(v) Genus: A group of closely related species having certain common characters.

Q. 10. Illustrate the taxonomical hierarchy with suitable examples of a plant and an animal.

[NCERT Ex. Q. 10 Page 9]

Ans. Taxonomical hierarchy consists of many steps and each step is mentioned as a rank or category. Each category is a unit of classification. Various levels in taxonomic hierarchy are:

Species → Genus → Family → Order → Class → Phylum → Kingdom.

(i) Similar individuals form a group called species. All the related species form the next rank genus. e.g., *Rana tigrina* (Frog), *Rana* is genus and *tigrina* is species.

(ii) Related genera are kept in a family e.g., *Petunia*, *Solanum* and *Datura* are the members of family Solanaceae. The related families comprises Order e.g., Solanaceae and Convolvulaceae comes in the order Polynomials.

(iii) All orders make classes, e.g., bony fishes and cartilaginous fishes are included in class Pisces.

(iv) Various classes like amphibia, aves, mamamalia form a Phylum (Chordata), and all Phylum comes in the Kingdom Animalia.

□□

CHAPTER 2

BIOLOGICAL CLASSIFICATION

Need for Classification and Five Kingdom Classification

System of Classification:

- Aristotle was the first who classified organisms on the scientific basis. He, on the basis of morphological characters, divided plants into three groups – trees, shrubs and herbs. He also classified animals into two groups – **enaima** (animals having red blood) and **anaima** (animals lacking red blood).
- **Two kingdom system of classification**
- Linnaeus classified all the organisms into two kingdoms – **Plantae** and **Animalia**. Kingdom plantae included all plants while kingdom animalia included all the animals.
- Although, this system of classification was popular for long time but with the discovery of some new organisms, it was found inadequate. Some of the demerits of the two kingdom system of classification are as follows:

1. Organisms with contrasting characters like eukaryotes and prokaryotes, unicellular and multicellular organisms and photosynthetic (green algae) and non-photosynthetic (fungi) organisms were placed together.
2. A large number of organisms did not fall into either category.

- **Three Domain System of classification:**
- The three domain system was developed by **Carl Woese**.
- It is a system for classifying biological organisms.
- Under this system, organisms are classified into three domains and six kingdoms. The domains are Archaea, Bacteria and Eukarya. Kingdoms are archaebacteria, Eubacteria, Protista, Fungi, Plantae and Animalia.

Scan to know more about this topic

Classification and Nomenclature

- **Five kingdom system of classification**
- In 1969, **R.H. Whittaker** proposed a Five Kingdom Classification. **Monera, Protista, Fungi, Plantae** and **Animalia** are the five kingdoms defined by him. The main criteria used by him for classifying organisms were as follows:

1. Cell structure
2. Body organisation
3. Mode of nutrition
4. Reproduction
5. Phylogenetic relationships

- **In five kingdom classification system:**
- All prokaryotic organisms were grouped together under **Kingdom Monera**.
- The fungi were placed in a separate kingdom – **Kingdom Fungi.**
- The unicellular eukaryotic organisms were placed in a separate kingdom – **Kingdom Protista.**
- It has put together organisms which, in earlier classifications, were placed in different kingdoms.
- For example, kingdom Protista has brought together *Chlamydomonas* and *Chlorella* (earlier placed in algae within plants and both having cell walls) with *Paramecium* and *Amoeba* (which were earlier placed in the animal kingdom).

Kingdom Monera

- They are **unicellular prokaryotes.** Bacteria are the only members of the kingdom monera. They are the most abundant micro-organisms found on the earth. They occur almost everywhere – in air, water, soil, snow and even in or on other organisms as parasites.

Scan to know more about this topic

Monera

- On the basis of shape, bacteria are grouped under four categories:
- **Coccus** (pl.: cocci): They have spherical shape.
- **Bacillus** (pl.: bacilli): They are rod-shaped bacteria.
- **Spirillum** (pl.: spirilla): They have long and spirally coiled bodies.
- **Vibrium** (pl.: vibrio): These bacteria have short and slightly curved bodies which appear like a shape of a comma.

Mnemonics

Concept: Shapes of Bacteria

Mnemonics: Valuable things **C**an **B**e **S**aved

Interpretation: Vibrium, Coccus, Bacillus, Spirillum

- Monerans have a cell wall which is mostly made up of peptidoglycan. They lack nuclear membrane. Their genetic material is present in the form of a coiled circular DNA which lies in the cytoplasm. This is called **nucleoid**.
- Monerans utilise different strategies to get their food.
- Some of the monerans (bacteria) are autotrophic that is, they synthesise their own food from inorganic substrates. They may be photosynthetic autotrophic or chemosynthetic autotrophic.

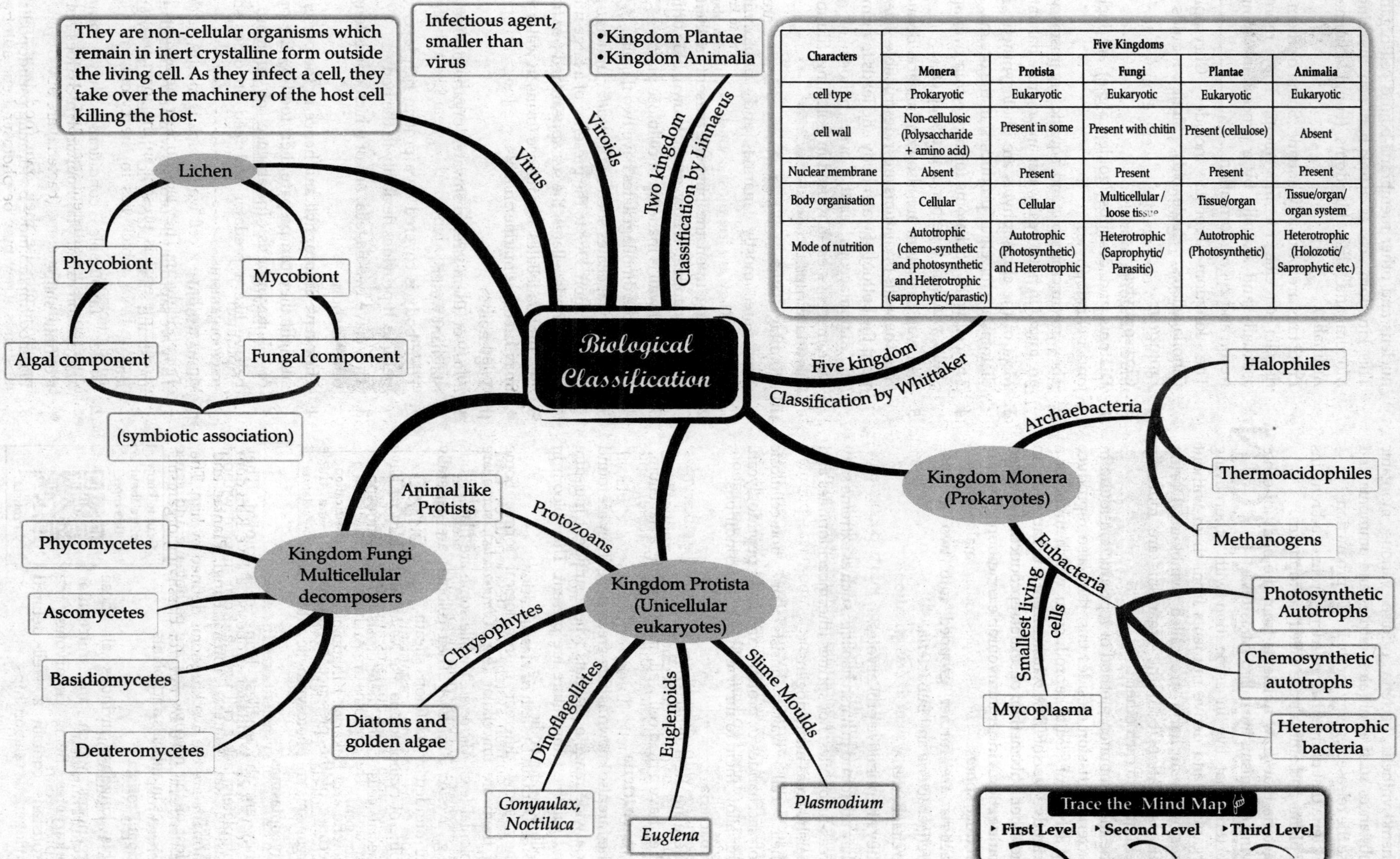

Characters	Five Kingdoms				
	Monera	Protista	Fungi	Plantae	Animalia
cell type	Prokaryotic	Eukaryotic	Eukaryotic	Eukaryotic	Eukaryotic
cell wall	Non-cellulosic (Polysaccharide + amino acid)	Present in some	Present with chitin	Present (cellulose)	Absent
Nuclear membrane	Absent	Present	Present	Present	Present
Body organisation	Cellular	Cellular	Multicellular / loose tissue	Tissue/organ	Tissue/organ/ organ system
Mode of nutrition	Autotrophic (chemo-synthetic and photosynthetic and Heterotrophic (saprophytic/parastic)	Autotrophic (Photosynthetic) and Heterotrophic	Heterotrophic (Saprophytic/ Parasitic)	Autotrophic (Photosynthetic)	Heterotrophic (Holozotic/ Saprophytic etc.)

- Chemosynthetic bacteria oxidise various inorganic substances such as nitrates, nitrites and ammonia and use the released energy for their ATP production.
- Bacteria that derive their nutrients from dead remains of plants and animals are called **saprophytes**.
- Bacteria that draw nutrients from the body of other living organisms are called **parasites**.
- Bacteria that live in association with other living organisms and derive nutrients from them without causing them harm are called symbiont. During this association, both the organisms are mutually benefitted to each other.

► The most common method of reproduction found in bacteria is **fission**. Besides this, they also reproduce by a type of sexual reproduction which involves a primitive type of DNA transfer from one bacterium to the other. This method of sexual reproduction is called **conjugation**. Under unfavourable conditions, bacteria produce spores.

► Bacteria are further grouped into two groups– Archaebacteria and Eubacteria.

- **Archaebacteria**

(i) They are primitive prokaryotes.

(ii) They are found in harsh habitats, such as extreme salty areas-halophiles; hot springs (thermoacidophiles and marshy areas methanogens).

(iii) Their cell wall consists of non-cellulosic polysaccharides or proteins and lacks peptidoglycan. This allow them to survive in extreme conditions.

- **Eubacteria**

(i) These are the true bacteria.

(ii) They have a rigid cell wall, and if motile, a flagellum.

- **Cyanobacteria**

(i) They are also known as blue-green algae. They are found in a wide range of habitats where sufficient moisture and suitable temperature are present. They bloom in polluted water bodies.

(ii) They show different morphological forms. Some of them are unicellular (e.g., *Chroococcus*), some are colonial (e.g., *Microcystis*) while some are filamentous (e.g., *Nostoc, Anabaena*). Their colonies are generally surrounded by gelatinous sheath.

(iii) Some of cyanobacteria like *Nostoc* and *Anabaena* have special cells called heterocysts to fix atmospheric nitrogen.

(iv) Because of the presence of chlorophyll – a, these organisms are photosynthetic autotrophs.

- **Mycoplasmas**

(i) They are the smallest living cells known. They completely lack a cell wall and can survive without oxygen.

(ii) Most of the mycoplasma are pathogenic and cause diseases in animals and plants.

Kingdom Protista

► This kingdom includes all those organisms which are **unicellular eukaryotes**. Being eukaryotes, the protistans contain a well defined nucleus and other membrane-bound cell organelles. This kingdom acts as a link between the kingdom Monera and other kingdoms (Fungi, Plantae and Animalia).

Scan to know more about this topic

Protista

► Protistans are primarily aquatic. Some of them have flagella or cilia for movement. They reproduce asexually and sexually by a process involving cell fusion and zygote formation.

► The kingdom Protista includes Chrysophytes, Dinoflagellates, Euglenoids, Slime moulds and Protozoans.

(i) **Chrysophytes**

1. **Diatoms** and **desmids** (golden algae) are included under chrysophytes.
2. They are microscopic and aquatic organisms which are found in both freshwater and marine habitats.
3. Most of the chrysophytes are photosynthetic. Infact diatoms are the chief 'producers' in the oceans.
4. The cell walls of diatoms form two thin overlapping shells, which fit together as in a soap case.
5. Cell wall of diatom are also rich in silica. Because of this, the walls of diatoms are indestructible. They pile up at the bottom of water body and leads to formation of '**diatomaceous earth**' over billions of years. Diatomaceous earth is used in polishing, filtration of oils and syrups.

(ii) **Dinoflagellates**

1. They are mostly marine and photosynthetic organisms.
2. Depending upon the pigment present in their cell, they may appear yellow, green, brown, blue or red.
3. Their cell wall is made up of cellulose plates.
4. Most of the dinoflagellates have two flagella.
5. Red dinoflagellates such as *Gonyaulax* undergo rapid multiplication. Due to the presence of a large number of red dinoflagellates, the sea appears red (*red tides*).
6. Red dinoflagellates also release toxins in water which may kill other marine animals.

(iii) **Euglenoids**

1. Most of them are freshwater organisms found in stagnant water.
2. Their body is covered by a protein rich layer called **pellicle**. It provides flexibility to the body.
3. They have two flagella, out of which one is long and other is short.
4. They have chlorophyll and hence in the presence of sunlight they can prepare their food by the process of photosynthesis. In absence of sunlight, they behave like a predator and feed on other smaller microorganisms.

(iv) **Slime Moulds**

1. They are saprophytic protists which are found in cool, moist and shady places rich in decaying twigs and leaves.
2. Under favourable conditions, they form an aggregation called **plasmodium** which does not have a definite shape.
3. Plasmodium can move by forming pseudopodia.

4. During unfavourable conditions, plasmodium transforms into fruiting bodies which bear spores at their tips.
5. The spores are extremely resistant and survive for many years, even under adverse conditions.

(v) Protozoans

They are heterotrophs and live as predators or parasites. Four major groups of protozoans are given below:

(a) Amoeboid protozoans

1. They are found in fresh water, sea water or moist soil.
2. They have pseudopodia to move and capture their prey.

Example: *Amoeba and Entamoeba.*

(b) Flagellated protozoans

1. They are either free-living or parasitic.
2. They have flagella.
3. The parasitic forms cause diseases like sleeping sickness.

Example: *Trypanosoma.*

(c) Ciliated protozoans

1. They are aquatic organisms.
2. Their body is covered with thousands of cilia which help in movement and capturing of food.
3. A cavity called *gullet* is present which opens to the outside of the cell surface and is the site of ingestion.

Example: *Paramecium.*

(d) Sporozoans

1. All sporozoans have an infectious spore-like stage in their life cycle.

Example: Plasmodium (malarial parasite).

Important Diagram

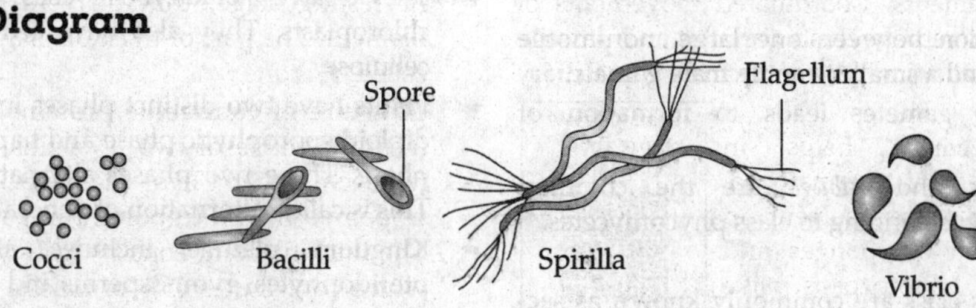

Bacteria of different shapes

Kingdom Fungi

Scan to know more about this topic
Kingdom Fungi

- Fungi prefer to grow in warm and humid places.
- Except the yeast, which is a unicellular organism, all fungi are filamentous. Their bodies consist of long, slender thread-like structures called hyphae. The network of hyphae is called mycelium.
- In some fungi, hyphae are continuous tubes filled with multinucleated cytoplasm. This type of hyphae is called **aseptate hyphae** or **coenocytic hyphae.** In contrast to this in some fungi septae or cross walls are present in the hyphae. Such type of hyphae is called **septate hyphae. Coenocytic** means something having multinuclei.
- The cell wall is made up of **chitin** and polysaccharides. **Chitin** is long-chain polymer of N-acetylglucosamine.
- All fungi are heterotrophic. They take their food by following methods:
  - Most of the fungi absorb soluble organic matter from dead substrates. Such fungi are called **saprophytes**.
  - Some of them depend on living plants and animals and are called **parasites.**
  - Some fungi live in association with other living organisms as symbionts, e.g., in lichen. Fungi live as symbiont with algae and in mycorrhiza with plant roots.
- **Fungi reproduce by three modes:**

(a) Vegetative means: It occurs through fragmentation, fission and budding.

(b) Asexual reproduction: This type of reproduction involves formation of spores which may be of different types like conidia, sporangiospores and zoospores.

(c) Sexual reproduction: Sexual reproduction involves formation of fruiting bodies inside which various types of spores (like oospores, ascospores and basidiospores) are produced.

- In fungi, the sexual cycle involves three steps which are given below:

(i) Plasmogamy: Fusion of the protoplasms of two motile or non-motile gametes is called plasmogamy. It is the first step of sexual reproduction.

(ii) Karyogamy: After plasmogamy, nuclei of both gametes fuse together. This is called karyogamy.

(iii) Meiosis: The last step of sexual reproduction involves meiotic division in zygote. As a result of this haploid spores are formed.

- Dikaryophase is a condition of having dikaryon in an intervening dikaryotic stage (i.e. two nuclei per cell) between plasmogamy and karyogamy in fungi.
- On the basis of morphology of the mycelium, mode of spore formation and fruiting bodies, kingdom fungi is divided into four classes.

(i) Phycomycetes

- Fungi belonging to this class are found in aquatic habitats and on decaying wood, in moist and damp places or as **obligate** parasites on plants.
- A **parasitic** organism which cannot complete its life-cycle without exploiting a suitable host is called **obligate parasite.**
- They have **aseptate mycelium** with **coenocytic condition.**
- They reproduce asexually either by means of zoospores (motile) or by aplanospores (non-motile). These spores are produced in sporangium endogeneously.
- Sexual reproduction involves fusion between two gametes which is of the following three types:

1. **Isogamous:** Fusion of two gametes which are similar in size.
2. **Anisogamous:** Fusion of two gametes which are dissimilar in size.
3. **Oogamous:** Fusion between one large, non-motile female gamete and a smaller, motile male gamete.

- Fusion of two gametes leads to formation of **zygospores.**
- *Mucor, Rhizopus* and *Albugo* are the common examples of fungi belonging to class phycomycetes.

(ii) Ascomycetes

- Members of this class are commonly known as sac-fungi.
- Some of them are unicellular, e.g., yeast (*Saccharomyces*) while most of them are multicellular, e.g., *Penicillium*.
- They are saprophytic, decomposers, coprophilous (growing on dung) or parasitic.
- They have branched and septate mycelium.
- They reproduce asexually through conidia which are produced on the special mycelium called conidiophores. Each conidia on germination gives rise to mycelium.
- Sexual reproduction occurs through special types of spores called ascospores. Ascospores are endogenously produced in sac like structures called asci and asci are arranged in fruiting bodies called ascocarps.
- *Aspergillus, Claviceps* and *Neurospora* are the common fungi belonging to the class Ascomycetes.

(iii) Basidiomycetes

- They grow in soil, on logs and tree stumps and in living plant bodies as parasites.
- They have branched and septate mycelium.
- They do not reproduce asexually, but vegetative reproduction by fragmentation is observed in them.
- Sexual reproduction is by fusion of vegetative or somatic cells to form basidium produced in basidiocarp.
- Basidium produces four basidiospores exogenously after meiosis.
- *Agaricus* (mushroom), *Ustilago* (smut) and *Puccinia* (rust fungus) are some common fungi belonging to class basidiomycetes.

(iv) Deuteromycetes

- Sexual or perfect stages of deuteromycetes are not known. Only asexual or vegetative stages are known. Because of this, they are commonly known as imperfect fungi.
- They reproduce only by asexual spores called conidia.
- They have septate and branched mycelium.
- Most of them are decomposers of litter and help in mineral cycling.
- Common examples of deuteromycetes are *Alternaria, Colletotrichum* and *Trichoderma.*

Kingdom Plantae

- The members of this kingdom are called plants. They are photosynthetic autotrophs, exceptionally insectivorous plants such as Bladderwort and Venus fly trap. *Cuscuta* is a parasite.
- They have eukaryotic cells with prominent chloroplasts. They also have cell wall made up of cellulose.
- Plants have two distinct phases in the life cycle– the diploid sporophytic phase and haploid gametophytic phase. These two phases alternate with each other. This is called alternation of generation.
- Kingdom plantae includes algae, bryophytes, pteridophytes, gymnosperms and angiosperms.

Kingdom Animalia

- The characteristic of this kingdom is heterotrophic eukaryotic organisms that are multicellular and their cells lack cell walls.
- They directly or indirectly depend on plants for food.
- They digest their food in an internal cavity and store food reserves as glycogen or fat.
- The mode of nutrition is holozoic ingestion of food.
- They follow a definite growth pattern and grow into adults that have a definite shape and size.
- Higher forms show elaborate sensory and neuromotor mechanism and most of them are capable of locomotion.
- The sexual reproduction is by copulation of male and female followed by embryological development.

Viruses, Viroids, Prions and Lichens

Viruses

- They are non-cellular organisms which remain in inert crystalline form outside the living cell. They are obligate parasites. As they infect a cell, they take over the machinery of the host cell to replicate themselves, killing the host.
- **W.M. Beijerinck** called fluids as '*contagium vivum fluidum*' as extracts of infected plants of tobacco that could cause infection in healthy plants.
- Virus means venom or poisonous fluid. Pasteur gave the term 'virus'.

- **D.J. Ivanowsky** found that certain microbes caused Tobacco Mosaic Disease in tobacco plant.
- **W.M Stanley** showed viruses could be crystallised to form crystals of protein, which are inert outside their specific host.
- A virus consists of a protein coat called capsid and a genetic material which may be either RNA or DNA. The genetic material of virus is infectious. Generally viruses which infect plants have single stranded RNA and viruses which infect animals have either single or double stranded RNA or double stranded DNA. Viruses which infect bacteria are known as **bacteriophages**. They have double stranded DNA as genetic material.
- The capsid is made of small sub-units called capsomeres which protect the nucleic acid. The number of capsomere varies in different viruses. For *e.g,* Tobacco Mosaic Virus (TMV) has 2130 capsomeres. The capsomeres may be arranged in helical or polyhedral geometric forms.
- Various diseases like mumps, small pox, herpes, influenza and AIDS are caused by viruses. Infection of viruses leads to development of diseases in plants also. Some common symptoms of plant viral diseases are formation of mosaic, rolling and curling of leaf, yellowing and vein clearing, dwarfing and stunted growth.

Viroids

- They are infectious agents of plants which are similar to virus but consist of only a short single stranded RNA. They are smaller than viruses and lack protein coat. The RNA of the viroids is of low molecular weight. One of the disease caused by viroids is potato spindle tuber disease.

Prions

- There are certain infections neurological diseases transmitted by an agent, similar in size to viruses, consisting of abnormally folded protein. These agents are called Prions.
- Some notable diseases caused by prions are spongiform encepolapathy (BSE) commonly called mad cow disease in cattle and its analogous variant Cr. Jacob disease (CJD) in humans.

Lichens

- They are symbiotic associations between algae and fungi. The algal component is called **phycobiont** and fungal component is known as **mycobiont.** In this symbiotic association both partners are mutually benefitted. Algae prepare food for fungi and fungi provide shelter and absorb mineral nutrients and water for its partner. As lichens are very sensitive to air pollution and do not grow in polluted area, they are very good pollution indicators.

Key Words

- **Nucleoid:** The irregularly-shaped region within the cell of a prokaryote which contains genetic material is called nucleoid. It is not surrounded by a nuclear membrane.
- **Saprophytes:** The organisms which obtain their food from the dead and decaying organic matter are called saprophytes.
- **Parasites:** The organisms which obtain their food from other living organisms without killing them are called parasites.
- **Heterocysts:** These are the specialised cells which are involved in nitrogen fixation in *Nostoc*, *Anabaena* and other cyanobacteria.
- **Pellicle:** It is a protein rich layer which covers the entire body of members of Euglenoids.
- **Hyphae:** The long thread-like structures which constitute vegetative body of fungi are called hyphae.
- **Mycorrhiza:** It is a symbiotic association of the mycelium of a fungus with the roots of certain plants.
- **Ascospores:** A type of spores which are formed as a result of sexual reproduction in class ascomycetes.
- **Basidiospores:** A type of spores which are formed as a result of sexual reproduction in class basidiomycetes.
- **Capsid:** A proteinaceous coat which encloses the nucleic acid of a virus is called capsid.
- **Capsomere:** Small protein subunits of a capsid is called capsomere.
- **Viroid:** An infectious agent of plants which is similar to a virus but comprises a short single stranded RNA without a protein coat is called viroid.

NCERT CORNER

Q. 1. Discuss how classification systems have undergone several changes over a period of time?

[NCERT Ex. Q. 1, Page 22]

Ans. The two kingdom system of classification was inadequate. So it was changed and finally five kingdom system of classification was devised by Whittaker in 1969. It takes the account of cell organisation, nature of cell wall, mode of nutrition, habitat, reproduction, ecological roles and evolutionary relationship etc. The five kingdoms are: Monera, Protista, Fungi, Plantae and Animalia.

Q. 2. State two economically important uses of:

(i) Heterotrophic bacteria

(ii) Archaebacteria. **[NCERT Ex. Q. 2, Page 22]**

Ans. (i) Use of heterotrophic bacteria:

(a) They help in making curd from milk.

(b) They are helpful in nitrogen fixation in roots of leguminous plants.

(ii) Uses of archaebacteria:

(a) They live in the gut of several ruminant animals such as cow and buffaloes and helps in their digestion.

(b) They help in the production of bio-gas such as methane.

Q. 3. What is the nature of cell walls in diatoms? **[NCERT Ex. Q. 3, Page 22]**

Ans. (i) In diatoms the cell walls form two thin overlapping shells which fit together as in a soap box.

(ii) These walls are embedded with silica forming siliceous frustules which are indestructible.

(iii) They pile up at the bottom of water reservoirs and form big heaps called diatomite.

(iv) Diatomite is used in filtration of sugars, alcohol and antibiotics.

Q. 4. Find out what do the terms 'algal bloom' and 'red tides' signify ? **[NCERT Ex. Q. 4, Page 22]**

Ans. (i) Algal bloom: When the algae in water body have excessive growth due to the enrichment of excessive nutrients in it, this refers to algal bloom.

(ii) Red tides: When the sea appears red due to the rapid multiplication of red dinoflagellates e.g., *Gonyaulax*, it is called as red tides.

Q. 5. How are viroids different from viruses ? **[NCERT Ex. Q. 5, Page 22]**

Ans.

	Viruses	Viroids
(i)	They have a protein coat.	They do not have a protein coat.
(ii)	The genetic material may be either DNA or RNA.	The genetic material is RNA.
(iii)	They can infect plants, animals and bacteria.	They can infect only plants.

Q. 6. Describe briefly the four major groups of protozoa. **[NCERT Ex. Q. 6, Page 22]**

Ans. Protozoa are microscopic unicellular protists with heterotrophic mode of nutrition. They may be holozoic, saprobic or parasitic. These are divided into four major groups.

(i) Amoeboid protozoa or sarcodines: They are unicellular, jelly-like protozoa found in fresh or sea water and in moist soil. Their body lacks a periplast. Therefore, they may be naked or covered by a calcareous shell. They usually lack flagella and have temporary protoplasmic outgrowths called pseudopodia. These pseudopodia or false feet help in movement and capturing prey. They include free living forms such as *amoeba* or parasitic forms such as *entamoeba*.

(ii) Flagellated protozoa or zooflagellates: They are free living, non-photosynthetic flagellates without a cell wall. They possess flagella for locomotion and capturing prey. They include parasitic forms such as *Trypanosoma*, which causes sleeping sickness in human beings.

(iii) Ciliated protozoa or ciliates: They are aquatic individuals that form a large group of protozoa.Their characteristics features are the presence of numerous cilia on the entire body surface and the presence of two types of nuclei. All the cilia beat in the same direction to move the water laden food inside a cavity called gullet. They include organisms such as *Paramecium, Vorticella*, etc.

(iv) Sporozoans: They include disease causing endo-parasites and other pathogens. They are uninucleate and their body is covered by a pellicle. They do not possess cilia or flagella. They include the malaria causing parasite *Plasmodium.*

Q. 7. Plants are autotrophic. Can you think of some plants that are partially heterotrophic? **[NCERT Ex. Q. 7, Page 22]**

Ans. Plants are generally autotrophic in nature because they contain chlorophyll. But a few members are partially heterotrophic i.e., they are not independent for their nutrition. Example includes:

(i) Insectivorous plants: Some plants have modified leaves which are used for trapping the insects within the leaves so that the insects are killed. Those insects are digested by the enzymes secreted by the epidermis of leaves. **Example:** Venus fly trap, Bladderwort, etc.

(ii) Parasite plants: Some plants have special and modified organs which penetrate into the host plant to absorb solutes and water.

Example: *Cuscuta.*

Q. 8. What do the terms phycobiont and mycobiont signify ? **[NCERT Ex. Q. 8, Page 22]**

Ans. The algal component of the lichen is called phycobiont and fungal component is known as mycobiont. Phycobiont prepare food for fungi and mycobiont provides shelter and absorb mineral nutrients and water for its partner.

Q. 9. Give a comparative account of the classes of kingdom Fungi under the following:

(i) Mode of nutrition

(ii) Mode of reproduction. **[NCERT Ex. Q. 9, Page 22]**

Ans.

Phycomycetes	Ascomycetes	Basidiomycetes	Deuteromycetes
Mode of Nutrition: These are obligate parasites on plants.	They are saprophytic, parasitic or coprophilous.	They are parasites.	They are saprophytes or parasites.
Mode of reproduction: True spores are produced in sporangia.	Asexual spores are called ascospores.	Asexual spores occur in basidiocarps.	The asexual spores are conidia.
Sexual spores are oospores or zygospores formed by union of the gametes	Asci are arranged in ascocarps (fruiting bodies).	Basidia are arranged in basidioscarps. (fruiting bodies)	Sexual reproduction unknown in them.

Sexually reproduces by zoospores or by aplanospores.	Sexual spores are called ascospores produced in sac shaped structure called the ascus.	Plasmogamy occurs by fusion of somatic and vegetative cells. Dikaryotic structure makes basidium. Karyogamy for production of 4 basidiospores.	They lack perfect or sexual stage.

Q. 10. What are the characteristic features of Euglenoids? [NCERT Ex. Q. 10, Page 22]

Ans. **(i)** These are unicellular flagellate protists. They are devoid of cellulose cell wall.

(ii) The body is covered by thin and flexible pellicle.

(iii) They bear two flagella, usually one long and one short.

(iv) They swim actively in a liquid medium by flagella.

(v) Nutrition is holophytic. They have chloroplasts. e.g., *Euglena*.

Q. 11. Give a brief account of viruses with respect to their structure and nature of genetic material. Also name four common viral diseases. [NCERT Ex. Q. 11, Page 22]

Ans. Viruses:

(i) They are non-cellular organisms.

(ii) They remain inert outside living cell. They have genetic material DNA or RNA. No virus has both RNA and DNA.

(iii) Plant infecting viruses have ssRNA but animal infecting viruses possess dsRNA.

Viruses causes diseases like (1) mumps, (2) small pox, (3) herpes and (4) influenza.

Q. 12. Organise a discussion in your class on the topic: Are viruses living or non-living?

[NCERT Ex. Q. 12, Page 22]

Ans. Viruses are the intermediate between living and non-living entities. They resemble non-living objects in:

(i) Lacking protoplast.

(ii) Ability to get crystallised. e.g., TMV, poliomyelitis virus.

(iii) Inability to live independent of a living cell.

(iv) High specific gravity which is found only in non-living objects.

(v) Absence of respiration. Absence of energy storing system.

(vi) Absence of growth and division.

Viruses resemble living beings which are as follows:

(i) It is formed of organic macromolecules, which occur only in living beings.

(ii) Presence of genetic material.

(iii) Ability to multiply or reproduce.

(iv) Occurrence of mutations. The most mutable virus is HIV or AIDS.

(v) Occurrence of enzyme transcriptase in most viruses.

(vi) They breed true to their type. Even variations are inheritable.

(vii) They take over biosynthetic machinery of the host cell and produce chemicals required for multiplication.

□□

PLANT KINGDOM

CHAPTER 3

Classification of Plants

Types of Classification:

- **Artificial System of Classification:** It was proposed by **Carolus Linnaeus** and is based on androecium structure and vegetative characters.
- **Natural System of Classification:** Proposed by **George Bentham** and **J.D. Hooker**. It was based on natural affinities among organisms.
- **Phylogenetic System of Classification:** It is based on evolutionary relationships between the various organisms. This system of classification believes that organisms belonging to the same taxa have a common ancestor.

Taxonomy:

- **Numerical Taxonomy** is based on all the observable characteristics. In this, numbers and codes are assigned to all the characters and then data is processed by using computers and each character is given equal importance where hundreds of characters are considered at the same time.
- **Cytotaxonomy** is based on cytological information like chromosome number, structure, and behaviour.
- **Chemotaxonomy** uses the chemical constituents of the organism to classify them.

Algae

- They are simple, thalloid, autotrophic and mostly aquatic organisms. They are found in different types of habitats like moist stones, soils and wood. Some of them are found in association with fungi (lichens) and animals (e.g., on sloth bear).
- Algae show variation in form and size. Some of them are microscopic unicellular (like *Chlamydomonas*), some are colonial (like *Volvox*) while some are filamentous (like *Ulothrix* and *Spirogyra*). Some marine algae like kelps have massive plant bodies. All modes of reproduction, i.e., Vegetative, asexual and sexual reproduction are found in algae.
- **Fragmentation:** A type of vegetative reproduction – is very common among filamentous algae. In this mode of reproduction, each fragment develops into a thallus.
- **Asexual reproduction** involves the production of different types of spores. Zoospores are the most common type of asexual spores. Due to presence of flagella, they are motile. They germinate to give rise to new plants.

> **Scan to know more about this topic**
> General characters of plant kingdom and Algae

- **Sexual reproduction** involves fusion of two gametes. On the basis of nature of gamete involved, sexual reproduction is of following three types:
  - **Isogamous reproduction:** In this type of reproduction, gametes are similar in size. Gametes may be flagellated as in *Chlamydomonas* or non-flagellated as in *Spirogyra*.
  - **Anisogamous reproduction:** This type of reproduction involves fusion of two gametes which are dissimilar in size as in some species of *Chlamydomonas*.
  - **Oogamous reproduction:** This type of reproduction involves fusion between one large, non-motile (static) female gamete and a smaller, motile male gamete. *Volvox* and *Fucus* exhibit oogamous reproduction.
- Algae are economically important for us. About half of the total carbon dioxide fixation on earth is carried out by algae through photosynthesis.
- Some marine brown and red algae produce hydrocolloids (like **algin** and **carrageen**). These colloids are used commercially.
- Agar is one of the commercial products. It is used to grow microbes and in preparations of ice-creams and jellies. It is also obtained from *Gelidium* and *Gracilaria*.
- Some unicellular algae like *Chlorella* and *Spirulina* are rich in proteins and hence they are used as food supplements.
- The algae are divided into three main classes: Chlorophyceae, Phaeophyceae and Rhodophyceae.

(i) Chlorophyceae (Green algae)

- The members of this class are commonly known as **green algae**. They possess pigments chlorophyll *a* and *b* in chloroplasts. Each chloroplast contains one or more storage bodies called pyrenoids. In addition to starch, pyrenoids also contain protein. In some algae, food may be stored in the form of oil droplets. Members of chlorophyceae have a rigid cell wall consisting of an inner layer of cellulose and an outer layer of pectose.
- Common examples of green algae are *Chlamydomonas, Volvox, Ulothrix, Spirogyra* and *Chara*.

(ii) Phaeophyceae (Brown algae)

- The members of this class are found chiefly in marine habitats. Some of them are simple branched, filamentous forms (like *Ectocarpus*) while some are profusely branched reaching a height of 100 metres. They possess chlorophyll *a*, *c*, carotenoids and xanthophylls. They store food in the form of complex carbohydrates (either laminarin or mannitol). The vegetative cells are covered

Classes	Common Name	Major Plgments	Stored Food	Cell Wall	Flagellar Number and Position of Insertion	Habitat
Chlorophy ceae	Green algae	Chlorophyll a, b	Starch	Cellulose	2-8, equal apical	Fresh water, brackish water, salt water
Phaeophy ceae	Brown algae	Chlorophyll a, C, fucoxanthin	Mannitol, laminarin	Cellulose and algin	2, unequal lateral	Fresh water (rare)brackish water, salt water
Rhodophy ceae	Red algae	Chlorophyll a, d, Phycoerythrin	Floridean starch	Cellulose, pectin and poly-sulphate esters	Absent	Fresh water (some), brackish water, salt water (most)

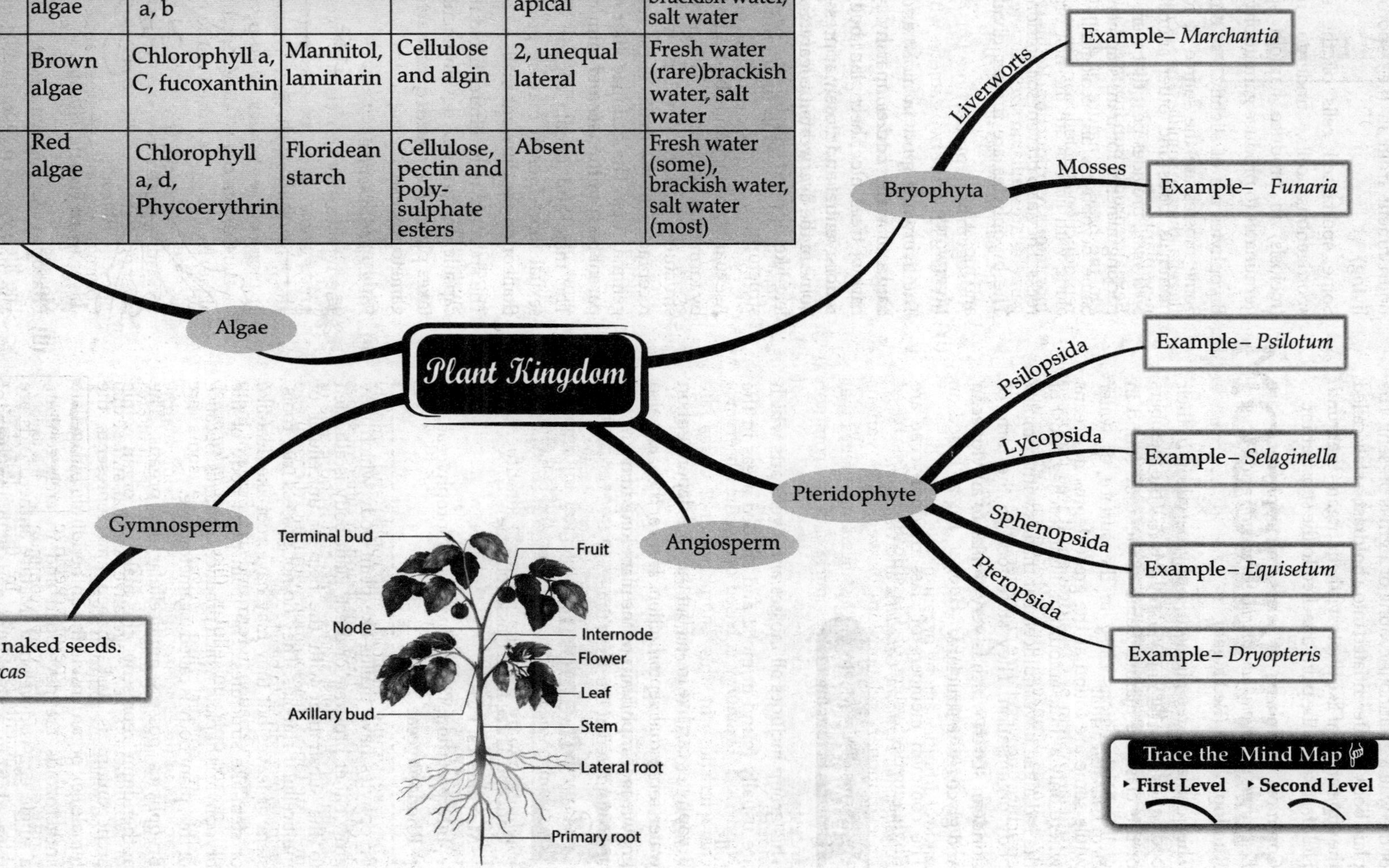

with a wall consisting of cellulose. On the outer side of the wall a gelatinous coating of **algin** is present. The plant body is differentiated into a **holdfast**, a stalk called the **stipe** and leaf like photosynthetic organ– the **frond**. Holdfast keeps the plant attached to the substratum.

- Common members of class phaeophyceae are *Ectocarpus, Dictyota, Laminaria, Sargassum* and *Fucus*.

(iii) Rhodophyceae (Red algae)

- They contain a red pigment, *r*-phycoerythrin in their body and hence they appear red. Most of the members of this class are marine. Some of them are found in well-lighted regions close to the surface of water while some are found at the great depths in oceans where only a little amount of light reaches. Most of the red algae have multicellular thallus with complex body organisation. They store food in the form of floridean starch which is very similar to amylopectin and glycogen in structure.
- The common members of class rhodophyceae are *Polysiphonia, Porphyra, Gracilaria* and *Gelidium*.

Bryophytes

- This group includes all mosses and liverworts which are usually found in moist and shaded areas in the hills.
- Bryophytes can live in soil but they are dependent on water for sexual reproduction. Hence, they are also known as "Amphibians of the plant kingdom".

Mnemonics

Concept: Three main classes of algae
Mnemonics: PCR
Interpretation: Phaeophyceae, **C**hlorophyceae, **R**hodophyceae.

- Bryophytes have thallus-like plant body which may grow either prostrate or erect. Plant body is attached to the substratum with the help of unicellular or multicellular rhizoids. They do not possess true roots, stem or leaves but they may have root-like, leaf-like or stem-like structures. The main plant body of the bryophyte is haploid which produces gametes. Because of this, plant body is called a gametophyte.
- Bryophytes possess multicellular sex organs. The antheridium represents the male sex organ while archegonium is flask shaped and represents the female sex organ. Inside the antheridium, biflagellate antherozoids are developed and in archegonium, a single egg is developed. Mature antherozoids are released from antheridium and with the help of water they reach to archegonium. In archegonium, antherozoid fuses with the egg to produce the zygote. After fertilisation, zygote undergoes a resting period and thereafter it undergoes reduction division. As a result a multicellular body called a sporophyte develops. The sporophyte is attached to the photosynthetic gametophyte and derives nourishment from it. (i.e., sporophyte is not free-living)
- Some specialised cells of the sporophyte, called sporogenous cells, undergo reduction division (meiosis) to produce haploid spores. Each spore germinates to produce gametophyte.
- Bryophytes are of slightly less economic importance. Some mosses are the source of food for herbaceous mammals, birds and other animals. A moss, named *Sphagnum*, provides peat that were used as fuel and as packing material for trans-shipment of living material. Some bryophytes are ecologically important. Mosses along with lichens are the first organisms to colonise rocks. They also prevent soil erosion.
- The bryophytes are further divided into liverworts and mosses.

(i) Liverworts

- The liverworts grow in moist and shady places like banks of water bodies, marshy ground, damp soil, bark of trees, etc. Their plant body is thalloid which is dorsiventral and closely appressed to the substrate. Some of the liverworts are leafy. Such forms have tiny leaf-like appendages in two rows on the stem-like structures.
- Asexual reproduction is by fragmentation of thalli or by formation of gemmae. The gemmae are specialised structures which develop in small cup-shaped receptacles on the thalli. These receptacles are called gemma cups. The gemmae after detaching from the parent body germinate and form new individuals.
- The male and female organs associated with the sexual reproduction may be produced on the same thalli or on the different thalli.
- The sporophyte is differentiated into a foot, seta and capsule. In capsule, development of haploid spores takes place. The spores germinate to form free-living gametophytes.
- For e.g., *Marchantia*.

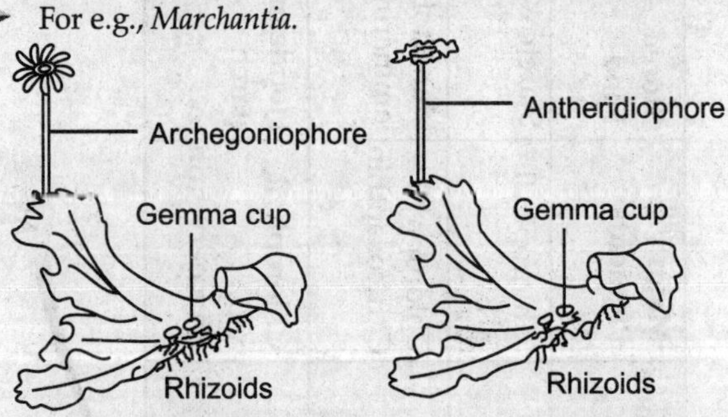

Liver wort: Female Thallus **Male thallus**

(ii) Mosses

- The life cycle of a moss involves both gametophytic phase and sporophytic phase, but the gametophytic phase is predominant one. Gametophytic phase consists of two stages - the first stage is the protonema stage and the second stage is leafy stage.
- Protonema stage develops directly from a spore. It is a creeping, green, branched and filamentous stage.

- Leafy stage develops from the secondary protonema. It consists of upright, slender axis bearing spirally arranged leaves. It bears multicellular and branched rhizoids which help the plant body to attach the soil. Leafy stage bears the sex organs.

Mnemonics

Concept: Divisions of plant kingdom
Mnemonics: A and B Plays Golf Alone
Interpretation: Algae, Bryophyta, Pteridophyta, Gymnosperms, Angiosperms

- Common examples of mosses are *Funaria, Polytrichum* and *Sphagnum.*
- The mosses exhibit following modes of reproduction:
- Vegetative reproduction in mosses takes place by fragmentation and budding in the secondary protonema.
- The sex organs *i.e.,* antheridia and archegonia are produced at the apex of the leafy shoots. After fertilisation, zygote is formed which develops into sporophyte.
- Sporophyte consists of a foot, seta and capsule. The sporophyte in mosses is more elaborate than that in liverworts. Inside the capsule, development of haploid spores takes place. Development of spores involves meiosis.

Pteridophytes

- They are the first terrestrial plants which possess vascular tissues – xylem and phloem. They are mostly found in cool, damp and shady places. The main plant body is a sporophyte which is differentiated into true root, stem and leaves. Each organ has well-differentiated vascular tissues. Some pteridophytes such as *Selaginella* bear small leaves (microphylls) while some other such as ferns bear large leaves (macrophylls).
- The sporophytic plant bears sporangia on the ventral side of leaf-like appendages called sporophylls. In some pteridophytes such as *Selaginella* and *Equisetum,* sporophylls form compact structures each called cone or strobilus. In sporangia, haploid spores are produced by meiotic division in spore mother cells. Each spore germinates and gives rise to inconspicuous, multicellular, thalloid gametophyte called **prothallus**. This prothallus is free-living, mostly photosynthetic and requires cool, damp, shady places to grow.
- The gametophyte bears male (antheridia) and female sex organs (archegonia). The transfer of antherozoids from the antheridia to the mouth of archegonium requires water. Fusion of male gamete with the egg leads to the formation of zygote.
- Later on, zygote develops into a multicellular well-differentiated sporophyte which is the dominant phase in the life cycle of the pteridophytes. Most of the pteridophytes bear same kind of spores. Such plants are called **homosporous**. Some pteridophytes such as *Selaginella* and *Salvinia* bear two kinds of spores – macrospore which are large in size and microspores which are small in size. Such pteridophytes are known as **heterosporous**. The megaspores and microspores germinate and give rise to female and male gametophytes, respectively.
- The pteridophytes are further classified into four classes:
- **Psilopsida** *e.g., Psilotum*
- **Lycopsida** *e.g., Selaginella and Lycopodium*
- **Sphenopsida** *e.g., Equisetum*
- **Pteropsida** *e.g., Dryopteris, Pteris, Adiantum*

Gymnosperms

Scan to know more about this topic
Gymnosperms

- In gymnosperms, ovules are naked without any covering and hence remain exposed. The seeds, which develop after fertilisation, are also naked.
- Gymnosperms are either shrub or tree. In some genera, e.g., in *Pinus*, roots are in association with fungi in the form of **mycorrhiza.** In some other genera of gymnosperms like *Cycas,* roots are associated with nitrogen-fixing cyanobacteria which are called **coralloid roots.**
- In some genera such as *Cycas,* stems are unbranched whereas in some other genera like *Pinus, Cedrus,* etc., stem is branched.
- The leaves may be simple or compound. *Cycas* has pinnately compound leaves which persist for a few years. Conifers such as *Pinus, Deodar,* etc., have needle-like leaves with thick cuticle and sunken stomata. All these features help to reduce water loss.
- The gymnosperms are heterosporous. They produce haploid microspores and megaspores within sporangia. Sporangia are formed on sporophylls which are arranged spirally along an axis to form compact strobili or cones.
- The strobili are of two types– male strobili/ cones and female strobili/cones. Male cones bear microsporophylls with microsporangia while female cones bear megasporophylls with ovules or megasporangia. The male or female cones may be borne on the same tree as in *Pinus* or on different trees as in *Cycas*.
- The microspore or pollen grain represents reduced gametophyte. The development of pollen grains take place within the microsporangia.
- In ovule, one of the cells of the nucellus differentiates into megaspore mother cell ($2n$). The megaspore mother cell divides meiotically to form four megaspores (n). One of the megaspores develops into a female gametophyte or embryo sac after nuclear division. The female gametophyte is retained within megasporangium.

- Unlike bryophytes and pteridophytes, in gymnosperms the male and the female gametophytes do not have an independent free-living existence. They remain within the sporangia retained on the sporophytes.
- After the release of pollen grains from the microsporangium, they are carried in air currents. When they come in contact with the opening of the ovules borne on megasporophylls, pollen tube carrying the male gametes grows towards archegonia in the ovules. The pollen tube discharge their contents near the mouth of the archegonia. Subsequently, fertilisation takes place and a zygote is formed. Zygote develops into an embryo and the ovules into seeds. These seeds are not covered.

Mnemonics

Concept: Examples of Gymnosperms
Mnemonics: Going to CP
Interpretation: *Gingko, Cycas, Pinus*

Angiosperms

- In angiosperms, the pollen grains and ovules are developed in specialised structures called flowers. The seeds are enclosed in fruits.
- The angiosperms are an exceptionally large group of plants occuring in wide range of habitats.
- They range in size from the smallest *wolffia* to tall trees of Eucalyptus (over metres).
- They provide us with food, fodder, fuel, medicines and several other commercially important products.
- They are divided into two classes: the dicotyledons and the monocotyledons.

Key Words

- **Isogamy:** It is the fusion of two morphologically and physiologically similar gametes.
- **Anisogamy:** It is the fusion of two gametes which are morphologically dissimilar but physiologically similar (both motile or both non-motile).
- **Oogamy:** Refers to the fusion of male and female gametes which are both morphologically and physiologically dissimilar.
- **Gametophyte:** Gametophyte is a haploid plant structure that produces gametes directly by mitosis.
- **Sporophyte:** Sporophyte is diploid ($2n$) plant structure that produces haploid (n) spores by meiosis.
- **Heterospory:** It is a phenomenon in which two different kinds of spores produced are produced on the same plant.

NCERT CORNER

Q. 1. What is the basis of classification of algae? **[NCERT Ex. Q. 1, Page 35]**

Ans. Algae are classified on the basis of:

(i) Type of pigments they possess.

(ii) Chemical nature of reserved food material.

(iii) Kinds, number and points of insertion of motile cells and

(iv) The presence or absence of organised nucleus in the cell.

Q. 2. When and where does reduction division take place in the life cycle of a liverwort, a moss, a fern, and a gymnosperm ? **[NCERT Ex. Q. 2, Page 35]**

Ans. Reduction divisions in the life cycle of a liverwort, a moss, a fern and a gymnosperm take place during the production of spores from spore mother cells.

Q. 3. Name three groups of plants that bear archegonia. Briefly describe the life cycle of any one of them. **[NCERT Ex. Q. 3, Page 35]**

Ans. Bryophytes, pteridophytes, and gymnosperms are the plants that bear archegonia.

The life cycle of bryophytes:

(i) Bryophytes produce gametes and are haploid. Bryophytes have multicellular sexual organs.

(ii) The antheridium, which produces biflagellate anterozoids, is the male sex organ. The archegonium is a female sexual organ that produces a single egg.

(iii) Anthrozoids are released into the water when antheridium comes into touch with archegonium.

(iv) An antherozoid fuses with the egg to produce the zygote.

(v) The zygote undergoes reduction division to produce a multicellular body called a sporophyte.

(vi) Saprophytes undergo reduction division to produce haploid spores.

(vii) These spores germinate to produce gametophyte.

Q. 4. Mention the ploidy of the following: protonemal cell of a moss; primary endosperm nucleus in dicot, leaf cell of a moss; prothallus cell of a fern; gemma cell in *Marchantia;* meristem cell of monocot, ovum of a liverwort, and zygote of a fern. **[NCERT Ex. Q. 4, Page 35]**

Ans. Protonemal cell of a moss: It is haploid (n).

Primary endosperms nucleus (PEN) in dicot: It is triploid ($3n$).

Leaf cell of a moss: It is haploid (n).

Prothallus cell of a fern: It is haploid (*n*).

Gemma cell in *marchantia*: It is haploid (*n*).

Meristem cell of monocot: It is diploid (2*n*).

Ovum of a liverwort: It is haploid (*n*).

Zygote of a fern: It is diploid (2*n*).

Q. 5. Write a note on economic importance of algae and gymnosperms. [NCERT Ex. Q. 5, Page 36]

Ans. Economic importance of algae:

(i) Agar is obtained commercially from *Gelidium* and *Gracilaria* which is widely used in the preparation of jellies, puddings, cream, etc.

(ii) Some brown algae are menace for shipping.

(iii) Some species of *Porphyra, Laminaria* and *Sargassum* are used as food.

(iv) An antibiotic chlorellin is extracted out from *Chlorella*.

Economic importance of Gymnosperms:

(i) Conifers provide enormous amount of soft wood for construction, plywood, paper industry, etc.

(ii) Seeds of *Pinus* are edible.

(iii) Saw dust of conifers is used in making linoleum and plastics.

(iv) Ephedrine drug is obtained from *Ephedra* used in asthma.

Q. 6. Both gymnosperms and angiosperms bear seeds, then why are they classified separately? [NCERT Ex. Q. 6, Page 36]

Ans. Both gymnosperms and angiosperms bear seeds, but they are yet classified separately. Because, in case of gymnosperms the seeds are naked, i.e., the seeds are not produced inside the fruit but in case of angiosperms the seeds are enclosed inside the fruit.

Q. 7. What is heterospory? Briefly comment on its significance. Give two examples. [NCERT Ex. Q. 7, Page 36]

Ans. Heterospory is the production of two kinds of spores and is the first step towards seed habit. Pteridophytes such as *Selaginella, Salvinia* and *Marsilea* produce two kinds of spores-microspores and macrospores.

Significance:

(i) The mega and microspores germinate and then give rise to male and female gametophytes.

(ii) The female gametophyte is retained on parent sporophyte for variable period of time.

(iii) The development of zygote into young embryo occurs within female gametophyte.

This step is said to be precursor of seed habit as exhibited by gymnosperms and angiosperms.

Q. 8. Explain briefly the following terms with suitable examples:
(i) Protonema (ii) Antheridium (iii) Archegonium (iv) diplontic (v) Sporophyll (vi) Isogamy [NCERT Ex. Q. 8, Page 36]

Ans. (i) Protonema: It is a juvenile stage of a moss that develops from the germinating meiospores. When fully grown, it comprises slender, green, branching system of filaments called protonema.

(ii) Antheridium: Male sex organs in bryophytes and pteridophytes are known as antheridium. They are jacketed and multicellular which produces a number of flagellated male gametes called sperms or antherozoids.

(iii) Archegonium: The female sex organs of bryophytes, pteridophytes and gymnosperms are called as archegonia. It is a flask shaped structure with tubular neck and a swollen venter. The single layered wall of neck has 5-6 rows of cell. It encloses a few sterile neck canal cells. The walls of venter encloses a few sterile venter canal cell and a fertile egg or oosphere.

(iv) Diplontic: It is a type of life cycle in which the gametophytic phase is represented by single to few called haploid gametophyte and sporophyte is doninant e.g., Fucus.

(v) Sporophylls: Spores bearing leaves of ferns are called as sporophylls. Sporangia occur on the leaves on clusters called sori, so they are also known as fertile leaves. A sorus is covered by a flap-like outgrowth from its surface or turned margins of sporophylls. They are of two types: microsporophyll which bear microsporangia and megasporophyll which bear megasporangia.

(vi) Isogamy: In isogamy the fusing gametes are morphologically and physiologically similar. They may be flagellate or non-flagellate.

Q. 9. Differentiate between the following:
(i) Red algae and brown algae
(ii) Liverworts and mosses
(iii) Homosporous and heterosporous pteridophyte [NCERT Ex. Q. 9, Page 36]

Ans. (i) Differences between red algae and brown algae:

S.No.	Red algae	Brown algae
(i)	It belongs to Rhodophyceae.	It belongs to the class phaeophyceae.
(ii)	Phycoerythrin, phycocyanin and phycobilins pigments are present with chlorophyll 'a'.	Chlorophyll a, c and fucoxanthin are the major pigments.
(iii)	Reserve food material is floridean starch.	Reserve food is laminarin and mannitol
(iv)	Unicellular and microscopic, only a few are filamentous and heterotrichous.	Unicellular, multi-cellular may be motile or flagellated.
(v)	Examples: *Gelidium, Porphyra, Chondrus.*	Examples: *Laminaria, Sargassum and Fucus*

(ii) Differences between liverworts and mosses:

S.No.	Liverworts	Mosses
(i)	They have a thallus like dorsoventrally flattened body.	There are differentiated into stem-like and leaf-like structures.
(ii)	Rhizoids unicellular.	Rhizoids multicellular and branched.

(iii)	Scales are present.	Scales are absent.
(iv)	Sporogonium is differentiated into foot, seta and capsule. In some cases, foot and seta may be absent.	Sporogonium is differentiated into foot, seta and capsule. The sporophyte is more elaborate.
(v)	The sporogonium does not synthesis its food.	The sporogonium sythesises its own food.
(vi)	Capsule has spores and elaters.	Elaters are not present.
(vii)	Peristomial teeth are absent.	Peristomial teeth are present on the upper end of the capsule. They usually help in the dispersal of spores.
(viii)	Columella is lacking.	Columella is present.
(ix)	Protonema is absent.	Spores germinate to form a filamentous protonema.
(x)	Spores germinate directly into a new plant.	Protonema bear buds laterally which give rise to leafy gametophyte.

(iii) Differences between homosporous and heterosporous pteridophytes:

Homosporous pteridophytes	Heterosporous pteridophytes
(i) Generally all the spores are of same kind, such plants are called homosporous.	Some plant of pteridophyta have different kind of spores. These plants are known as heterosporous. e.g., *Selaginella, Salvinia.*
(ii) It has no evolutionary significance.	It has an evolutionary significance as hetero-spory is precursor to the seed habit.

Q. 10. Match the following (column I with column II)

Column I	Column II
(a) *Chlamydomonas*	(i) Moss
(b) *Cycas*	(ii) Pteridophyte
(c) *Selaginella*	(iii) Algae
(d) *Sphagnum*	(iv) Gymnosperm

[NCERT Ex. Q. 10, Page 36]

Ans.

Column I	Column II
(a) *Chlamydomonas*	(iii) Algae
(b) *Cycas*	(iv) Gymnosperm
(c) *Selaginella*	(ii) Algae
(d) *Sphagnum*	(i) Moss

Q.11. Describe the important characteristics of Gymnosperms? [NCERT Ex. Q. 11, Page 36]

Ans. The main characters of gymnosperms are as follows:

(i) All gymnosperms are perennial, growing as woody trees or bushy shrubs.

(ii) Vascular tissues are arranged into vascular bundles.

(iii) Gymnosperms are heterosporous, i.e., they produce two type of meiospores: Microspores and megaspores. Microspores are produced on the microsporangia and megaspores are produced on megasporangia. The megasporangia are integumented and are called ovules.

(iv) Flowers are absent, however, microsporophylls and megasporophylls usually aggregate to form distinct cones or strobili called male cones and female cones respectively.

(v) Ovules are borne on megasporophyll and have three layered integument with an opening called micropyle.

(vi) Pollination is accomplished by wind.

(vii) Fertilisation is affected by pollen tube produced by the male gametophyte. It is called siphonogamy.

(viii) A food laden tissue called endosperm is produced in a seed. Seeds are naked i.e., without any seed-coat.

□□

ANIMAL KINGDOM

CHAPTER 4

Basis of Classification

- There are fundamental features common to various individuals in relation to the arrangement of cells, body symmetry nature of coelom, patterns of digestive, circulatory or reproductive systems. These features are used as the basis of classification of animals.

Levels of Organisation

- All the members of Animalia are multicellular, but some of them do not exhibit the same pattern of organisation of cells. Example: the cells in sponges are arranged as loose cell aggregates i.e., they exhibit cellular level of organisation.
- The cells performing the same function, in coelenterates, are arranged into tissues, hence is called tissue level of organisation.
- Organs level is the higher level of organisation, exhibited by members of Platyhelminthes and other higher phyla where tissues are grouped together to form organs.
- The pattern in which organs associate to form functional systems and each system is concerned with a specific physiological function is called organ system level of organisation.
- The digestive system in Platyhelminthes has only a single opening to the outside of the body that serves as both mouth and anus and hence is called incomplete. A complete digestive system has two opening, mouth and anus.
- **The circulatory system may be of two types:**

(i) Open type in which blood is pumped out of the heart and the cells and tissues are directly bathed in it and

(ii) Closed type in which the blood is circulated through a series of vessels of varying diameter, e.g., arteries, veins and capillaries.

Symmetry

- Animals can be categorised on the basis of their symmetry.
- Sponges are mostly asymmetrical, i.e., any plane that passes through the centre does not divide them into two equal halves.
- When any plane passing through the central axis of the body divides the organism into two equal halves, it is called radial symmetry. Example: Coelenterates, ctenpolores and echinoderms.
- When the body of an organism can be divided into identical left and right halves in only one plane, it is called lateral symmetry. Example: annelids, arthropods etc.

Diploblastic and Triploblastic Organisation

- Diploblastic animals are those in which the cells are arranged in two embryonic layers, an external ectoderm and an internal endoderm. Example: Coelenterates. An undifferentiated layer, mesoglea, is present in between the ectoderm and the endoderm.
- Triploblastic animals are those in which the developing embryo has a third germinal layer, **mesoderm,** in between the ectoderm and endoderm. Example: platyhelminthes.

Coelom

- Coelem is the body cavity, which is lined by mesoderm.
- Animals possessing coelom are called coeomates. Example: annelids, mollusces, arthropods, hemichordates and chordates.
- Animals in which the body cavity is not lined by mesoderm but it is present as scattered pouches in between the ectoderm and endoderm are called pseudocoelomates. Example: aschelminthes, Such a body cavity is called pseudocoelom.
- Animals in which the body cavity is absent are called acoelomates. Example: platyhelminthes.

Segmentation

- The pattern in which the body of animal is externally and internally divided into segments with a serial repetition of at least some organs, is called metameric segmentation. Example: earthworm.
- This phenomenon is known as metamerism.

Notochord

- Notochord is a mesodermally derived rod like structure formed on the dossal side during embryonic development in some animals.
- Animals with notochord are called chordates and those animals which do not form this structure are called non-chordates. Example: porifera to echinoderms.

Classification of Animals

- Animals are classified on the basis of arrangement of cells, body symmetry, nature of coelom, patterns of digestive, circulatory or reproductive systems.

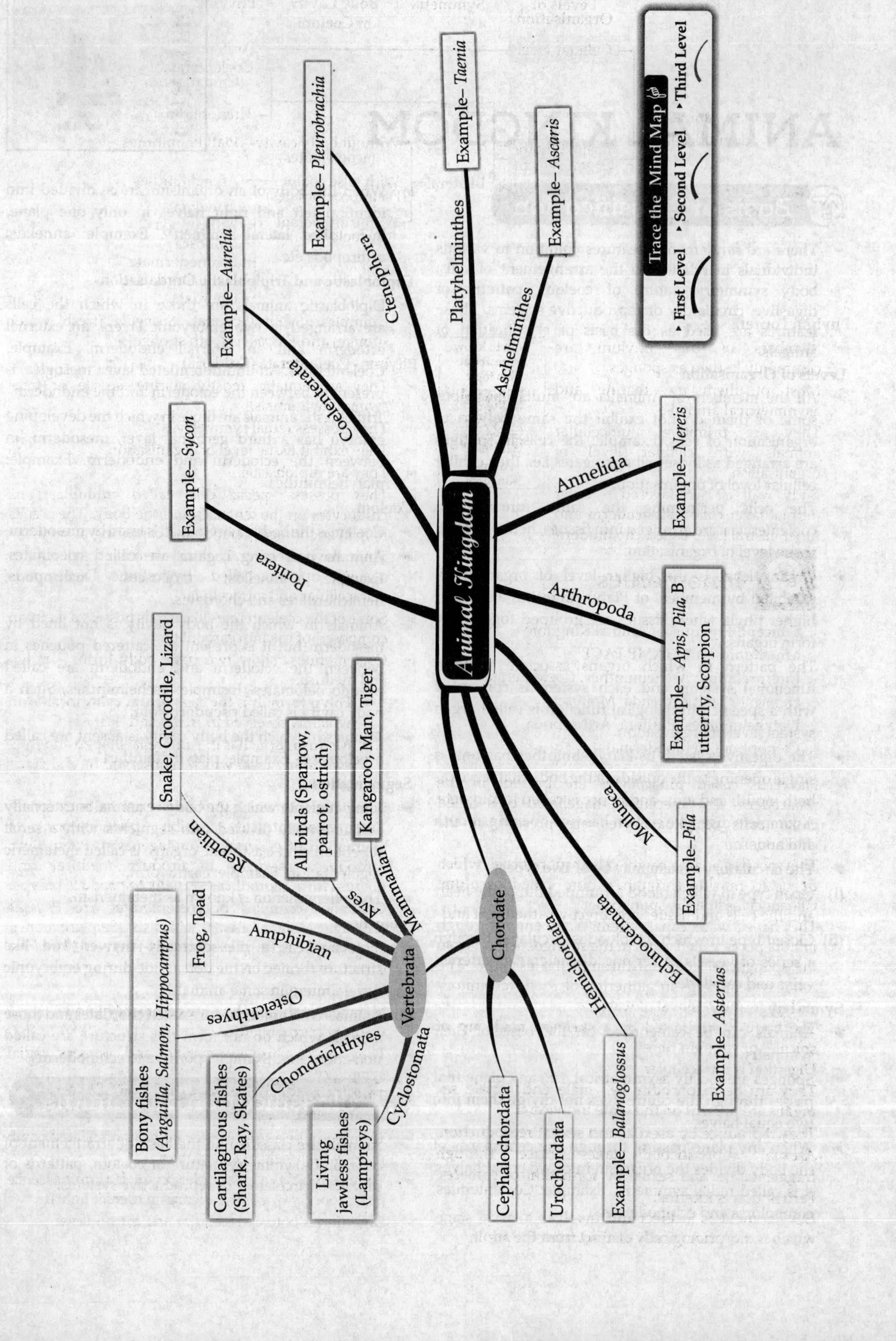
Trace the Mind Map
First Level
Second Level
Third Level
Animal Kingdom
Porifera
Example– Sycon
Coelenterata
Example– Aurelia
Ctenophora
Example– Pleurobrachia
Platyhelminthes
Example– Taenia
Aschelminthes
Example– Ascaris
Annelida
Example– Nereis
Arthropoda
Example– Apis, Pila, B utterfly, Scorpion
Mollusca
Example– Pila
Echinodermata
Example– Asterias
Hemichordata
Example– Balanoglossus
Chordate
Urochordata
Cephalochordata
Vertebrata
Cyclostomata
Living jawless fishes (Lampreys)
Chondrichthyes
Cartilaginous fishes (Shark, Ray, Skates)
Osteichthyes
Bony fishes (Anguilla, Salmon, Hippocampus)
Amphibian
Frog, Toad
Reptilian
Snake, Crocodile, Lizard
Aves
All birds (Sparrow, parrot, ostrich)
Mammalian
Kangaroo, Man, Tiger

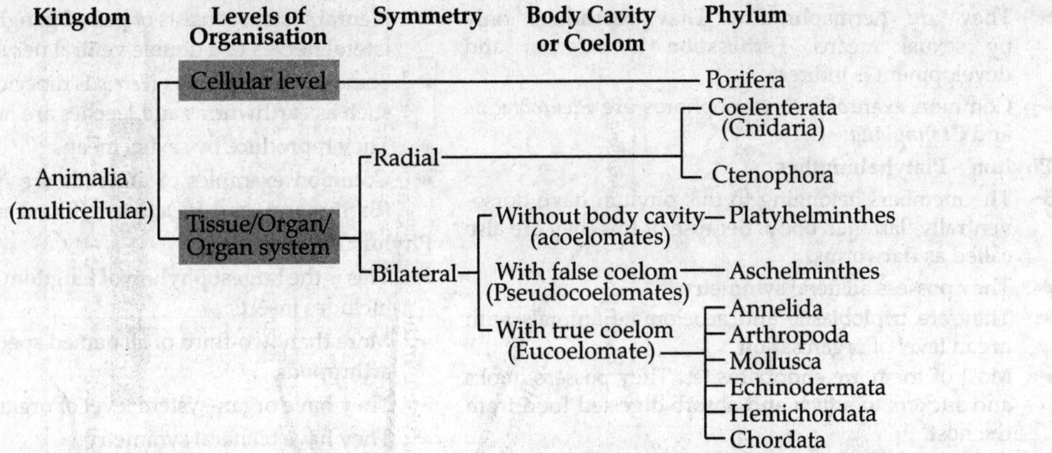

Phylum Porifera

- Members of this phylum are commonly known as sponges.
- Most of them are marine and **asymmetrical** animals.
- They are primitive multicellular animals with cellular level of organisation.
- Body wall is two layered – outer dermal layer called **pinacoderm** and inner gastral layer called **choanoderm**.

Scan to know more about this topic

Animal Kingdom

Mnemonics

Concept: Phylums of Animal Kingdom
Mnemonics: A CHAMP PACE
Interpretation: Aschelminthes, Coelenterata, Hemichordata, Annelida, Mollusca, Platyhelminthes, Porifera, Arthropoda, Ctenophora, Echinodermata.

- Flat cells called **pinacocytes** are present in the pinacoderm and specialised flagellated cells called **collar cells or choanocytes** are present in the choanoderm.
- They possess a large cavity called spongocoel, which opens to outside through a pore called **osculum**. Choanocytes line the spongocoel.
- They have a water canal system. Water enters through minute pores called **ostia** in the spongocoel and from the spongocoel goes out through the osculum. The canal system helps in gathering of food, respiratory exchange and removal of waste.
- The body is supported by a skeleton made up of spicules or spongin fibres.
- Digestion is intracellular.
- They are hermaphrodite i.e., male and female sex organs are present on the same individual.
- They reproduce by asexual and sexual reproduction. Asexual reproduction takes place through fragmentation and sexual by formation of gametes. Fertilisation is internal.
- Development is indirect and involves a larval stage which is morphologically distinct from the adult.
- Examples: *Sycon* (Scypha), *Spongilla* (fresh water sponge) and *Euspongia* (bath sponge).

Phylum- Coelenterata (Cnidaria)

- They are aquatic, mostly marine, sessile or free-swimming animals.
- They possess radial symmetry.
- They exhibit tissue level of organisation.
- They are diploblastic.
- They possess special cells called **cnidoblasts** or **cnidocytes** on the tentacles and the body. These cells help in anchorage, defence and capturing of prey.
- They have a central gastro-vascular cavity with a single opening called **hypostome**. Digestion is extracellular and intracellular.
- Some of the coelenterates like corals possess a skeleton composed of calcium carbonate.
- Coelenterates show two basic body forms – polyp and medusa.
    - **Polyp form:** It is the sessile and cylindrical form which is observed in *Hydra* and *Adamsia*.
    - **Medusa form:** It is the umbrella-shaped and free-swimming form which is observed in *Aurelia* or jelly fish.
- Some coelenterates e.g., *Obelia* exist in both forms. These coelenterates exhibit phenomenon of alternation of generation (metagenesis). Polyp form reproduces asexually to produce medusae and medusa form reproduces sexually to produce polyps.
- Common examples of coelenterates are *Physalia* (Portuguese man-of-war), *Adamsia* (Sea anemone), *Pennatula* (Sea-pen), *Gorgonia* (Sea-fan) and *Meandrina* (Brain coral).

Phylum – Ctenophora

- Members of this phylum are commonly known as **sea walnuts** or **comb jellies**.
- They are exclusively marine and possess radial symmetry.
- They are diploblastic organisms with tissue level of organisation.
- Their body bears eight external rows of ciliated comb plates which help in locomotion.
- They exhibit the phenomenon of bioluminescence (the property of a living organism to emit light).
- Digestion is both extracellular and intracellular.

- They are hermaphrodite. They reproduce only by sexual means. Fertilisation is external and development is indirect.
- Common examples of ctenophores are *Pleurobrachia* and *Ctenoplana*.

Phylum – Platyhelminthes

- The members belonging to this phylum have dorso-ventrally flattened body. Because of this they are also called as **flatworms**.
- They possess bilateral symmetry.
- They are triploblastic and acoelomate animals with organ level of organisation.
- Most of them are endoparasites. They possess hooks and suckers to attach and absorb digested food from the host.
- Specialised cells called **flame cells** are present in them. These cells help in osmoregulation and excretion.
- They are hermaphrodite.
- Fertilisation is internal and development is through many larval stages.
- Common examples of flat worms are *Taenia* (Tapeworm) and *Fasciola* (Liver fluke).

Phylum – Aschelminthes

- As their body is circular in cross-section, they are also know as round worm.
- They are found in variety of habitats. For example, some of them are aquatic, some are terrestrial and some are parasitic in plants and animals.
- They have organ-system level of body organisation.
- They possess bilateral symmetry.
- They are triploblastic and pseudocoelomate animals.
- They possess complete digestive system with well developed muscular pharynx.
- They have an excretory tube which removes body wastes from the body cavity through the excretory pore.
- They are dioecious, i.e., males and females are distinct. Usually, females are longer than males.
- Fertilisation is internal and development may be direct or indirect.
- Some examples of aschelminthes are *Ascaris* (Round Worm), *Wuchereria* (Filarial worm) and *Ancylostoma* (Hookworm).

Phylum – Annelida

- They may be aquatic (marine and freshwater) or terrestrial; free-living, and sometimes parasitic.
- They have organ-system level of body organisation.
- They have bilateral symmetry.
- They are triploblastic and coelomate animals.
- Their body surface is distinctly marked out into segments or metameres.
- They possess longitudinal and circular muscles which help in locomotion.
- Aquatic annelids like *Nereis* possess lateral appendages called **parapodia** which help in swimming.
- They possess closed circulatory system.
- Nephridia (sing. nephridium) help in osmoregulation and excretion.
- Neural system consists of paired ganglia connected by lateral nerves to a double ventral nerve cord.
- Some of them such as *Nereis* is dioecious, while some such as earthworms and leeches are monoecious.
- They reproduce by sexual means.
- Common examples of annelids are *Nereis, Pheretima* (Earthworm) and *Hirudinaria* (Blood sucking leech).

Phylum Arthropoda

- This is the **largest phylum** of kingdom animalia which includes insects.
- More than two-third of all named species on earth are arthropods.
- They have organ-system level of organisation.
- They have bilateral symmetry.
- They are triploblastic, segmented and coelomate animals.
- Their body is covered by chitinous exoskeleton.
- The body is divisible into three parts – head, thorax and abdomen.
- They have jointed appendages.
- They have gills, book gills, book lungs or tracheal system as respiratory organ.
- They have open circulatory system.
- They possess sensory organs like antennae and eyes.
- They have malpighian tubules as excretory organ.
- Most of them are dioecious and oviparous.
- Fertilisation is usually internal. Development may be direct or indirect.
- Some of the arthropods such as *Apis* (Honey bee), *Bombyx* (Silkworm), *Laccifer* (Lac insect) are economically important insects while some other insects like *Anopheles*, *Culex* and *Aedes* (Mosquitoes) are vectors and some insects like *Locusta* (Locust) are pest. *Limulus* (King crab) is a living fossil.

Phylum – Mollusca

- This is the second largest phylum of kingdom Animalia.
- Molluscs are terrestrial or aquatic (marine or freshwater) organisms.
- They have an organ-system level of organisation.
- Their body is bilaterally symmetrical.
- They are triploblastic and coelomate animals.
- They have soft and unsegmented body covered by a calcareous shell.
- Their body is differentiated into head, muscular foot and visceral hump. A soft and spongy layer of skin forms a mantle over the visceral hump. The space between the hump and the mantle is called the mantle cavity.
- The anterior region of the head bears sensory tentacles. The mouth contains a rasping organ for feeding, called radula.
- In terrestrial forms, respiration takes place through lungs and in aquatic forms, respiration takes place through feather-like gills which are present in the mantle cavity.

- Molluscs are usually dioecious and oviparous with indirect development.
- Common examples of molluscs are *Pila* (Apple snail), *Pinctada* (Pearl oyster), *Sepia* (Cuttlefish), *Loligo* (Squid), *Octopus* (Devil fish), *Aplysia* (Sea- hare), *Dentalium* (Tusk shell) and *Chaetopleura* (Chiton).

Phylum – Echinodermata

- The echinoderms are marine organisms which have an endoskeleton of calcareous ossicles.
- They have organ-system level of organisation.
- The echinoderms, in larval stage, are bilaterally symmetrical but adults are radially symmetrical.
- They are triploblastic and coelomate animals.
- The digestive system is complete. The mouth is situated on the lower (ventral) side and anus is present on the upper (dorsal) side.
- Their unique characteristic is presence of water vascular system. This system helps in locomotion, capture and transport of food and respiration.
- Echinoderms lack excretory system.
- They reproduce by sexual means. Sexes are separate.
- Fertilisation is usually external and development is indirect with free-swimming larva.
- Common echinoderms are *Asterias* (Star fish), *Echinus* (Sea urchin), *Antedon* (Sea lily), *Cucumaria* (Sea cucumber) and *Ophiura* (Brittle star).

Phylum – Hemichordata

- It was earlier considered as a sub-phylum under phylum Chordata. But now it is considered as a separate phylum under non-chordata.
- This phylum incorporates worm-like marine animals with organ-system level of organisation.
- Hemichordates are bilaterally symmetrical, triploblastic and coelomate animals.
- Their body is cylindrical and differentiated into an anterior proboscis, a collar and a long trunk.
- They have open circulatory system.
- They respire through gills.
- Proboscis gland is their excretory organ.
- Sexes are separate. Fertilisation is external and development is indirect.
- Common hemichordates are *Balanoglossus* and *Saccoglossus*.

Phylum-Chordata

- Animals belonging to phylum Chordata are fundamentally characterised by the presence of a notochord, a dorsal hollow nerve cord and paired pharyngeal gill slits.

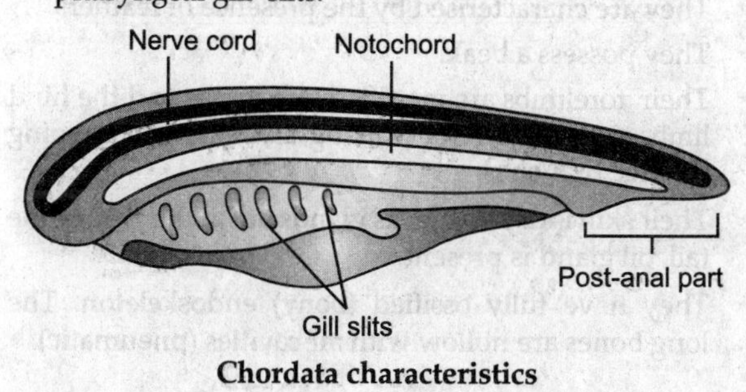

Chordata characteristics

- They are bilaterally symmetrical, triploblastic, coelomate with organ-system level of organisation.
- They possess a post anal tail and a closed circulatory system.

Table: Comparison of chordates and non-chordates.

S.No.	Chordates	Non-chordates
(i)	Notochord present.	Notochord absent.
(ii)	Central nervous system is dorsal, hollow and single.	Central nervous system is ventral, solid and double.
(iii)	Pharynx perforated by gill slits.	Gill slits are absent.
(iv)	Heart is ventral.	Heart is dorsal (if present).
(v)	A post-anal part (tail) is present.	Post-anal tail is absent.

- **Phylum chordata is divided into three subphyla:**

(i) Urochordata: In urochordates, notochord is present only in larval tail. Their examples are *Ascidia*, *Salpa* and *Doliolum*.

(ii) Cephalochordata: In cephalochordates, notochord extends from head to tail region and is persistent throughout their life. Examples of cephalochordates is *Branchiostoma*.

(iii) Vertebrata: The members of this sub-phylum possess notochord during the embryonic period. In adults, this notochord is replaced by a cartilaginous or bony vertebral column.

- Subphyla Urochordata and Cephalochordata are often referred to as protochordate.
- They have a ventral muscular heart with two, three or four chambers.
- They have kidneys for excretion and osmoregulation.
- They have paired appendages either in the form of fins or in the form of limbs.
- Subphylum vertebrata is divided into two Divisions: Agnatha and Gnathostomata.

Divisions : Agnatha (The jawless vertebrates).

Class – Cyclostomata

- All the members of class cyclostomata are marine and ectoparasites on some fishes.
- They possess an elongated body containing 6-15 pairs of gill slits for respiration.
- They have a sucking and circular mouth without jaws.
- They lack scales and paired fins.
- Their cranium and vertebral column are cartilaginous.
- They have closed circulatory system.
- They are marine creatures but for spawning they migrate to freshwater. Thereafter, they die within a few days.
- Their larvae, after metamorphosis, return to the ocean.

Scan to know more about this topic

Hemichordata and chordata

- Some common members of class cyclostomata are *Petromyzon* (Lamprey) and *Myxine* (Hagfish).

Divisions : Gnathostomata (The jawed vertebrates)

Gnathostomata is divided into two super classes : Pisces and Tetrapod.

Super Class I: Pisces (bear fins)

Class 1 – Chondrichthyes

- They are marine animals.
- Their body is streamlined and endoskeleton is cartilaginous.
- Their mouth is located on the ventral side.
- Notochord is persistent throughout life.
- Gill slits are separate and not covered by operculum.
- They contain minute placoid scales. Because of their presence, the skin is tough.
- Their teeth are modified placoid scales which are backwardly directed. Their jaws are very powerful. These animals are predaceous.
- They lack air bladder and hence to avoid sinking they have to swim constantly.
- Their heart is two-chambered (one auricle and one ventricle).
- Some of cartilaginous fishes e.g., *Torpedo* have electric organs and some of them e.g., *Trygon* possess poison sting.
- They do not have capacity to regulate their body temperature. Such type of animals are called cold-blooded animals or poikilothermous animals.
- Sexes are separate. In males, pelvic fins bear claspers.
- They show internal fertilisation and many of them are viviparous.
- Some examples of chondrichthyes are *Scoliodon* (Dog fish), *Pristis* (Saw fish) and *Carcharodon* (Great white shark) and *Trygon* (Sting ray).

Class 2 – Osteichthyes

- This class includes those marine and freshwater fishes which have bony endoskeleton.
- Their body is streamlined and mouth is terminal.
- They possess four pairs of gills which are covered by an operculum on each side.
- Skin is covered with cycloid/ctenoid scales.
- They possess air bladder which regulates buoyancy.
- They have two- chambered (one auricle and one ventricle) heart.
- They are cold-blooded animals.
- Sexes are separate.
- Fertilisation is usually external and most of them are oviparous.
- Development is direct.
- Common examples of marine bony fishes are *Exocoetus* (Flying fish), *Hippocampus* (Sea horse) while *Labeo* (Rohu), *Catla* (Katla), *Clarias* (Magur) are examples of freshwater bony fishes. Some of them such as *Betta* (Fighting fish), and *Pterophyllum* (Angel fish) are aquarium fishes.

Super class 2. Tetrapoda (bear two pairs of limbs).

Class 1. – Amphibia

- Amphibians can live in aquatic as well as terrestrial habitats.
- Their body is differentiated into head and trunk. Some amphibians also possess tail.
- Their skin is moist and lack scales.
- They have two pairs of limbs.
- The eyes have eyelids and tympanum represents the ear.
- Respiration takes place by gills, lungs and through skin.
- They possess three-chambered heart. Out of the three chambers, two are auricles and third one is ventricle.
- They are cold-blooded animals.
- Sexes are separate. They are oviparous.
- Fertilisation is external and development is direct or indirect.
- Some common amphibians are *Bufo* (Toad), *Rana* (Frog), *Hyla* (Tree frog), *Salamandra* (Salamander) and *Ichthyophis* (Limbless amphibia).

Class 2. – Reptilia

- Members of this class are mostly terrestrial animals and have creeping or crawling mode of locomotion.
- Their body is covered with dry and cornified skin, epidermal scales or scutes.
- They lack external ear openings. Tympanum represents ear.
- Most of them possess two pairs of limbs while some do not have limbs.
- Except the crocodiles, all reptiles have three-chambered heart. (Crocodiles have four-chambered heart).
- They are cold blooded animals.
- Sexes are separate.
- They are oviparous.
- Fertilisation is internal and development is direct.
- Some common reptiles are *Chelone* (Turtle), *Testudo* (Tortoise), *Chameleon* (Tree lizard), *Calotes* (Garden lizard), *Crocodilus* (Crocodile), *Alligator* (Alligator), *Hemidactylus* (Wall lizard) and poisonous snakes like *Naja* (Cobra), *Bangarus* (Krait), *Vipera* (Viper).

Class 3. – Aves

- This class includes all the birds which have ability to fly (except flightless birds like ostrich).
- They are characterised by the presence of feathers.
- They possess a beak.
- Their forelimbs are modified into wings and the hind limbs are modified for walking, swimming or clasping the tree branches.
- Their skin is dry and lacks glands but at the base of the tail, oil gland is present.
- They have fully ossified (bony) endoskeleton. The long bones are hollow with air cavities (pneumatic).

- In birds, there are additional chambers in digestive tract called the crop and gizzard.
- Heart is four – chambered.
- They are able to maintain a constant body temperature. Such type of animals are called warm-blooded or homoiothermous animals.
- They respire through lungs.
- Sexes are separate and fertilisation is internal.
- They are oviparous and development is direct.
- Common members of this class are *Corvus* (Crow), *Columba* (Pigeon), *Psittacula* (Parrot), *Struthio* (Ostrich), *Pavo* (Peacock), *Aptenodytes* (Penguin) and *Neophron* (Vulture).

Class 4. – Mammalia

- They are found in a variety of habitats like polar ice caps, deserts, mountains, forests, grasslands and dark caves. Some of them are also adapted to fly or live in water.
- They have milk producing mammary glands to nourish their young ones.
- They possess two pairs of limbs which are adapted for walking, running, climbing, burrowing, swimming or flying.
- They possess hair on the skin.
- External ears or pinnae are present.
- They possess different types of teeth in the jaw.
- The heart is four-chambered.
- They are homoiothermous.
- They respire through lungs.
- Sexes are separate and fertilisation is internal.
- They are viviparous with few exceptions and development is direct.
- Common mammals are *Macropus* (Kangaroo), *Pteropus* (Flying fox), *Camelus* (Camel), *Macaca* (Monkey), *Rattus* (Rat), *Canis* (Dog), *Felis* (Cat), *Elephas* (Elephant), *Equus* (Horse), *Delphinus* (Common dolphin), *Balaenoptera* (Blue whale), *Panthera tigris* (Tiger), *Panthera leo* (Lion). Exceptionally *Ornithorhynchus* (Platypus) is an oviparous mammal.

Salient Features of Different Phyla in the Animal Kingdom

Phylum	Level of Organisation	Symmetry	Coelom	Segmentation	Digestive System	Circulatory System	Respiratory System	Distinctive Features
Porifera	Cellular	Asymmetrical	Absent	Absent	Absent	Absent	Absent	Body with pores and canals in walls.
Coelenterate (Cnidaria)	Tissue	Radial	Absent	Absent	Incomplete	Absent	Absent	Cnidoblasts present.
Ctenophora	Tissue	Radial	Absent	Absent	Incomplete	Absent	Absent	Comb plates for locomotion.
Platyhelminthes	Organ & Organ system	Bilateral	Absent	Absent	Incomplete	Absent	Absent	Flat body, suckers.
Aschelminthes	Organ system	Bilateral	Pseudocoelomate	Absent	Complete	Absent	Absent	Often worm-shaped elongated
Annelida	Organ system	Bilateral	Coelomate	Present	Complete	Present	Present	Body segmentation like rings.
Arthropoda	Organ system	Bilateral	Coelomate	Present	Complete	Present	Present	Exoskeleton of cuticle, jointed appendages.
Mollusca	Organ system	Bilateral	Coelomate	Absent	Complete	Present	Present	External skeleton shell usually present.
Echinodermata	Organ system	Radial	Coelomate	Absent	Complete	Present	Present	Water vascular system, radial symmetry.
Hemichordata	Organ system	Bilateral	Coelomate	Absent	Complete	Present	Present	Worm-like with proboscis, collar and trunk.
Chordata	Organ system	Bilateral	Coelomate	Present	Complete	Present	Present	Notochord, dorsal hollow nerve cord, gill slits with limbs or fins.

Key Words

- **External fertilisation:** When fertilisation occurs outside the female body, it is called external fertilisation
- **Internal fertilisation:** When fertilisation occurs inside the female body, it is called internal fertilisation.
- **Direct development:** In this, the young ones resemble the adults in all respects except colour, size.
- **Indirect development:** In this, the young ones do not resemble the adults.

NCERT CORNER

Q. 1. What are the difficulties that you would face in classification of animals, if common fundamental features are not taken into account?

[NCERT Ex. Q. 1, Page 53]

Ans. For the classification of living organisms, common fundamental characteristics are considered. This common fundamental features helps in grouping animals in certain categories or sub-categories. If we consider specific characteristics, then each organism will be placed in a separate group and the entire objective of classification would not be achieved. Sometimes, classification of animals, plays an important role in comparing different organisms and judging their individual evolutionary significance. If only one characteristic is considered, then this objective would not be achieved.

Q. 2. If you are given a specimen, what are the steps that you would follow to classify it ?

[NCERT Ex. Q. 2, Page 53]

Ans. To classify the given specimen, firstly we will consider some of its fundamental features in a given manner:

(i) Arrangement of cell and level of organisation.
(ii) Body symmetry.
(iii) Body cavity and nature of coelom.
(iv) Segmentation.
(v) Diploblastic and triploblastic organisation.

Q. 3. How useful is the study of the nature of body cavity and coelom in the classification of animals?

[NCERT Ex. Q. 3, Page 53]

Ans. The nature of body cavity and coelom is very important in classification.

(i) The body cavity which is lined by mesoderm is called coelom and the animal possessing coelom are called coelomates.

(ii) The animals in which the coelom is absent are called acoelomate animals.

(iii) In some animals, the body cavity in not lined by mesoderm, instead, the mesoderm is present as scattered pouches in between the ectoderm and endoderm.

Such a body cavity in known as pseudocoel and the animals are called pseudocoelomates.

Q. 4. Distinguish between intracellular and extracellular digestion. [NCERT Ex. Q. 4, Page 53]

Ans. Differences between intracellular and extracellular digestion are:

	Intracellular digestion	Extracellular digestion
(i)	It occurs within the cells.	It occurs outside the cell in a cavity.
(ii)	In this, the digestive enzymes are poured into the food vacuoles, where digestion of food takes place.	In this, the digestive enzymes are poured into the cavity for digestion to take place.
(iii)	e.g., Protozoans and Sponges	e.g., Higher invertebrates and all vertebrates.

Q. 5. What is the difference between direct and indirect development? [NCERT Ex. Q. 5, Page 53]

Ans. (i) In oviparous animals, the newly hatched young may resemble the adult. Such a development is called direct development.

(ii) In some cases, the young hatched from eggs do not resemble the adult. They lead independent life for some period and finally undergo important changes to become adults. These changes from larvae to adult are called metamorphosis and such a development is called indirect development.

Q. 6. What are the peculiar features that you find in parasitic Platyhelminthes? [NCERT Ex. Q. 6, Page 53]

Ans. The main features of Platyhelminthes are given below:

(i) They have dorsoventrally flattened body, hence are called flatworms.

(ii) Hooks and suckers are present, which absorb nutrients from the host directly through their body surface.

(iii) Flame cells are present, which helps in osmo-regulation and excretion.

(iv) Some members like *Planaria* possess high regeneration capacity.

(v) Example: *Taenia* (Tapeworm), *Fasciola* (liver fluke).

Q. 7. What are the reasons that you can think of for the arthropods to constitute the largest group of the animal kingdom? [NCERT Ex. Q. 7, Page 53]

Ans. (i) Tough cuticle protects the arthropods against predators and forms jointed exoskeleton for muscles attachment. This has enabled the arthropods to survive on land in almost any environment

(ii) Bilaterally symmetrical, 'segmented', triploblastic, coelomate animals, found almost everywhere in all habitats.

(iii) Body enclosed by chitinous cuticle (exoskeleton).

(iv) They have joined appendages.

(v) They have mouth parts of various types.

(vi) Trachea/book lungs or book gills for respiration.

Q. 8. Water vascular system is the characteristic of which group of the following:

(i) Porifera (ii) Ctenophora (iii) Echinodermata (iv) Chordata [NCERT Ex. Q. 8, Page 53]

Ans. Option (iv) is correct.

Water vascular system is the characteristic of *Echinodermata*.

Q. 9. "All vertebrates are chordates but all chordates are not vertebrates". Justify the statement.
[NCERT Ex. Q. 9, Page 53]

Ans. All vertebrates are chordates. This is so because they possess three basic chordates features.

(i) All chordates possess a notochord.
(ii) All chordates have a dorsal, hollow nerve cord.
(iii) All chordates have pharyngeal gill clefts in some stage of their life cycle.

All chordates are not vertebrates: Vertebrates have vertebral column but protochordates and agnatha have notochord that is not replaced by vertebral column.

Q.10. How important is the presence of air bladder in Pisces? [NCERT Ex. Q. 10, Page 53]

Ans. (i) A gas filled swim bladder or air sac is always present above the alimentary canal which acts as buoyancy regulator. It enables the fish to stay at a particular depth without expending energy in swimming.
(ii) In some bony fishes, the swim bladder is used as lung for breathing air.

Q.11. What are the modifications that are observed in bird that help them fly? [NCERT Ex. Q. 11, Page 53]

Ans. (i) Birds have feathers which help them to fly.
(ii) Forelimbs are modified into wings for flight.
(iii) The avian flight muscles are used for flying.
(iv) The long bones are hollow and contain air cavities to reduce weight.
(v) The bones are light.
(vi) Feathers decrease water loss from body.
(vii) High metabolic rate to lift body from ground.
(viii) Urinary bladder is absent. Excreta is passed out at once these features help in reducing the weight of the body.

Q.12. Could the number of eggs or young ones produced by an oviparous and viviparous mother be equal? Why? [NCERT Ex. Q. 12, Page 53]

Ans. The number of eggs produced by an oviparous mother will be more than the viviparous mother. This is because, in oviparous animals, the development of young one takes place outside the mother's body. As a result, their eggs are more prone to environmental conditions and predators. Therefore, to overcome the loss, more eggs are produced by mothers so that even under harsh environmental conditions, some eggs might be able to survive and produce young ones. On the other hand, a viviparous mother gives rise to fewer number of young ones because there are less chances of their death, as the development of young ones takes place in safe conditions inside the body of the mother.

Q.13. Segmentation in the body is first observed in which of the following:

(A) Platyhelminthes **(B) Aschelminthes**
(C) Annelida **(D) Arthropoda**
[NCERT Ex. Q. 13, Page 53]

Ans. Option (iii) is correct.

Segmentation in the body is first observed in Annelida.

Q. 14. Match the following:

(i) Operculum	**(a)** Ctenophora
(ii) Parapodia	**(b)** Mollusca
(iii) Scales	**(c)** Porifera
(iv) Comb plates	**(d)** Reptilia
(v) Radula	**(e)** Annelida
(vi) Hairs	**(f)** Cyclostomata and Chondricthyes
(vii) Choanocytes	**(g)** Mammalia
(viii) Gill slits	**(h)** Osteichthyes

[NCERT Ex. Q. 14, Page 53]

Ans.

(i)	Operculum	**(h)**	Osteichthyes
(ii)	Parapodia	**(e)**	Annelida
(iii)	Scales	**(d)**	Reptilia
(iv)	Comb plates	**(a)**	Ctenophora
(v)	Radula	**(b)**	Mollusca
(vi)	Hairs	**(g)**	Mammalia
(vii)	Choanocytes	**(c)**	Porifera
(viii)	Gill slits	**(f)**	Cyclostomata and Chondricthyes

Q.15. Prepare a list of some animals that are found parasitic on human beings. [NCERT Ex. Q. 15, Page 54]

Ans. Parasitic animals on human beings are:

Parasite	Phylum	In part of human body
Taenia solium	Platyhelminthes	Intestine
Ascaris lumbricoides	Aschelminthes	Small intestine
Fasciola hepatica	Platyhelminthes	Liver and bile ducts
Wuchereria bancrofti	Aschelminthes	Lymphatic and muscular system
Leishmania donovani	Protozoan	Blood
Plasmodium vivax	Protozoan	Blood

MORPHOLOGY OF FLOWERING PLANTS

CHAPTER 5

Morphology of Root, Stem and Leaf

Scan to know more about this topic

Morphology of flowering plants

- **Morphology** is the branch of biological science that deals with the study of form, size, colour, structure and relative position of various parts of organisms.
- **Importance of Morphology:**
- Knowledge of morphology is essential for recognition or identification of plants.
- It gives information about the range of variations found in a species.
- **Parts of Flowering Plants**:
- All the flowering plants have roots, stem, leaves, flower and fruits. The underground parts of flowering plant are the root system and the portion above the ground forms the shoot system.
- **The Root:**
- In dicotyledons, elongation of radicle forms the primary roots which bears lateral roots of several orders called secondary roots, tertiary roots, etc. Primary roots along with lateral roots forms the **tap root system**. Examples: Mustard, gram, etc.
- In monocotyledons, primary root is replaced by large number of roots at its base of stem to constitute the **fibrous root system. Example: Wheat, rice, etc.**
- The roots that arise from other parts of plant beside radicle are called **adventitious roots.** Examples: Grass, Prop roots of Banyan tree, Maize, etc.
- The main functions of root system is the absorption of water and minerals from soil, providing proper anchorage to the plant parts and storing reserve food materials.
- **Regions of Root:**
- The apex of root is covered by a thimble like structure called **root cap**. It protects the tender apex of root while making way through soil.
- Above the root cap is **region of meristematic activity** having small cells with dense cytoplasm.
- The cells above the region of meristematic activity is **region of elongation** where cells undergo elongation and enlargement to increase the length of root.
- **Region of maturation** contain root hairs that help in absorption of water and minerals.

The Stem

- The ascending part of axis bears branches, leaves, flowers and fruits. It develops from plumule of the embryo.
- Stem bears nodes and internodes. The region of stem where leaves are born are called nodes and portion between two nodes are called internodes.
- The main function of stem is to spread branches, bear leaves, flowers and fruits. It also conducts water and minerals from root to leaves.
- Some stem perform special functions like storage of food, support, protection and vegetative propagation.

The Leaf

- Leaf is a green, dissimilar exogenous lateral flattened outgrowth which is borne on the node of a stem or its branches. It is specialised to perform photosynthesis.
- Leaves originate from shoot apical meristem and are arranged in an acropetal order.
- A typical leaf consists of three parts- leaf base, petiole, lamina. Leaf is attached with stem by leaf base which may bear two small leaf like structure called stipules.
- Middle prominent vein is called midrib. Veins provide rigidity to the leaf blade and act as channel for the transport of water minerals and food material.
- The arrangement of vein and veinlets in the lamina is called venation.
- A leaf having a single or undivided lamina is called **simple leaf**. Here, the incisions do not touch the mid rib. Examples: Mango, guava, etc.
- When the incision of lamina reach up to the midrib and breaks it into a number of leaflets, it is called **compound leaves.**
- The compound leaves may be of two types. In a **pinnately compound leaves**, a number of leaflets are present on common axis called **rachis**. Example- Neem.
- In **palmately compound leaves**, the leaflets are attached at a common point. Example- Silk cotton.
- The pattern of arrangement of leaves on the stem or branch is called **phyllotaxy**.
- In **alternate type of phyllotaxy,** single leaf arise at each node as in China rose.
- In **opposite types of phyllotaxy,** a pair of leaves arise from each node opposite to each other as in guava.
- If more than two leaves arise at a node and form a whorl it is called **whorled type** of phyllotaxy as in *Alstonia*.

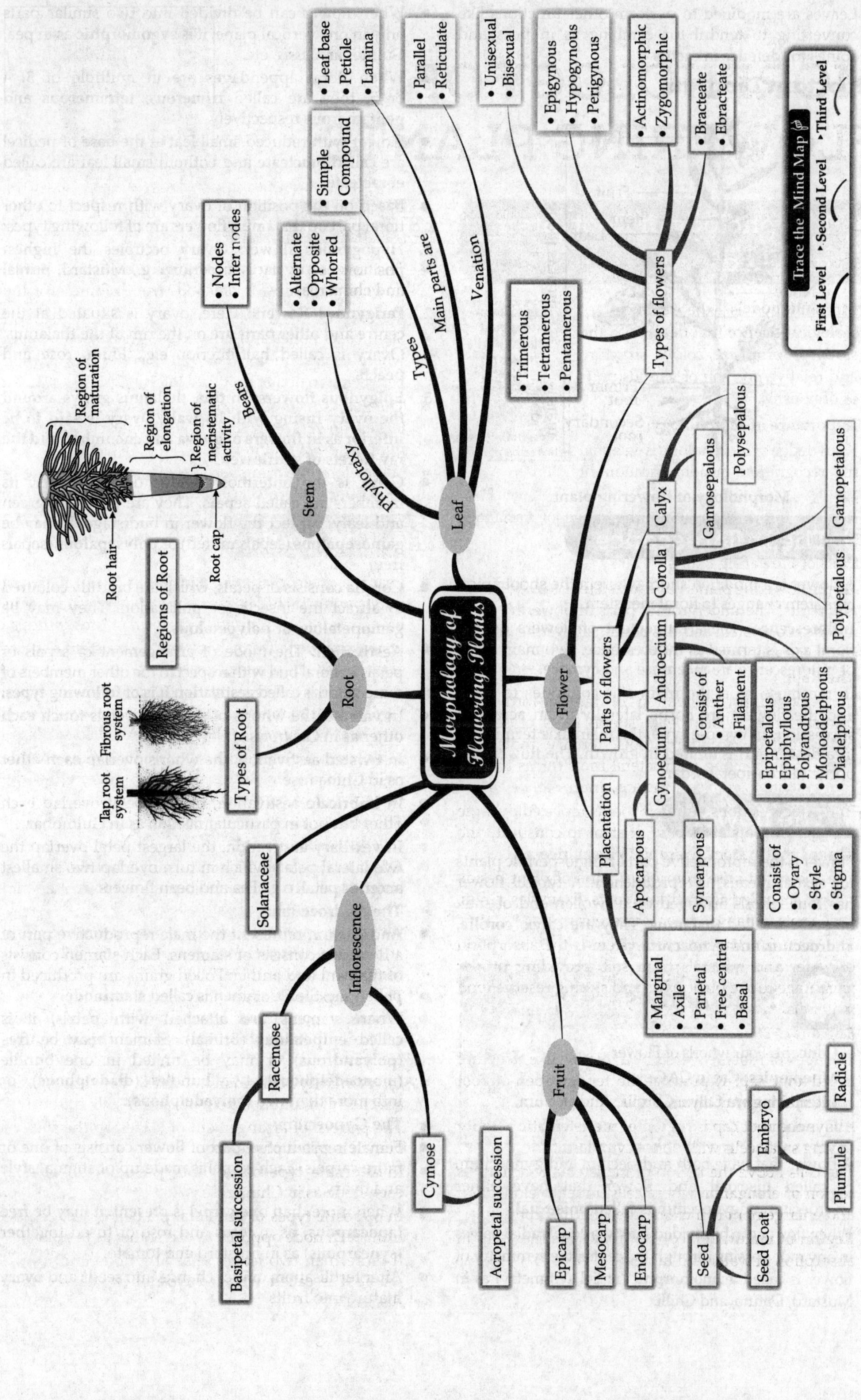
Morphology of Flowering Plants
Root
Types of Root
Tap root system
Fibrous root system
Regions of Root
Root hair
Root cap
Region of maturation
Region of elongation
Region of meristematic activity
Stem
Bears
• Nodes
• Inter nodes
Phyllotaxy
• Alternate
• Opposite
• Whorled
Leaf
Types
• Simple
• Compound
Main parts are
• Leaf base
• Petiole
• Lamina
Venation
• Parallel
• Reticulate
Flower
Types of flowers
• Unisexual
• Bisexual
• Epigynous
• Hypogynous
• Perigynous
• Actinomorphic
• Zygomorphic
• Bracteate
• Ebracteate
• Trimerous
• Tetramerous
• Pentamerous
Parts of flowers
Calyx
Gamosepalous
Polysepalous
Corolla
Polypetalous
Gamopetalous
Androecium
Consist of
• Anther
• Filament
• Epipetalous
• Epiphyllous
• Polyandrous
• Monoadelphous
• Diadelphous
Gynoecium
Consist of
• Ovary
• Style
• Stigma
Apocarpous
Syncarpous
Placentation
• Marginal
• Axile
• Parietal
• Free central
• Basal
Fruit
Epicarp
Mesocarp
Endocarp
Seed
Seed Coat
Embryo
Plumule
Radicle
Inflorescence
Racemose
Basipetal succession
Cymose
Acropetal succession
Solanaceae
Trace the Mind Map
First Level
Second Level
Third Level

- Leaves are modified to perform other functions like converting to tendril for climbing as in peas and spines for defence in cactus.

Important Diagram

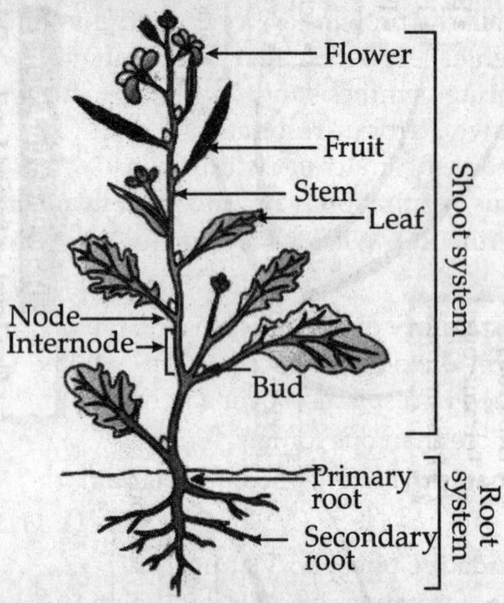

Morphology of flowering plant

The Inflorescence

- A flower is a modified shoot wherein the shoot apical meristem changes to floral meristem.
- **Inflorescence:** The arrangement of flowers on the floral axis is termed as inflorescence. Two main types of inflorescence are **racemose** and **cymose.**
- In racemose type, the main axis continues to grow and the flowers are borne laterally in an acropetal succession. In cymose type, the main axis terminates in a flower and is limited in growth. The flowers are borne in a basipetal order.

The flower

- Flower is the reproductive part of angiospermic plants for sexual means of reproduction. A typical flower has four whorls arranged on a swollen end of stalk or pedicel called **thalamus**. They are **calyx, corolla, androecium** and **gynoecium**.

Mnemonics

Concept: Four whorls of Flower
Mnemonics: Cat in CAGe
Interpretation: Calyx, Corolla, Androecium, Gynoecium

- A flower that have both androecium and gynoecium, is called **bisexual** and flower that have either androecium or gynoecium is called **unisexual**.
- When flower can be divided into two equal radial halves in any radii passing through the center, the symmetry of flower is called **actinomorphic** (radial symmetry) as in Mustard, Datura, and Chilli.
- When flower can be divided into two similar parts only in one vertical plane, it is **zygomorphic** as in pea, Gulmohar, *Cassia,* etc.
- When floral appendages are in multiple of 3, 4 or 5, they are called **trimerous, tetramerous** and **pentamerous** respectively.
- Flower with reduced small leaf at the base of pedicel are called **bracteate** and without small leaf are called **ebracteate**.
- Based on the position of ovary with respect to other floral part on thalamus, flowers are of following types:

1. **Hypogynous flower:** Ovary occupies the highest position i.e., ovary is superior. e.g., Mustard, brinjal and china rose.
2. **Perigynous flowers:** Here, ovary is situated at the centre and other parts are on the rim of the thalamus. Ovary is called half-inferior. e.g., Plum, rose and peach.
3. **Epigynous flowers: In this, thalamus grows around the ovary fusing with its wall. Ovary is said to be inferior as in flowers of guava and cucumber, and the ray florets of sunflower.**

- **Calyx** is the outermost whorls of the flower; its members are called **sepals**. They are generally green and leafy; protect the flower in bud stage. It may be **gamosepalous** (sepals united) or **polysepalous** (sepals free).
- **Corolla** consists of petals, which are brightly coloured to attract the insects for pollination. They may be **gamopetalous** or **polypetalous**.
- **Aestivation:** The mode of arrangement of sepals or petals in floral bud with respect to the other members of same whorl is called **aestivation It is of following types:**
- In **valvate**, the whorls of sepals or petals touch each other as in *Calotropis*.
- In **twisted** aestivation, the whorls overlap each other as in China rose.
- In **imbricate** aestivation, margin petal overlap each other but not in particular fashion as in Gulmohar.
- In **vexillary** aestivation, the largest petal overlap the two lateral petals which in turn overlap two smallest anterior petal. e.g., Pea and bean flowers.
- **The Androecium:**
- Androecium represent the male reproductive part of a flower. It consists of stamens. Each stamen consists of filament and anther. Pollen grains are produced in pollen sac. Sterile stamen is called **staminode**.
- When stamens are attached with petals, it is called **epipetalous** (Brinjal). Stamen may be free (**polyandrous**) or may be united in one bundle (**monoadelphous**), two bundles (**diadelphous**), or into more than two (**polyadelphous**).
- **The Gynoecium:**
- Female reproductive part of flower consists of one or more carpels. Each carpel is made up of stigma, style and ovary.
- When more than one carpel is present, it may be free (**apocarpous**) as in lotus and rose or fused together (**syncarpous**) as in mustard and tomato.
- After fertilisation, ovules change into seeds and ovary mature into fruits.

- **Placentation:**
- The arrangement of ovules within the ovary is called placentation.
- The placentation are of different types namely marginal, axile, parietal, basal, central and free central.

The Fruit

- Mature and ripened ovary developed after fertilisation is fruit. If a fruit is formed without fertilisation of ovary, it is called **parthenocarpic fruit.**
- Fruit consists of seeds and pericarp. Thick and fleshy pericarp is three layered called epicarp, mesocarp and endocarp.
- In mango and coconut, the fruit is known as a drupe. They develop from monocarpellary superior ovaries and are one seeded.
- **The Seeds**
- The ovules after fertilisation, develop into seeds.
- A seed is made up of a seed coat and an embryo.
- The embryo is made up of radicle, an embroyonal axis and one or two cotyledons.

Structure of a Dictyoledonous Seed

- Dicotyledonous seed is made up of a seed coat and an embryo. **Embryo** is made up of embryonal axis, radicle and cotyledons.
- Seed coat has two layers: outer **testa** and inner **tegmen**. **Hilum** is scar through which seed is attached to the ovary. Small pore above the hilum is called micropyle.

Structure of Monocotyledonous Seed:

- In monocotyledonous seed, outer covering of endosperm separate the embryo by a proteinaceous layer called **aleurone layer.**
- Single cotyledon is called as **scutellum** having a short axis bearing plumule and radicle.
- Plumule and radicle are closed inside sheaths called as **coleoptile** and **coleorhiza** respectively.

Semi-Technical Description of a Typical Flowering Plant

- The plant is described beginning with its habit, vegetative characters–roots, stem and leaves and then floral characters inflorescence and flower parts.
- After describing various parts of plant, a floral diagram and a floral formula are presented.

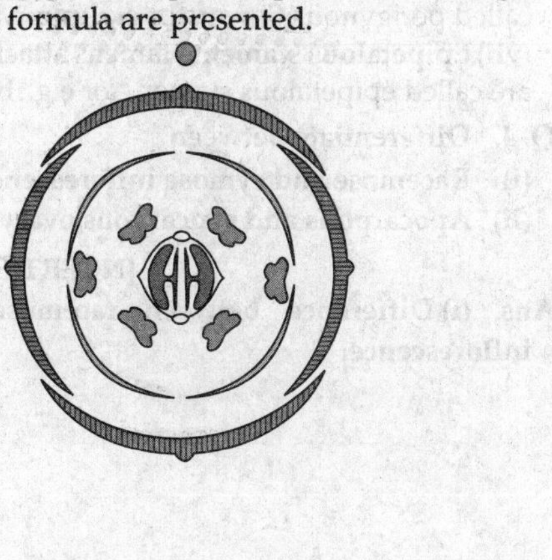

- In the floral formula, Br stands for bracteate, K stands for calyx, C for corolla, P for perianth, A for androceium and G for Gynoecium, $\underline{G}$ for superior ovary and $\overline{G}$ for inferior ovary, ♂ for male, ♀ for bisexual plants, ⊕ for actinomorphic and % for zygomorphic nature of flower.
- Fusion is indicated by enclosing the figure within bracket and adhesion by a line drawn above the symbols of the floral parts.
- A floral diagram provides information about the number of parts of a flower, their arrangement and the relation they have with one another.
- **Solanaceae**
- It is a large family, commonly called as the 'potato family'. It is widely distributed in tropics, subtropics and even temperate zones.
- **Vegetative Characters:** Plants mostly herbs, shrubs and rarely small trees
  - **Stem:** Herbaceous rarely woody, aerial; erect, cylindrical, branched, solid or hollow, hairy or glabrous, underground stem in potato (*Solanum tuberosum*).
  - **Leaves:** Alternate, simple, rarely pinnately compound, exstipulate; venation reticulate
- **Floral Characters**
  - **Inflorescence:** Solitary, axillary or cymose as in Solanum
  - **Flower:** Bisexual, actinomorphic
  - **Calyx:** Sepals five, united, persistent, valvate aestivation
  - **Corolla:** Petals five, united; valvate aestivation
  - **Androecium:** Stamens five, epipetalous
  - **Gynoecium:** Bicarpellary obligately placed, syncarpous; ovary superior, bilocular, placenta swollen with many ovules, axile.
  - **Fruits:** Berry or capsule
  - **Seeds:** Many, endospermous.
  - Many plants belonging to this family are source of food (tomato, brinjal, potato), spice (chilli); medicine (belladonna, ashwagandha); fumigatory (tobacco); ornamentals (petunia).

Scan to know more about this topic

Description of Solanaceae family

- **Floral Formula:** $\oplus$ ⚥ $K_{(5)}\overparen{C_{(5)}A_5}\underline{G}_{(2)}$
- Many of them are source of food (potato, tomato, brinjal, etc.), spices (chilli), etc.

Key Words

- **Root cap:** It is a thimble like structure that covers the root apex.
- **Phyllotaxy:** It is the pattern of arrangement of leaves on the stem or branch.
- **Inflorescence:** The arrangement of flowers on the floral axis is known as inflorescence.

Key Words

- **Unisexual flowers:** Flowers, which contain either gynoecium (stamen) or androecium (carpels), are called unisexual flowers.
- **Bisexual flowers:** Flowers, which contain both androecium (carpels) and gynoecium (stamens), are called bisexual flowers.
- **Hypogynous flowers (Superior ovary):** Flowers in which ovary occupies the highest position on the thalamus while other floral parts are situated below it.
- **Perigynous flowers (Half inferior ovary):** Flowers in which, ovary is situated at the centre and other floral parts are arranged on the rim of the thalamus
- **Epigynous flowers (Inferior ovary):** Flowers in which, the thalamus grows around the ovary fusing with its wall.
- **Aestivation:** It is the mode in which sepals or petals are arranged in a floral bud with respect to other floral members.
- **Placentation:** It refers to the arrangement of ovules within the ovary of a flower.
- **Fruit:** It is the matured or ripened ovary developed after fertilisation.

NCERT CORNER

Q. 1. How is a pinnately compound leaf different from a palmately compound leaf ? [NCERT Ex. Q. 1, Page 70]

Ans. Difference between pinnately compound leaf and palmately compound leaf:

S.No.	Features	Pinnately Compound Leaf	Palmately Compound Leaf
(i)	Shape	Feather like.	Like palm of hand.
(ii)	Origin of leaflets	Leaflets appear in two rows.	Leaflets are clustered together.
(iii)	Joint in its axis.	Joint absent between leaflet and point of attachment.	Joint usually present between leaflet and point of attachment.
(v)	Origin	Branch of midrib.	Tip of petiole represents the leaflet bearing point.

Q. 2. Explain with suitable examples the different types of phyllotaxy. [NCERT Ex. Q. 2, Page 70]

Ans. Phyllotaxy is the arrangement or distribution of leaves on the stem or its branches in such a way that they receive maximum sunlight to perform photosynthesis. Phyllotaxy is of three types:

(i) Alternate or Spiral: In this type, a single leaf arise at each node in an alternate manner, e.g., *Hibiscus rosa sinensis*.

(ii) Opposite: Two leaves are borne from the node in opposite directions. It is of two types:
(a) Opposite Superposed: e.g., *Quisqualis*.
(b) Opposite Decussate: e.g., *Calotropis*.

(iii) Whorled or Verticillate: More than two leaves are borne on a node, which form a whorl.

Q. 3. Define the following terms:

(i) Aestivation	**(ii) Placentation**
(iii) Actinomorphic	**(iv) Zygomorphic**
(v) Superior ovary	**(vi) Perigynous flower**
(vii) Epipetalous stamen	**[NCERT Ex. Q. 3, Page 70]**

Ans. (i) Aestivation: The arrangement of accessory floral organs (sepals or petals) in relation to one another in the floral bud is called aestivation.

(ii) Placentation: The number, position and arrangements or distribution of ovules inside the ovary is called placentation.

(iii) Actinomorphic: A cyclic flower which can be divided into two equal vertical halves or mirror image by any vertical plane is said to be actinomorphic. e.g., *Hibiscus, Solanum*, etc.

(iv) Zygomorphic: The flowers which can be divided into two similar halves by a single vertical plane is known as zygomorphic flower. for e.g., peas and beans.

(v) Superior ovary: Superior ovary flowers are those flowers in which the gynoecium is present at the highest position, while other floral parts are arranged below it. for e.g., brinjal and mustard.

(vi) Perigynous flower: Flowers in which the gynoecium are present in the centre and rest of the floral parts are arranged at the rim of the thalamus at the same level are called perigynous flower. for e.g., plum and rose.

(vii) Epipetalous stamen: Stamens attached to the petals are called epipetalous stamen. for e.g., brinjal.

Q. 4. Differentiate between

(i) Racemose and cymose inflorescence

(ii) Apocarpous and syncarpous ovary

[NCERT Ex. Q. 4, Page 70]

Ans. (i) Difference between racemose and cymose inflorescence:

S.No.	Racemose Inflorescence	Cymose Inflorescence
(i)	The main axis continues to grow.	The main axis terminate in a flower, hence is limited in growth.
(ii)	The flowers are borne laterally in an acropetal succession.	Flowers are borne in basipetal order.
(iii)	e.g., Radish, mustard.	e.g., Cotton, jasmine.

(ii) Difference between apocarpous and syncarpous ovary:

Apocarpous ovary	Syncarpous ovary
When, in gynoecium, more than one carpel is present, that are free, it is called apocarpous ovary. e.g., Lotus, Rose	When carpels are fused, it is called syncarpous ovary. e.g., Mustard and tomato.

Q. 5. Draw the labelled diagram of the following:
(i) Gram seed (ii) V.S. of maize seed
[NCERT Ex. Q. 5, Page 70]

Ans. (i)

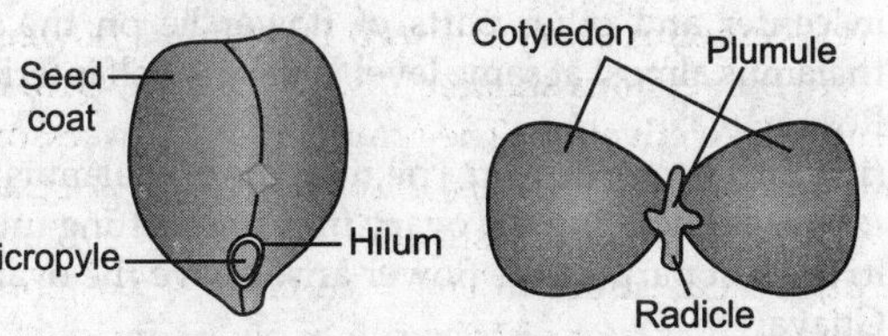

(ii)

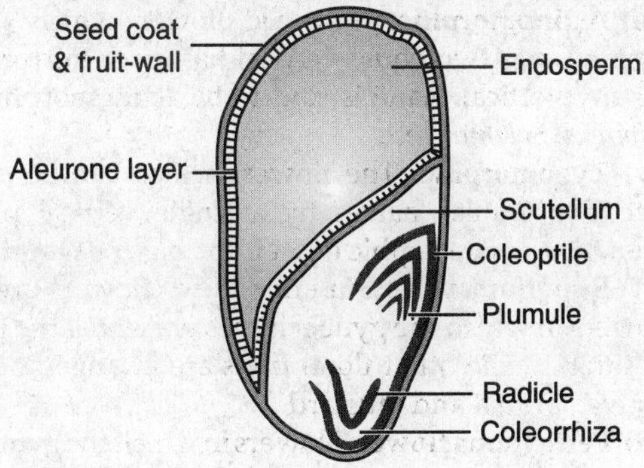

Q. 6. Take one flower of the family Solanaceae and write its semi-technical description. Also draw their floral diagram. [NCERT Ex. Q. 6, Page 70]

Ans. Characteristics of family Solanaceae:

- The solanaceae family, also known as the potato family, consists primarily of herbs, shrubs, and small trees.
- Stems are herbaceous, rarely woody, and aerial; they are erect, cylindrical, branching, solid or hollow, hairy or glabrous, and underground in potatoes.
- Leaves are ex-stipulate with reticulate venation, alternating, simple, rarely pinnately compound.

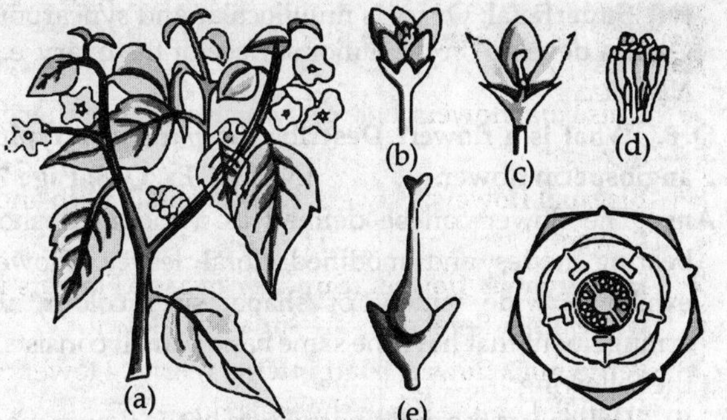

Floral Characters:

- **Inflorescence:** Solitary, axillary or cymose as in Solanum
- **Flower:** bisexual, actinomorphic
- **Calyx:** sepals five, united, persistent, valvate aestivation
- **Corolla:** petals five, united; valvate aestivation
- **Androecium:** stamens five, epipetalous
- **Gynoecium:** bicarpellary obligately placed, syncarpous; ovary superior, bilocular, placenta is swollen with many ovules, axile.
- **Fruits:** berry or capsule
- **Seeds:** many, endosperms endospermic

Economic importance: Plants belonging to this family are used as food, spices, medicines and ornamentals.

Floral diagram:

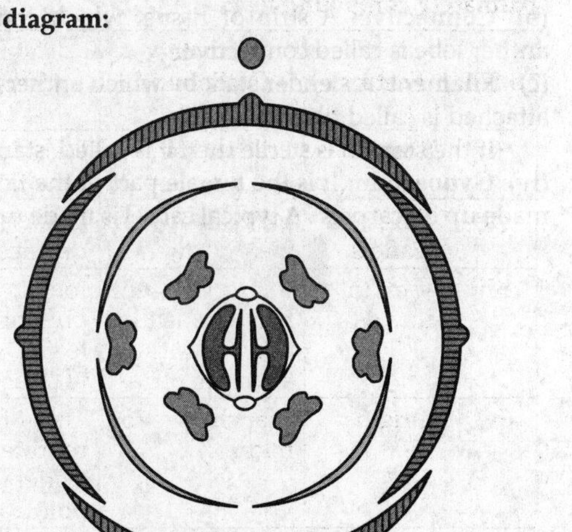

$\oplus$ ⚥ $K_{(5)}\overbrace{C_{(5)}A_5}\underline{G}_{(2)}$

E.g. : Brinjal, chilli, ashwagandha, petunia

Q. 7. Describe the various types of placentations found in flowering plants. [NCERT Ex. Q. 7, Page 70]

Ans. (i) Marginal: Ovary one chambered and ovules lie along the margin of the ovary. e.g., Gram and pea.

(ii) Parietal: Ovary one chambered and ovules lie at the level of the fusion of two carpels. e.g., Mustard.

(iii) Axile: Ovary many chambered and the ovules are attached to the central column. e.g., Onion and lemon.

(iv) Free central: Ovary one chambered. The center bears many ovules. e.g., *Dianthus* and *Primula*.

(v) Basal: Ovary one chambered and ovules develop on the thalamus. e.g., Sunflower.

(vi) Superficial: Ovary is multilocular and syncarpous. Ovules develop on the minor surface of the ovary. e.g., *Nymphea.*

Q. 8. What is a flower? Describe the parts of a typical angiosperm flower. [NCERT Ex. Q. 8, Page 70]

Ans. The flower can be defined as a modified shoot bearing nodes and modified floral leaves. Flowers exhibit a wide variety of shape, size, colour and arrangement that have the same basic plan. It consists of the following:

(i) Calyx: It is the outermost whorl of the flower made up of sepals. This is green, leaf-like structure. It may be polysepalous (sepals free), gamosepalous (sepals united), calyx may be regular or irregular.

(ii) Corolla: It is the second whorl of the flower inside the sepals. The petals (units of corolla) are usually brightly coloured. The insects are attracted due to the attractive colour of the petals. The corolla may be polypetalous (petals not united) or gamopetalous (petals united).

(iii) Androecium: It is the third whorl of the flower inside the petals. It represents the male reproductive whorl. Its units are stamen. In each stamen there are three parts viz:

(a) Anther: Knob-like bilobed structure containing the pollen grains. Each lobe contains two chambers called pollen sac.

(b) Connective: A strip of tissue, which connect the anther lobe is called connective.

(c) Filament: A slender stalk by which anther lobes are attached is called filament.

If the stamen is sterile then it is called 'staminode'.

(iv) Gynoecium: It is the female part of the flower. It is made up of 'carpels'. A typical carpel is made up of three parts:

(a) Stigma: Upper part which receives pollen grains.

(b) Style: The stalk between stigma and ovary.

(c) Ovary: Basal part containing ovules. The sterile gynoecium is known as **'pistillode'**.

Q. 9. Define the term inflorescence. Explain the basis for the different types inflorescence in flowering plants. [NCERT Ex. Q. 9, Page 70]

Ans. Inflorescence: An axis bearing a cluster of flower is called as inflorescence.

(i) Racemose: In racemose type of inflorescence the main axis continues to grow, the flowers are borne laterally in an acropetal succession.

(ii) Cymose: In this type of inflorescence, the main axis terminates in a flower, hence is limited in growth. The flowers are borne in a basipetal order.

Q.10. Describe the arrangement of floral members in relation to their insertion on thalamus. [NCERT Ex. Q. 10, Page 70]

Ans. Based on the position of calyx, corolla and the androecium in respect of ovary on the thalamus, flowers may be of three kinds:

(i) Hypogynous flower: Gynoecium located at highest position and rest whorls of flower lies below it e.g., Mustard.

(ii) Perigynous flower: The gynoecium is situated in center and other parts of flower lie on the rim of thalamus almost at same level. Ovary is half inferior e.g., Rose.

(iii) Epigynous flower: The margins of thalamus grows upwards enclosing the ovary fully and getting united to it, the rest parts of the flower arise above the ovary e.g., Guava.

□□

ANATOMY OF FLOWERING PLANTS

CHAPTER 6

The Tissue System

- Anatomy is the study of internal structure of organism. In plants, anatomy includes histology, that is, organisation and structure of tissues. Anatomy helps in knowing the structural peculiarities of different group of plants and indicates the structural adaptation to diverse environments.
- The cells that have become structurally and functionally specialised and have lost the ability of cell division are called permanent tissue.
- **Epidermal Tissue System :**
  - It forms the outermost covering of whole plant body, which consists of epidermal cells, stomata and the epidermal appendages (trichomes and hairs).
  - Epidermis is single layered, parenchymatous with waxy thick layers of cuticle to prevent water loss.
  - Stomata is present in epidermis of leaves. It regulates the transpiration and gaseous exchange. In dicots, stomata are bean-shaped having two guard cells closing the stomatal pore. In monocots, stoma is dumb-bell shaped. Guard cells contain chloroplasts to carry out the process of photosynthesis. Guard cells also help in opening and closing of stomata.
  - Epidermis also contains a number of hairs. Root hairs are unicellular elongation of epidermal cells. Trichomes are present on stems, which are multicellular, branched or unbranched preventing water loss due to transpiration.
- **The Ground Tissue System :**
  - All the tissue between epidermis and vascular bundle forms the ground tissues. It consists of simple permanent tissues. Parenchyma is present in pericycle, cortex, pith and medullary rays in stem and roots.
  - In leaves, the ground tissue consists of thin-walled chloroplast containing cells and is called **mesophyll**.

Scan to know more about this topic
Plant Tissue Systems

- **The Vascular Tissue System :**
  - The vascular system consists of complex tissues, xylem and phloem that together form vascular bundles.
  - The cambium is present between phloem and xylem. Such vascular bundles because of the presence of cambium possess the ability to form secondary xylem, and hence called **open** vascular bundles.
  - In monocots, the vascular bundles have no cambium and are called **closed**.
  - When xylem and phloem within a vascular bundle are arranged in alternate manner on different radii, the arrangement are called **radial** as in roots. When xylem and phloem are situated at the same radius of vascular bundle, it is called **conjoint** as in stem and leaves.

Anatomy of Dictoyledonous and Monocotyledonous Plants

- **Dicotyledonous Root :**
  - The outermost layer of dicot root is epidermis containing unicellular root hairs.
  - Below epidermis is the cortex which consists of many layers of thin-walled parenchymatous cells with intercellular spaces.
  - The innermost layer of cortex is called endodermis having waxy material suberin as casparian strips, which is impermeable to water.
  - Pericycle is present below endodermis. The parenchymatous cells lying between xylem and phloem are called conjunctive tissue.
  - Two to four xylem and phloem patches are present. All the tissues inside the endodermis constitute the stele.
- **Monocotyledonous Roots :**
  - Anatomically in monocot roots, epidermis, cortex, endodermis, pith are similar to dicots except having more than six vascular bundles with larger pith.
- **Dicotyledonous Stem :**
  - Epidermis is the outermost layer of dicot stems having thin layer of cuticle, may contain trichomes and hairs.
  - Cortex is divided into three sub-layers, outer hypodermis (collenchymatous), middle cortical layer (parenchymatous) and inner endodermis, which is rich in starch grains so, also known as starch sheath.
  - Vascular bundles are conjoint, open, endarch with protoxylem. Pith is parenchymatous with intercellular spaces.

Scan to know more about this topic
Anatomy of Dicot and Monocot roots

- **Monocotyledonous Stem :**
  - They have sclerenchymatous hypodermis, large number of scattered vascular bundles surrounded by sclerenchymatous bundle sheath. Vascular bundles are closed and conjoint. Phloem parenchyma is absent.
- **Dicotyledonous Leaf (Dorsiventral) :**
  - Vertical section through lamina shows three regions : epidermis, mesophyll and vascular system.
  - Epidermis covers both upper (adaxial) and lower (abaxial) surface. Abaxial surface have more stomata.

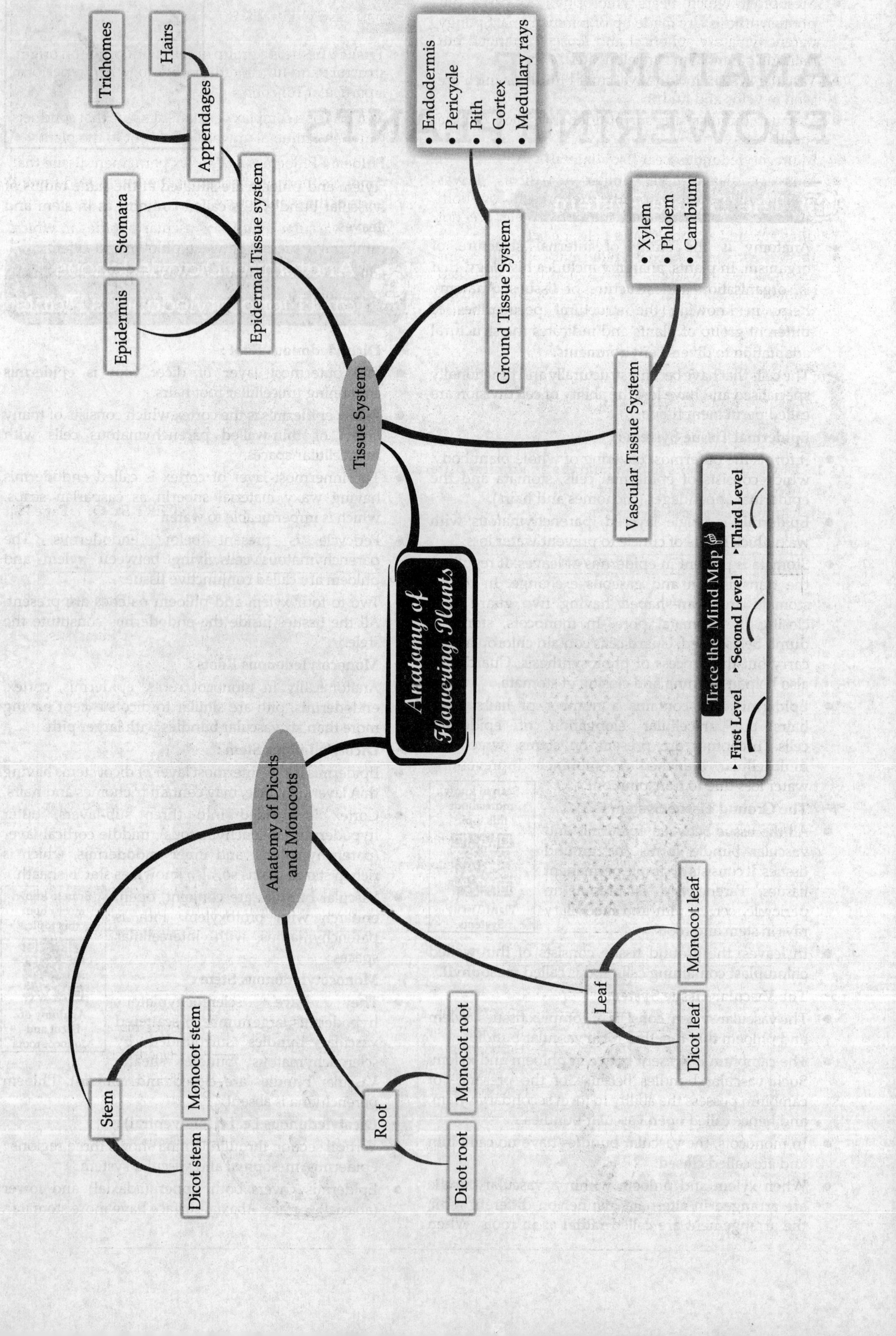
Anatomy of Flowering Plants
Tissue System
Epidermal Tissue system
Epidermis
Stomata
Appendages
Trichomes
Hairs
Ground Tissue System
• Endodermis
• Pericycle
• Pith
• Cortex
• Medullary rays
Vascular Tissue System
• Xylem
• Phloem
• Cambium
Anatomy of Dicots and Monocots
Stem
Dicot stem
Monocot stem
Root
Dicot root
Monocot root
Leaf
Dicot leaf
Monocot leaf
Trace the Mind Map
First Level
Second Level
Third Level

- Mesophyll which bears chlorophyll to carry out photosynthesis, are made up of parenchyma. Spongy parenchyma are spherical and loosely arranged but palisade parenchyma are elongated.
- Vascular system includes vascular bundles, which are seen in veins and midribs.
- Vascular bundles are surrounded by thick bundle sheath cells.

➤ **Monocotyledonous Leaf (Isobilateral) :**

- Monocots leaves are similar to dicots leaves anatomically except stomata are present on both surfaces of epidermis and mesophyll cells are not differentiated as spongy and palisade cells.
- In grasses, some adaxial epidermal cell with veins are modified into large, empty, colourless cells called bulliform cells. These cells make the leaves turgid when water is absorbed and curls in case of water stress.

Key Words

➤ **Tissue :** Tissue is a group of cells with common origin, structure and function that work together to perform a particular function.

➤ **Xylem :** It is a complex permanent tissue that conducts water and mineral upward from root to the plant.

➤ **Phloem :** Phloem is a complex permanent tissue that conducts food synthesised in the leaves to different parts of the plant body.

➤ **Open vascular bundles :** Vascular bundles in which cambium is present between phloem and xylem.

➤ **Closed vascular bundles :** Vascular bundles which lack cambium.

NCERT CORNER

Q. 1. Draw illustrations to bring out the anatomical difference between :

(i) Monocot root and dicot root

(ii) Monocot stem and dicot stem **[NCERT Ex. Q. 1, Page 78]**

Ans. (i)

Dicot root	Monocot root

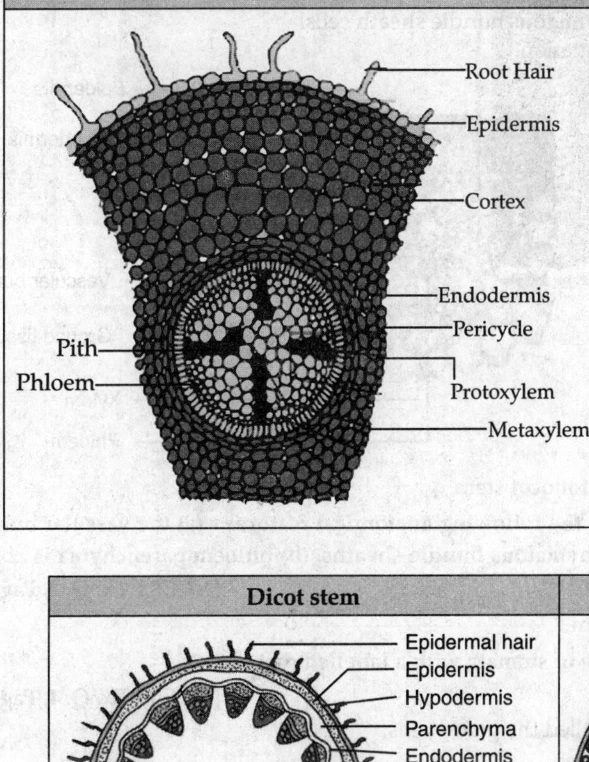

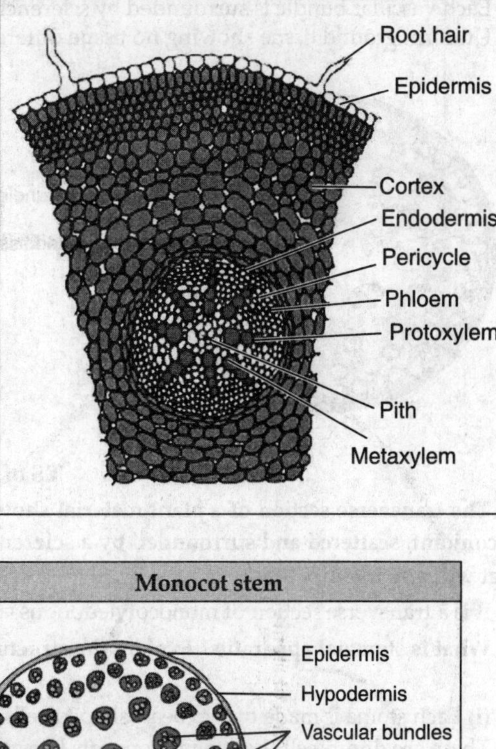

(ii)

Dicot stem	Monocot stem

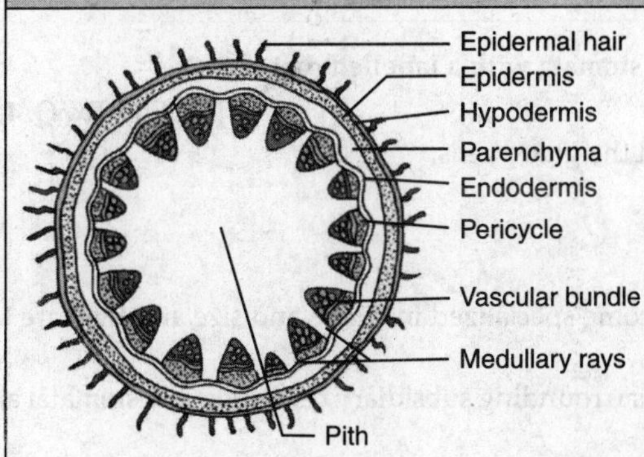

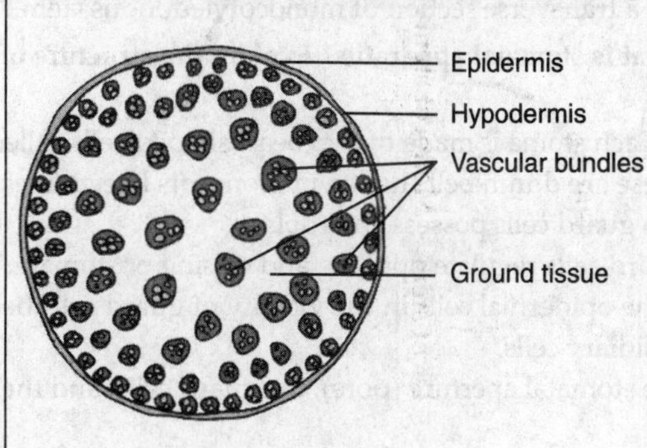

Q. 2. Cut a transverse section of young stem of a plant from your school garden and observe it under the microscope. How would you ascertain whether it is a monocot stem or a dicot stem? Give reasons. [NCERT Ex. Q. 2, Page 78]

Ans. T.S. of dicot stem possess following characters :

(i) Presence of conjoint, collateral and open vascular bundles, with a strip of cambium between xylem and phloem.

(ii) Vascular bundles are arranged in the form of a ring, around the centrally located pith.

(iii) Ground tissue is differentiated into the collenchyma, parenchyma, endodermis, pericycle and pith.

(iv) Medullary rays are present between the vascular bundles.

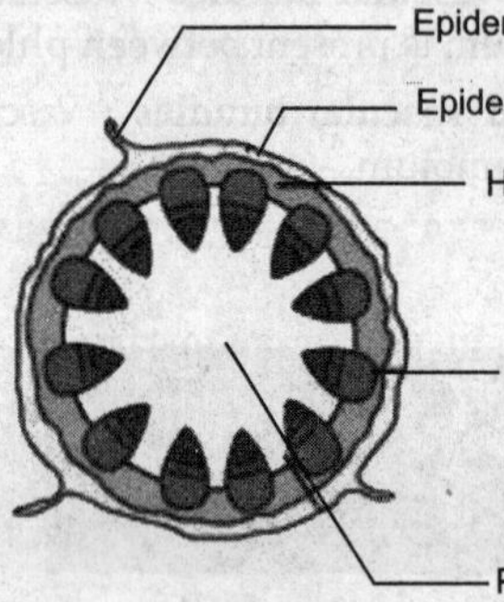

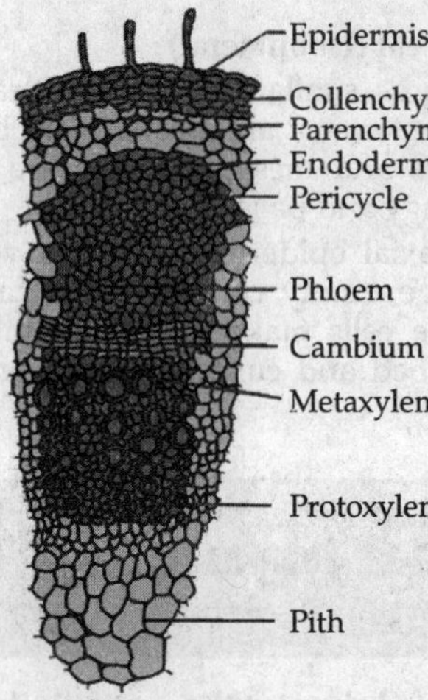

T.S. of Dicot Stem.

T.S. of monocot stem possess following characters :

(i) Conjoint, collateral and closed vascular bundles each surrounded by a sclerenchymatous bundle sheath.

(ii) Vascular bundles are scattered in the ground tissue containing the parenchyma. Peripheral vascular bundles are generally smaller than the centrally located ones.

(iii) Each vascular bundle is surrounded by sclerenchymatous bundle sheath cells.

(iv) Uniform ground tissue showing no tissue differentiation.

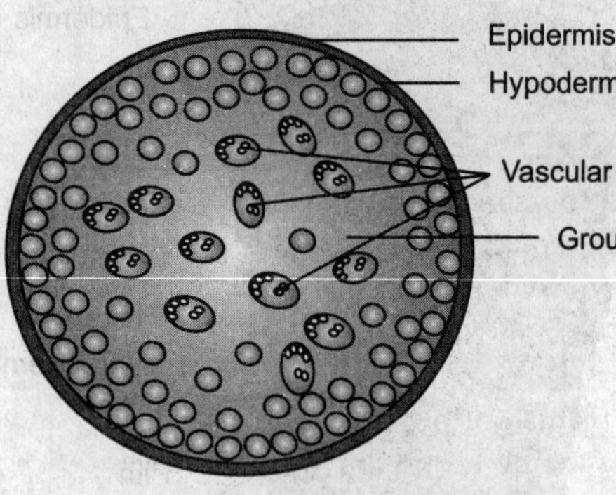

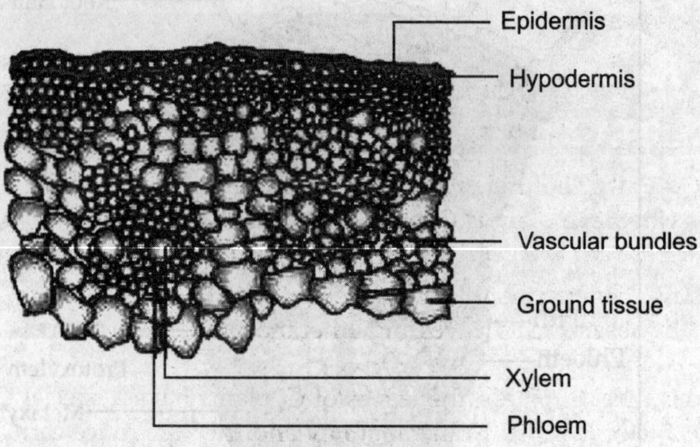

T.S of Monocot stem.

Q. 3. The transverse section of a plant material shows the following anatomical features - (a) the vascular bundles are conjoint, scattered and surrounded by a sclerenchymatous bundle sheaths. (b) phloem parenchyma is absent. What will you identify it as? [NCERT Ex. Q. 3, Page 78]

Ans. It is a transverse section of monocotyledonous stem.

Q. 4. What is stomatal apparatus? Explain the structure of stomata with a labelled diagram. [NCERT Ex. Q. 4, Page 78]

Ans. (i) Each stoma is made of two bean-shaped cells called the guard cells.

(ii) These are dumb-bell shaped in monocots like grasses.

(iii) The guard cells possess chloroplast.

(iv) Guard cells regulate opening and closing of stomata.

(v) Some epidermal cells in the vicinity of guard cells become specialized in shape and size and they are termed as the subsidiary cells.

(vi) The stomatal aperture (pore), the guard cells, and the surrounding subsidiary cells make the stomatal apparatus.

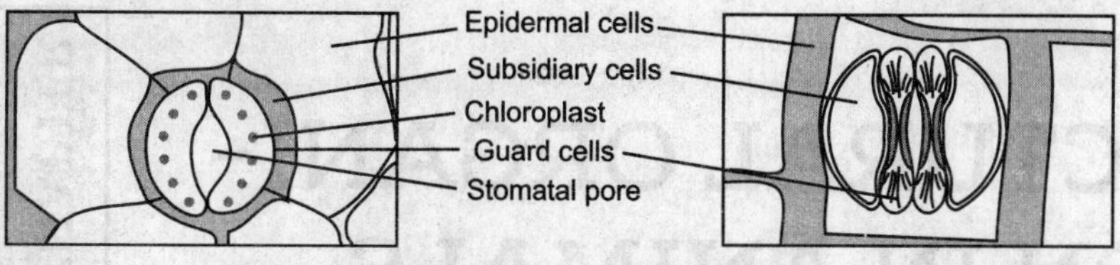

Structure of a stomata

Q. 5. Name the three basic tissue systems in the flowering plants. Give the tissue names under each system. [NCERT Ex. Q. 5, Page 78]

Ans. There are three basic types of tissues found in flowering plants according to Sachs (1975).

These are :

(i) Epidermal plant tissue system. e.g., Epidermis, cuticle, stomata, trichomes and hairs.

(ii) Vascular plant tissue system: Xylem and phloem, endodermis, pericycle, medullary rays pith and mesophyll in leaves.

(iii) Ground or fundamental tissue system. e.g., Cortex.

Q. 6. How is the study of plant anatomy useful to us? [NCERT Ex. Q. 6, Page 78]

Ans. Importance of plant anatomy :

(i) It helps us to understand the structural adaptations of plants with respect to diverse environments.

(ii) Plant anatomy helps us to study plant physiology. Thus, it helps in the improvement of food crops.

(iii) Study of various plant fibres such as jute, flax etc. helps in their commercial exploitation.

Q. 7. Describe the internal structure of a dorsiventral leaf with the help of labelled diagrams. [NCERT Ex. Q. 7, Page 78]

Ans. Anatomy of Dicot/Dorsiventral Leaf :

(i) Epidermis is present on both the upper surface (adaxial epidermis) and the lower surface (abaxial epidermis). The epidermis on the outside is covered with a thick cuticle.

(ii) The lower epidermis is interrupted by a number of openings called stomata.

(iii) Each stomata is surrounded by two kidney/bean shaped cells called guard cells, which is responsible for the opening and closing of stomata.

(iv) The mesophyll consists of two types of cells :

(a) Elongated cells arranged compactly in rows or stacks called palisade parenchyma.

(b) Irregularly arranged cells with large intercellular spaces, called spongy parenchyma.

(v) The mesophyll cells contain a number of chloroplasts.

(vi) The vascular bundles are present in the midrib and other veins.

(vii) In each vascular bundle, the xylem is towards the adaxial side (upper surface) and phloem is towards the abaxial side (under surface).

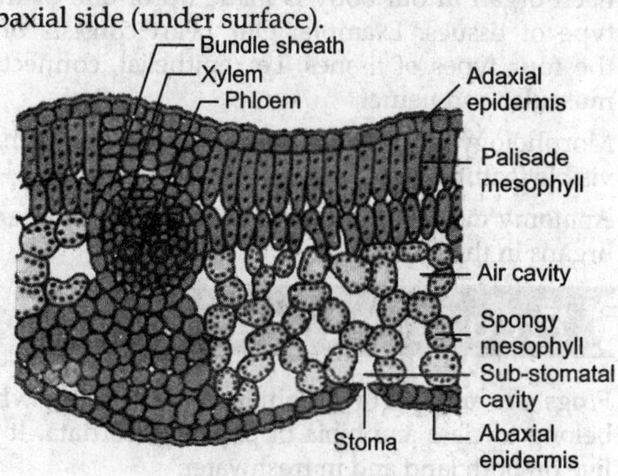

T.S Dicot leaf

□□

CHAPTER 7

STRUCTURAL ORGANISATION IN ANIMALS

Organ and Organ System

- The human body is composed of billions of cells to perform various function. In multicellular animals, a group of similar cells along with inter cellular substances perform a specific function. Such an organisation is called tissue.
- All complex animals consist of only four basic types of tissues. These tissues are organised in specific proportion and pattern to form an organ like stomach, lung, heart and kidney.
- When two or more organs perform a common function by their physical and/or chemical interaction, they together form organ system, e.g., digestive system, respiratory system etc.
- Each organ in our body is made up of one or more type of tissues. Example: Our heart consists of all the four types of tissues, i.e., epithelial, connective, muscular and neural.
- Morphology refers to the study of form or externally visible features.
- Anatomy means the study of morphology of internal organs in the family.

Frog (*Rana Tigrina*)

- Frogs are a type of amphibious vertebrate, which belong to class amphibia of phylum chordata. It can live on both land and in freshwater.
- *Rana tigrina* is the most common Indian species.
- They are called cold-blooded or poikilotherms.
- **Poikilotherms:** These are organisms whose body temperature changes in response to their surroundings. As a result, they do not maintain a constant body temperature.
- They also have the ability to change the color of their skin in order to blend in with their surroundings and hide from their enemies. This ability is known as camouflage.
- During extreme hot conditions, frogs take shelter in deep burrows to protect themselves from extreme hot environment called as aestivation.
- Aestivation is defined as an organism's dormant state during the summer. This assists the organism in surviving extreme heat of summers.
- An organism's dormant state during the winter is known as hibernation or winter sleep. This assists the organism in surviving the bitter cold of winter. At this stage, the organism's metabolic and physiological activities are minimal.

Morphology:

- The skin of the frog is smooth and slippery because of the presence of mucus. This aids in keeping the skin moist at all times. The frog does not consume water. Instead, it absorbs it through the skin.
- The dorsal side of the body is olive green with dark irregular spots. The ventral side is a light yellow in colour.
- A frog's body is divided into head and the trunk. There is no neck or tail.
- The body of a frog has a pair of nostrils, bulged eyes covered by a nictitating membrane, and a membranous tympanum (ear)
- Nictitating membrane is a whitish or translucent membrane that forms an inner eyelid.
- Tympanum is a membranous structure that represents the ear on either side of the eye. It is capable of receiving sound signals.
- The forelimbs and hind limbs aid in walking, swimming, leaping, and burrowing.
- The hind limbs are larger and more muscular than the forelimbs. They all end in five digits.
- Forelimbs are smaller and less muscular than hind limbs. They all have four digits at the end. Webbed digits on the feet aid in swimming.

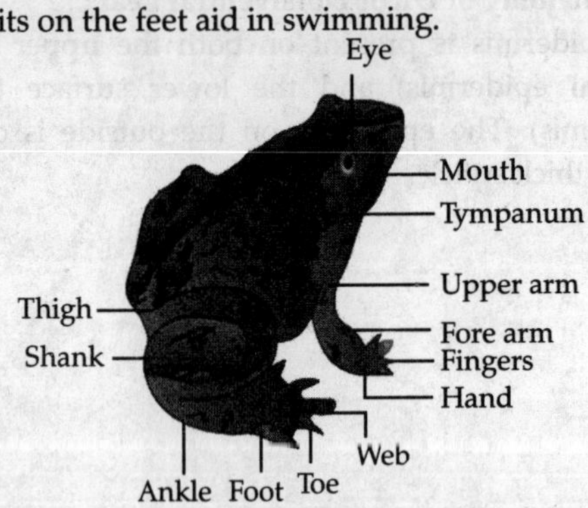

Structure of frog

- Frogs have two sexes. Male frogs are distinguished by the presence of sound-producing vocal sacs and a copulatory pad on the first forelimb digit.

Digestive system of a frog:

- It is made up of a short alimentary canal and digestive glands. The mouth opens into the buccal cavity, which leads to the oesophagus via the pharynx.
- The oesophagus is a narrow tube. It connects to the stomach. The stomach is followed by the intestine.

Scan to know more about this topic

Frog: Digestive System

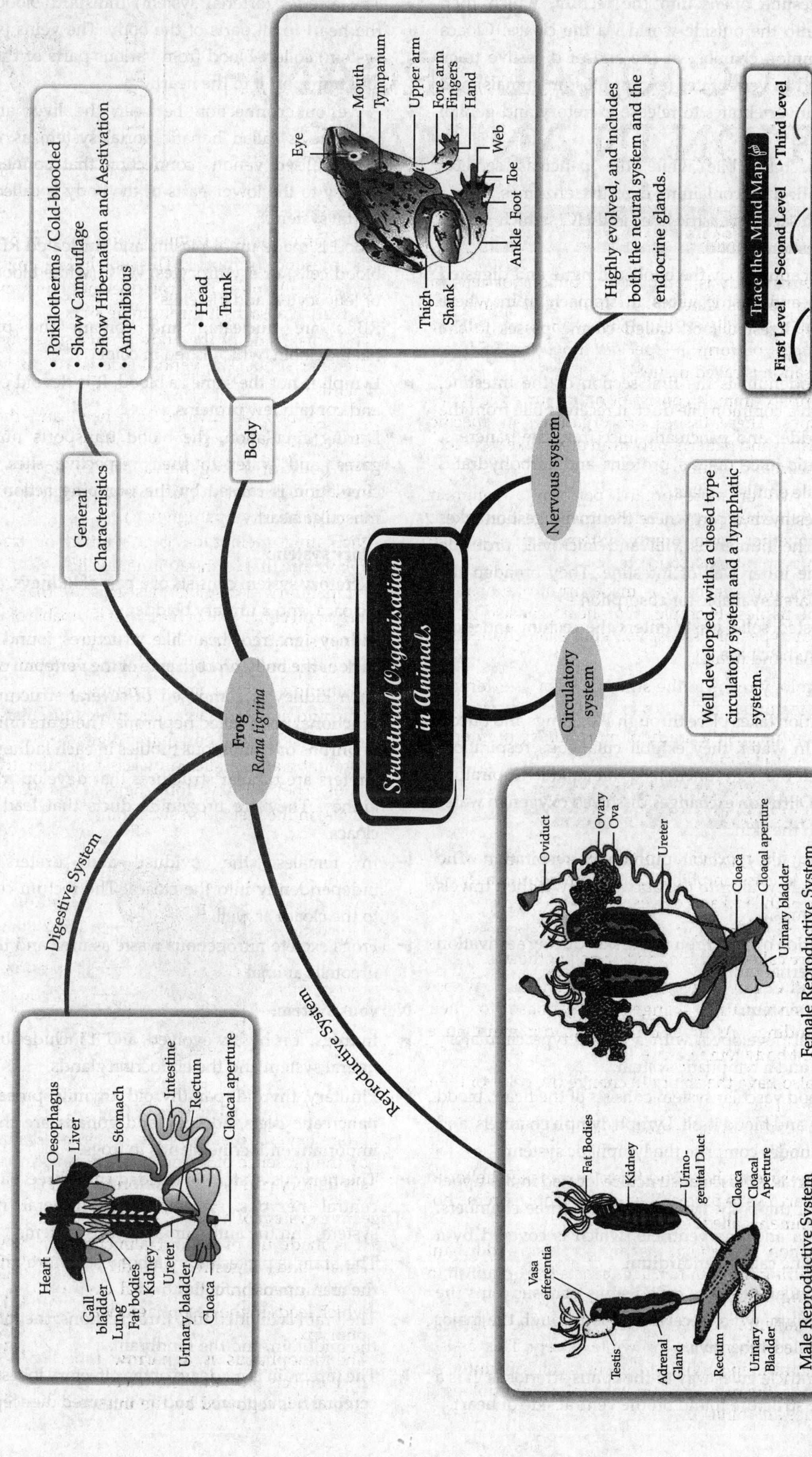
Structural Organisation in Animals
Frog
Rana tigrina
General Characteristics
• Poikilotherms / Cold-blooded
• Show Camouflage
• Show Hibernation and Aestivation
• Amphibious
Body
• Head
• Trunk
Eye
Mouth
Tympanum
Upper arm
Fore arm
Fingers
Hand
Web
Toe
Foot
Ankle
Shank
Thigh
Nervous system
Highly evolved, and includes both the neural system and the endocrine glands.
Circulatory system
Well developed, with a closed type circulatory system and a lymphatic system.
Trace the Mind Map
• First Level
• Second Level
• Third Level
Digestive System
Oesophagus
Liver
Stomach
Intestine
Rectum
Cloacal aperture
Heart
Gall bladder
Lung
Fat bodies
Kidney
Ureter
Urinary bladder
Cloaca
Reproductive System
Vasa efferentia
Testis
Adrenal Gland
Rectum
Urinary Bladder
Fat Bodies
Kidney
Urino-genital Duct
Cloaca
Cloacal Aperture
Male Reproductive System
Oviduct
Ovary
Ova
Ureter
Cloaca
Cloacal aperture
Urinary bladder
Female Reproductive System

The intestine opens into the rectum, which then opens into the outside world via the cloaca. Cloaca is a common chamber at the end of digestive tract. It is used in vertebrates (except most mammals) and certain invertebrates to release excretory and genital products.

- Liver secretes bile while the pancreas secretes pancreatic juice containing digestive enzymes.
- Stomach secretes gastric juice and HCl, which aids in the digestion of food.
- Food is captured by the bilobed tongue and digested by HCl and gastric juices in stomach from where partially digested food called chyme passes to the duodenum.
- The duodenum is the first section of the intestine. Through a common bile duct, it receives bile from the gall bladder and pancreatic juice from the pancreas. Pancreatic juice digests proteins and carbohydrates while bile emulsifies fats.
- The intestine is a part where the final digestion takes place. The numerous villi and microvilli protrude from the inner wall of intestine. They broaden the surface area available for absorption.
- Undigested solid waste enters the rectum and exits through the cloaca.

Respiration

- Respiration takes place through skin, lungs and buccal cavity. In water, they exhibit cutaneous respiration, in which the skin functions as an aquatic respiratory organ. Diffusion exchanges dissolved oxygen in water through the skin.
- On land, they exhibit pulmonary respiration. The nostrils allow air into the buccal cavity. It then travels to the lungs.
- Respiration occurs through the skin during aestivation and hibernation.

Circulatory system:

- It is well developed, with a closed type circulatory system and a lymphatic system.
- The blood vascular system consists of the heart, blood vessels, and blood itself. Lymph, lymph channels, and lymph nodes comprise the lymphatic system.
- The heart is a muscular structure located in the upper cavity of the body. It is made up of three chambers: two atria and one ventricle, which is covered by a membrane called pericardium.
- A triangular structure called sinus venosus joins the right atrium, which receives blood through the major veins called vena cava.
- The ventricle gives way to the conus arteriosus. It is a sac-like structure found on the ventral side of heart.
- The arteries (arterial system) transport blood from the heart to all parts of the body. The veins (venous system) collect blood from various parts of the body and transport it to the heart.
- A venous connection between the liver and the intestine is called hepatic portal system as well as a specialised venous connection that connects the kidney to the lower parts of the body is called renal portal system.
- Blood is made up of plasma and nucleated RBC (red blood cells) or erythrocytes, WBC (white blood cells) or leucocytes, and platelets.
- RBCs are nucleated and contain the pigment haemoglobin, which is red in color.
- Lymph is not the same as blood. It is devoid of RBCs and contain few proteins.
- During circulation, the blood transports nutrients, gases, and water to their respective sites. Blood circulation is caused by the pumping action of the muscular heart.

Excretory system:

- Excretory system consists of a pair of kidneys, ureters, a cloaca, and a urinary bladder.
- Kidneys are red, bean-like structures found in the back of the body on both side of the vertebral column.
- Each kidney is composed of several structural and functional units called nephrons. There are numerous nephrons or uriniferous tubules in each kidney.
- Ureters are tubular structures that develop from the kidney. They are urogenital ducts that lead to the cloaca.
- In females, the oviduct and ureters open independently into the cloaca. The rectum connects to the cloaca as well.
- Frogs excrete nitrogenous waste as urea and thus is a ureotelic animal.

Nervous system:

- In frogs, it is highly evolved, and it includes both the neural system and the endocrine glands.
- Pituitary, thyroid, parathyroid, thymus, pineal body, pancreatic islets, adrenal, and gonads are the most important endocrine glands in frogs.
- The nervous system is divided into three parts: the central nervous system, the peripheral nervous system, and the autonomic nervous system.
- The brain is protected by a bony structure known as the cranium or brain box.
- The brain is divided into three sections: the forebrain, the midbrain, and the hindbrain.
- The forebrain is made up of the olfactory lobes, paired cerebral hemispheres, and an unpaired diencephalon.

- The midbrain is distinguished by a pair of optic lobes.
- The cerebellum and the medulla oblongata make up the hindbrain. The medulla oblongata exits the foramen magnum and enters the spinal cord. The vertebral column protects the spinal cord.

Scan to know more about this topic

Frog: Reproductive System

- The sensory organs present are:
  - Organs of sense: Sensory papillae
  - Organs of taste: Taste buds
  - Organs of smell: Nasal epithelium
  - Organs of vision: Eyes
  - Hearing organs: Tympanum
- Internal ears and eyes are well-organised structures.

Reproduction:

- They have well-organised reproductive systems for both males and females.
- Male reproductive organs consist of a pair of yellowish ovoid testes adhered to the upper part of kidneys by a double fold of peritoneum called mesorchium, vasa efferentia enter the kidneys on their side and open into Bidder's canal, which finally communicates with the urinogenital duct that opens into the small, median chamber cloaca.
- The female reproductive organs include a pair of ovaries with a pair of oviduct opening into the cloaca separately.
- Fertilisation is external, development involves a larval stage called tadpole, which undergoes metamorphosis to form the adult.

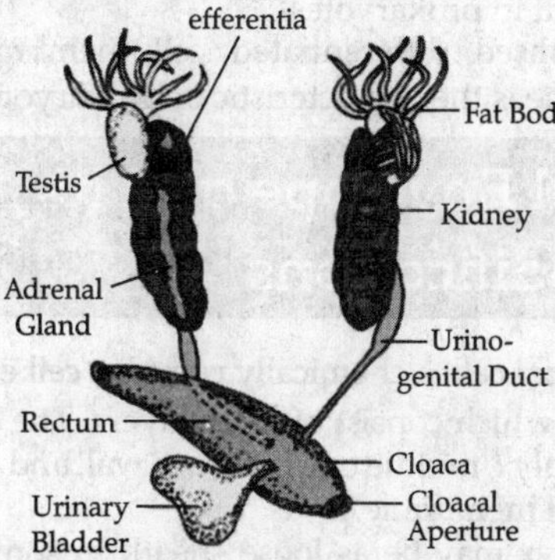

Male Reproductive System

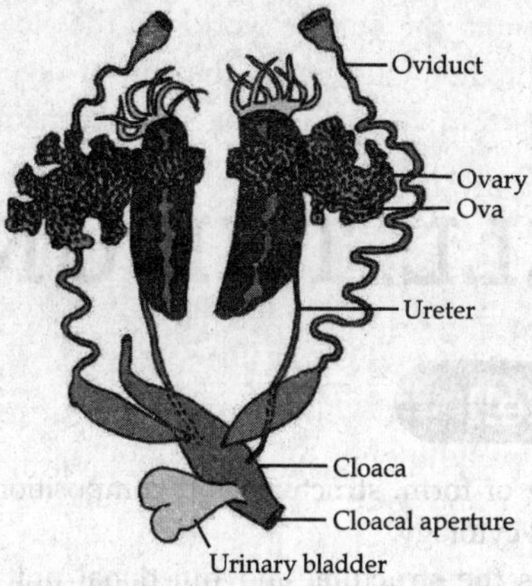

Female Reproductive System

Importance of frogs:

- Frogs are beneficial to humans because they eat insects and protect crops.
- Frogs maintain ecological balance in the ecosystem because they serve as an important link in the food chain and food web.
- Man eats the muscular legs of frogs in some countries.

Important Diagram

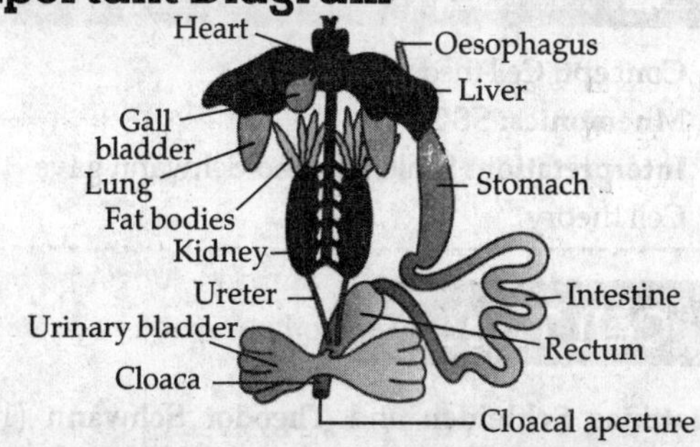

Alimentary canal and digestive glands

Key Words

- **Aestivation:** An organism's dormant state during the summer.
- **Hibernation:** An organism's dormant state during the winter is known as hibernation or winter sleep.
- **Blood:** It is a bright red coloured fluid connective tissue.

NCERT CORNER

Q. 1. Draw a neat diagram of digestive system of frog.

[NCERT Ex. Q. 1, Page 84]

Ans. For Diagram : Refer to Revision notes/ Important diagram/ Fig Alimentary canal and digestive glands.

Q. 2. Mention the function of the ureters in frog.

[NCERT Ex. Q. 2, Page 84]

Ans. A ureter acts as a urinogenital duct, which carries sperms along with urine in male frogs.

CHAPTER 8

CELL: THE UNIT OF LIFE

Cell

- Study of form, structure, and composition of cell is called cytology.
- Cell is the structural and functional unit of life. In unicellular organism (*Amoeba*, *Paramecium*, yeast, bacteria), single cell perform all the essential functions of life.
- In multicellular organisms, different kinds of tissues perform different function and have division of labour.

Mnemonics

Concept: Cell theory
Mnemonics: SSC
Interpretation: Schleiden and Schwann gave Cell theory

Cell Theory

- **Matthias Schleiden** and **Theodor Schwann** (1839) proposed the cell theory.
- All living organisms are composed of cells and products of cells.
- All cells arise from pre-existing cells.
- Shape and size of cells varies greatly according to their position and function.
- Mycoplasma is the smallest cell and largest isolated cell is the ostrich egg.
- The shape of cell may be cuboid, columnar, polygonal, thread like or irregular.

Scan to know more about this topic
Cell Theory

An Overview of Cell

- Inside each cell is a dense membrane bound structure called nucleus.
- This nucleus contains the chromosomes which in turn contain the DNA.
- Cells that have membrane bound nuclei are called eukaryotic whereas cells that lack a membrane bound nucleus are prokaryotic.
- In both prokaryotic and eukaryotic cells, a semi-fluid matrix called cytoplasm occupies the volume of the cell.
- Besides the nucleus, the eukaryotic cells have other membrane bound distinct structures called organelles like the endoplasmic reticulum (ER), the golgi complex, lysosomes, mitochondria, microbodies and vacuoles. The prokaryotic cells lack such membrane bound organelles.
- Ribosomes are non-membrane bound organelles found in all cells both eukaryotic as well as prokaryotic.
- Animal cells contain another non-membrane bound organelle called controsome which helps in cell division.

Prokaryotic Cells

- Prokaryotic cells are represented by Bacteria, Blue green algae, Mycoplasma and PPLO.
- They multiply rapidly and vary in size greatly.
- Bacterial cells may be bacillus (rod shaped), coccus (spherical), vibrio (comma-shaped) and spirillum (spiral).
- All prokaryotic cells have cell wall surrounding the cell membrane except in Mycoplasma.
- Genetic material is naked. Besides the genomic DNA (single chromosome) many bacteria have small circular DNA outside the genomic DNA called as plasmids.
- The plasmid DNA, in some bacteria, provides some special features like resistance to antibiotic.
- Cell organelles like Mitochondria, Golgi bodies, etc., are absent in prokaryotes.
- A specialised differentiated cell membrane called mesosome is the characteristic of prokaryotes.

Cell Envelope and its modifications

- In bacterial cell, a chemically complex cell envelope is present, which consist of three layers. The outermost is glycocalyx, middle one is the cell wall and innermost is the cell membrane.
- Glycocalyx may be as loose sheath in some bacteria called as slimy layer. In some other bacteria, glycocalyx may be thick and tough called capsule.
- Plasma membrane is semi-permeable having mesosome in the form of vesicles, tubules and lamellae. They help in cell wall formation, DNA replication and distribution of daughter cells.
- Motile bacterial cell contain flagella, which is composed of filament, hook and basal body. Pili and fimbriae are the other surface structure that help the bacteria in attaching with host and other substance.

Ribosomes

- In prokaryotes, ribosomes are attached with cell membrane having two sub-units – 50S and 30S to form together 70S prokaryotic ribosomes.
- Ribosomes are site of protein synthesis. Ribosomes attach with mRNA to form a chain called polyribosomes.

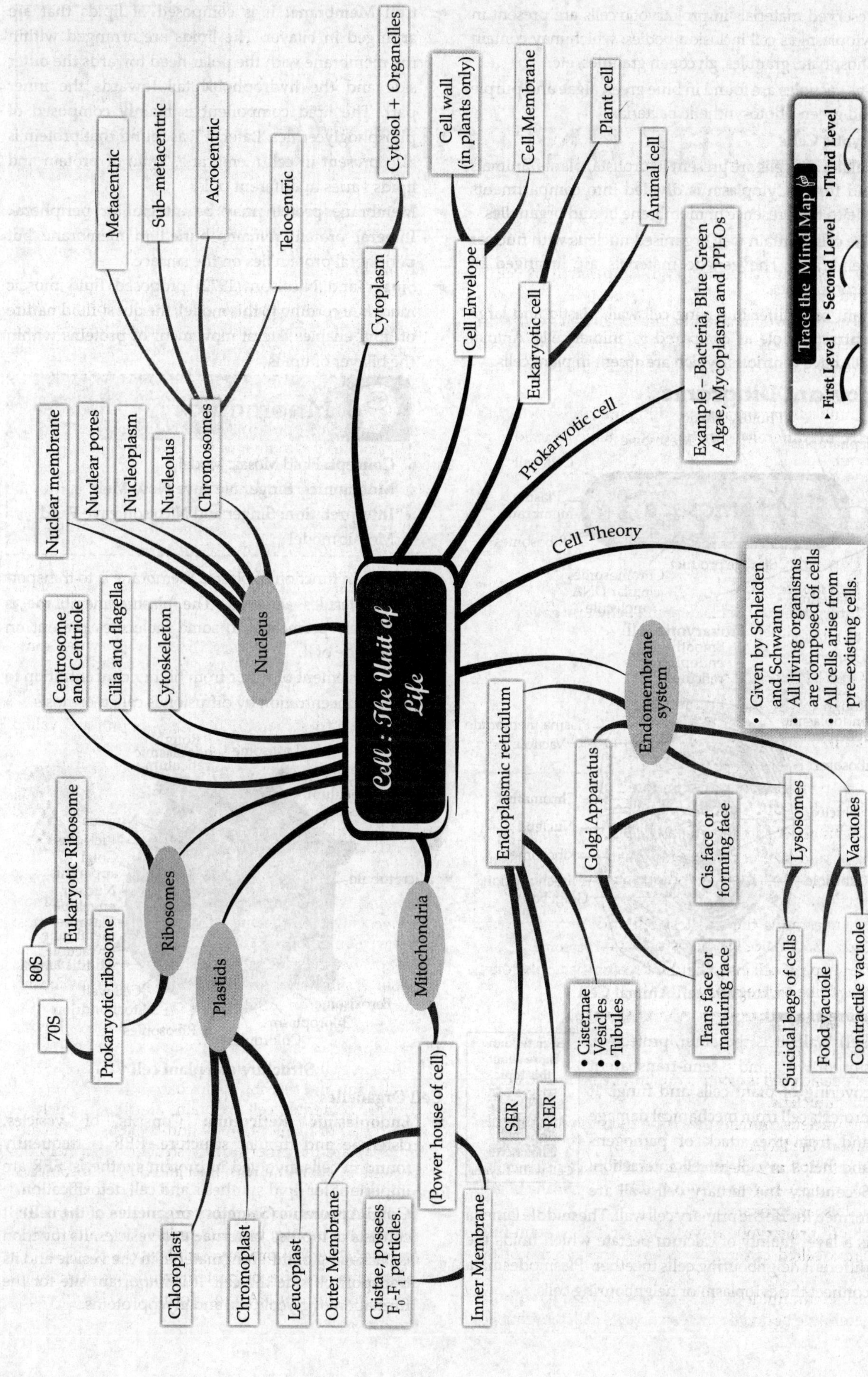

Trace the Mind Map
First Level
Second Level
Third Level
Cell : The Unit of Life
Nucleus
Nuclear membrane
Nuclear pores
Nucleoplasm
Nucleolus
Chromosomes
Metacentric
Sub–metacentric
Acrocentric
Telocentric
Cytoplasm
Cytosol + Organelles
Cell Envelope
Cell wall (in plants only)
Cell Membrane
Eukaryotic cell
Plant cell
Animal cell
Prokaryotic cell
Example – Bacteria, Blue Green Algae, Mycoplasma and PPLOs
Cell Theory
Given by Schleiden and Schwann
All living organisms are composed of cells
All cells arise from pre–existing cells.
Endomembrane system
Endoplasmic reticulum
Cisternae
Vesicles
Tubules
SER
RER
Golgi Apparatus
Cis face or forming face
Trans face or maturing face
Lysosomes
Suicidal bags of cells
Vacuoles
Food vacuole
Contractile vacuole
Mitochondria
(Power house of cell)
Outer Membrane
Inner Membrane
Cristae, possess F_0-F_1 particles.
Plastids
Chloroplast
Chromoplast
Leucoplast
Ribosomes
Eukaryotic Ribosome
80S
Prokaryotic ribosome
70S
Centrosome and Centriole
Cilia and flagella
Cytoskeleton

- Reserved materials in prokaryotic cells are present in cytoplasm as cell inclusion bodies, which may contain phosphate, granules, glycogen granules, etc.
- Gas vacuoles are found in blue green algae and purple and green photosynthetic bacteria.

Eukaryotic Cells

- Eukaryotic cells are present in protista, plants, animals and fungi. Cytoplasm is divided into compartments due to the presence of membrane bound organelles.
- The cells contain well organised nucleus with nuclear membrane. The genetic materials are arranged in chromosomes.
- Plant cells differ in having cell wall, plastid and large central vacuole as compared to animal cells. Animal cells have centrioles, which are absent in plant cells.

Important Diagrams

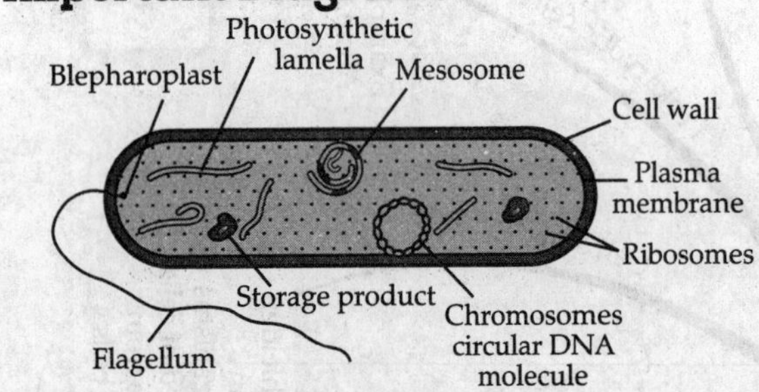

Prokaryotic cell

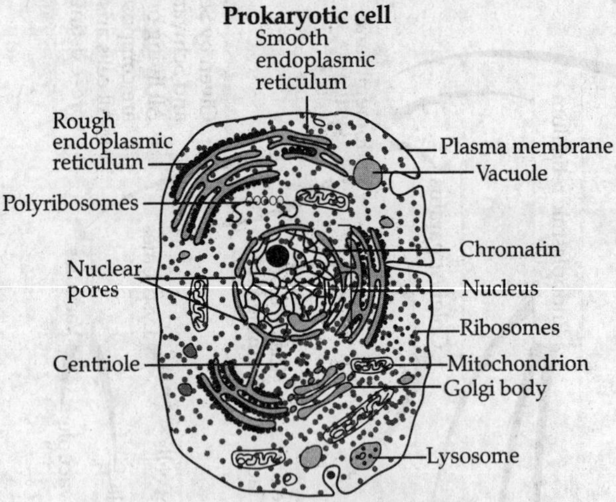

Eukaryotic cell Animal Cell

Structure of a cell:

- **Cell Wall:** It is the outer, protective, supportive and semi-transparent covering of plant cells and fungi. It protects cell from mechanical damage and from the attack of pathogens and helps in cell to cell interaction. Secondary and tertiary cell wall are formed inside the primary cell wall. The middle lamella is a layer mainly of calcium pectate which holds the different neighbouring cells together. Plasmodesmata connect the cytoplasm of neighbouring cells.

Scan to know more about this topic

Cell wall- Layers

- **Cell Membrane:** It is composed of lipids that are arranged in bilayer. The lipids are arranged within the membrane with the polar head towards the outer side and the hydrophobic tail towards the inner part. The lipid component is mainly composed of phosphoglycerides. Later, it was found that protein is also present in cell membrane. Ratio of protein and lipids varies in different cells.
- Membrane protein may be integral or peripheral. Integral protein remains buried in membrane but peripheral protein lies on the surface.
- Singer and Nicolson (1972) proposed fluid mosaic model. According to this model, the quasi-fluid nature of lipid enables lateral movement of proteins within the bilayer of lipids.

Mnemonics

Concept: Fluid Mosaic Model
Mnemonics: Singer Ne gaya **Flow Mein**
Interpretation: Singer and **Nicolson** gave **Fluid** Mosaic model

- The main function of plasma membrane is to transport the molecules across it. The plasma membrane is selectively permeable to some molecules present on either side of it.
- The movement of water from higher concentration to lower concentration by diffusion is called osmosis.

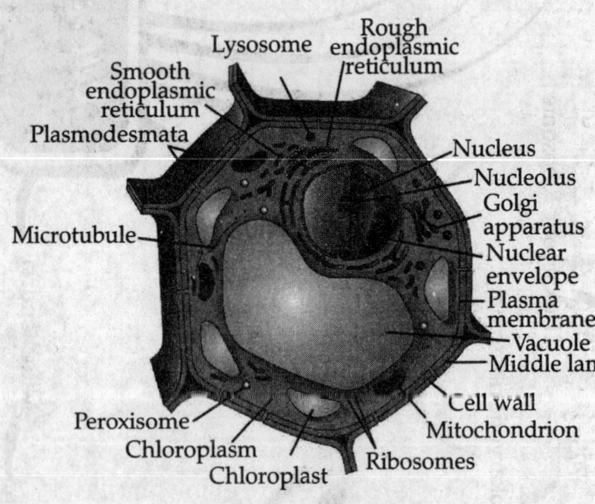

Structure of a plant cell

Cell Organelles:

- **Endoplasmic Reticulum:** Consists of vesicles, cisternae and tubular structure. RER is frequently found in cells involved in protein synthesis. SER are important for lipid synthesis and cell detoxification.
- **Golgi Apparatus (Secretory organelles of the cell):** It consists of tubules, cisternae and vesicles. Its function is packaging of different material in the vesicle and its transport outside the cell. It is important site for the formation of glycolipids and glycoproteins.

- **Lysosomes (Suicidal bags of cell):** They are formed from Golgi and E.R. They contain hydrolytic enzyme (hydrolases), active at acidic pH.
- **Vacuoles:** The vacuoles are membrane bound space in the cytoplasm. It contain water, sap and excretory products. Tonoplast covers the vacuoles in plant cell. It regulates the concentration of cell.

Scan to know more about this topic

Mitochondria

- **Mitochondria (Power House of cell):** Double membrane bound structure. Matrix is inside the inner membrane and number of infolding of inner membrane is called cristae. Enzymes are found in both membrane. Energy is generated in the form of ATP in the mitochondria. It has its own DNA and 70S ribosomes.
- **Plastids (Kitchen of the cell):** Based on the types of pigments, plastids can be classified into chloroplast, chromoplast and leucoplast. Chromoplast contain coloured pigments like carotene. Leucoplast are colourless with stored nutrients, amyloplast (starch storing), elaioplast (fat storing) and alueroplast (protein storing). Chloroplast are green, composed of thylakoids (which form grana and stroma) where photosynthesis takes place, contain 70S ribosome and DNA.
- **Ribosomes (Protein factories of cell):** They are composed of RNA and protein and are not surrounded by any membrane. In Prokaryotes, 70S and in eukaryotes, 80S ribosomes are found.
- **Cytoskeleton, cilia and flagella:** These are filamentous proteinaceous structures in cytoplasm. Cytoskeletons are involved in mechanical support, motility and shape maintenance while cilia and flagella are meant for attachment and movement.
- **Centrosome and centrioles:** Two centriole forms centrosome perpendicularly. They have cartwheel organisation made up of nine spaced fibres of tubulin composed of central hub and peripheral spokes. These are important in cell division.
- **Nucleus (Brain of the cell):** It consists of nuclear membrane and nucleoplasm. Nuclear membrane is bilayered and is selectively permeable. In outer membrane R.E.R. is present. Movement of RNA and protein takes place between nucleus and cytoplasm. Nucleoplasm contain nucleolus and chromatin. Nucleolus is the site for RNA synthesis. Chromatin contains DNA, RNA, histone and non-histone proteins.
- Based on the position of the centromere, the chromosomes are classified into four types: acrocentric, telocentric, sub-metacentric and metacentric.
- Many membrane bound minute vesicles called microbodies that contain various enzymes, are present in both plant and animal cells.

Key Words

- **Cell:** Cell is the biological, functional and structural unit of life.
- **Totipotency:** It is the ability of living cells to form the whole organism, unless and until they have become extremely specialised.
- **Undifferentiated cells:** These are unspecialised cells that have the ability to divide.
- **Differentiated cells:** The cells that have become specialised to perform specific functions are called differentiated cells.
- **Dedifferentiated cells:** The cells which revert to undifferentiated state to take over the function of division are known as dedifferentiated cells.
- **Prokaryotes:** Organisms whose cells do not possess a well defined nucleus is known as prokaryotes.
- **Eukaryotes:** Organisms whose cells have a nucleus with a well-defined nuclear membrane is known as eukaryotes.
- **Mesosome:** Mesosome is specialised membranous structures defined by the invagination of the cell membrane in bacteria.
- **Polyribosome:** Several ribosomes may attach to a single mRNA and form a chain called polyribosomes or polysome.
- **Diffusion:** The process of movement of substance from the region of higher water concentration to the region of lower concentration, so as to spread the substance uniformly in the given space is known as diffusion.
- **Osmosis:** It is defined as the diffusion of water from region of higher concentration to region of lower concentration across the semi-permeable membrane.
- **Hypotonic Solution:** Hypotonic is the solution which has lower osmotic concentration than the cell.
- **Hypertonic Solution:** Hypertonic is the solution that has higher osmotic concentration than the cell.
- **Isotonic Solution:** It is the solution that has same osmotic concentration as inside the cell.
- **Plasmolysis:** It is the phenomenon of the loss of water from a plant cell by osmosis when kept in a hypertonic solution.
- **Active transport:** It is the process of transport of molecules across the plasma membrane against the concentration gradient.
- **Endomembrane system:** The endomembrane system is the grouping of some membrane organelles as their functions are coordinated. It includes endoplasmic reticulum (ER), golgi complex, lysosomes and vacuoles.

NCERT CORNER

Q. 1. Which of the following is not correct?

(a) Robert Brown discovered the cell.

(b) Schleiden and Schwann formulated the cell theory.

(c) Virchow explained that cells are formed from pre-existing cells.

(d) A unicellular organism carries out its life activities within a single cell. [NCERT Ex. Q. 1, Page 103]

Ans. (a) Robert Brown did not discover the cell. Cell was discovered by Robert Hooke. Robert Brown discovered the cell nucleus.

Q. 2. New cells generate from:

(a) Bacterial fermentation (b) Regeneration of old cells

(c) Pre-existing cells (d) Abiotic materials

[NCERT Ex. Q. 2, Page 103]

Ans. (c) According to biogenetic theory, new cells generate from pre-existing cells.

Q. 3. Match the following:

	Column I		Column II
(i)	**Cristae**	**(a)**	**Flat membranous sacs in stroma**
(ii)	**Cisternae**	**(b)**	**Infoldings in mitochondria**
(iii)	**Thylakoids**	**(c)**	**Disc-shaped sacs in Golgi apparatus**

[NCERT Ex. Q. 3, Page 103]

Ans.

	Column I		Column II
(i)	**Cristae**	**(b)**	**Infoldings in mitochondria**
(ii)	**Cisternae**	**(c)**	**Disc-shaped sacs in Golgi apparatus**
(iii)	**Thylakoids**	**(a)**	**Flat membranous sacs in stroma**

Q. 4. Which of the following is correct ?

(a) Cells of all living organisms have a nucleus.

(b) Both animal and plant cells have a well-defined cell wall.

(c) In prokaryotes, there are no membrane bound organelles.

(d) Cells are formed *de novo* from abiotic materials.

[NCERT Ex. Q. 4, Page 103]

Ans. (c) Membrane bound organelles are absent in prokaryotes.

Q. 5. What is a mesosome in a prokaryotic cell? Mention the functions that it performs.

[NCERT Ex. Q. 5, Page 103]

Ans. Mesosomes are extensions of plasma membrane into the cell in the form of vesicles, tubules and lamellae.

Its functions are:

(i) They help in the synthesis of cell wall and replication of DNA.

(ii) The also help in respiration, secretion processes to increase the surface area of plasma membrane to carry out various enzymatic activities.

Q. 6. How do neutral solutes move across the plasma membrane? Can the polar molecules also move across it in the same way? If not, then how are these transported across the membrane? [NCERT Ex. Q. 6, Page 103]

Ans. Neutral solutes move across the plasma membrane by means of diffusion along the concentration gradient. It moves from higher to lower concentration.

No, the polar molecule cannot move across it in the same way.

Polar molecules require a carrier protein of the membrane to facilitate their transport across the membrane. Some ions or molecules are transported across the membrane against their concentration gradient, which is an energy dependent process. It is called active transport. In active transport, ATP is utilised.

Q. 7. Name two cell-organelles that are double membrane bound. What are the characteristics of these two organelles? State their functions and draw labelled diagrams of both. [NCERT Ex. Q. 7, Page 103]

Ans. Mitochondria and chloroplast

Mitochondria:

(i) Each mitochondrion is a double membrane-bound structure with the outer membrane and the inner membrane.

(ii) The outer membrane forms the continuous limiting boundary of the organelle whereas the inner membrane forms a number of infolding called the cristae. The cristae increase the surface area.

(iii) The matrix possesses single circular DNA molecule, a few RNA molecules and 70S ribosomes.

Function:

(i) Mitochondria are the sites of aerobic respiration and produce cellular energy in the form of ATP, hence they are called powerhouses of the cell.

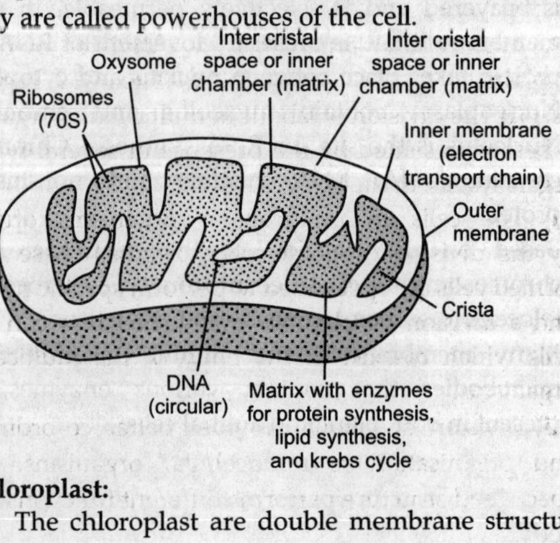

Chloroplast:

(i) The chloroplast are double membrane structures.

They are divided into outer and inner membranes, further divided into two distinct regions: Grana and stroma.

(ii) Between the outer and inner membranes, intermembrane space is present.

(iii) The inside of chloroplast is clearly marked into a colourless ground matrix called **stroma**.

(iv) A number of organised flattened membranous sacs called the thylakoids are present in the stroma.

(v) Thylakoids are arranged in stacks called grana. Besides these, there are flat membranous tubules called the stroma lamellae connecting the thylakoids of the different grana.

(vi) The stroma of the chloroplast contains small, double-stranded circular DNA and 70S ribosomes.

Functions:

(i) Chloroplasts are the centres of photosynthesis.

(ii) They are able to trap solar energy and convert it into chemical energy.

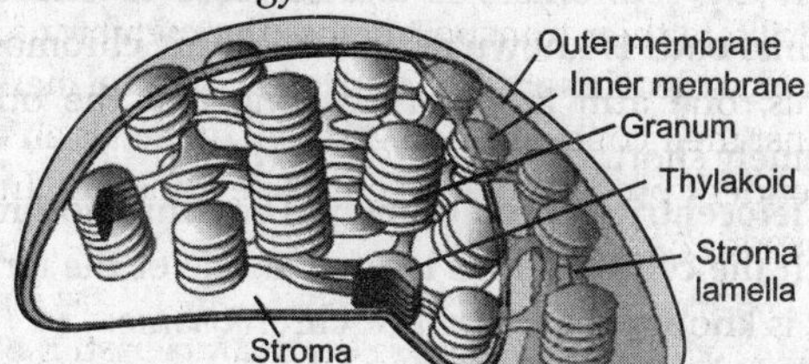

Q. 8. What are the characteristics of prokaryotic cells? **[NCERT Ex. Q. 8, Page 103]**

Ans. (i) The outer covering of protoplasm of bacterial cell is called as cell envelope, which comprises three components: Glycocalyx, cell wall and cell membrane.

(ii) Cytoplasm is granular, crystallo-colloid complex that forms the protoplasm.

(iii) The genetic material of prokaryotes is called as nucleoid. Nucleoid consists of a single circular strand of DNA duplex.

(iv) Some additional rings of extra chromosomal DNA called plasmids are present which can replicate independently.

(v) Bacteria bear flagella for locomotion. Bacterial flagellum is made up of 3 parts: basal body, hook and filament.

Q. 9. Multicellular organisms have division of labour. Explain. **[NCERT Ex. Q. 9, Page 103]**

Ans. (i) The division of labour in multicellular organisms is best represented by the presence of several types of organ system in the body.

(ii) The cells in multicellular organisms originate by the division of single-celled zygote. These newly formed cells are specialised to perform specific function and a division of labour is established between these cells which co-exist in the body of the multicellular organisms.

(iii) Division of labour provides better co-ordination and organisation to multicellular organisms. Thus, specialised structure performs different functions in the body.

Q. 10. Cell is the basic unit of life. Discuss in brief. **[NCERT Ex. Q. 10, Page 103]**

Ans. Cell is the basic unit of life because:

(i) All life begins as a single cell.

(ii) All life activities of an organism are present in miniature form in each and every cell of its body.

Q. 11. What are nuclear pores? State their function. **[NCERT Ex. Q. 11, Page 103]**

Ans. At number of places, the nuclear envelop is interrupted by minute pores, called nuclear pores. A nuclear pore has complex structure.

Some pores passes membranous annuli or pocket shaped outgrowths called bleeds. A pore along with additional structure is called pore complex.

Function: Helps in exchange of materials between nucleus and cytoplasm.

Q. 12. Both lysosomes and vacuoles are endomembrane structures, yet they differ in terms of their functions. Comment. **[NCERT Ex. Q. 12, Page 103]**

Ans. (i) Both lysosomes and vacuoles are the endomembrane structures yet they differ in terms of their functions because they contain different materials.

(ii) The isolated lysosomal vesicles have been found to be very rich in almost all type of hydrolytic enzymes such as lipase, proteases, carbohydrases.

These enzymes are optically active at the acidic pH and capable of digesting carbohydrates, proteins, lipids and nucleic acids.

(iii) On the other hand, the vacuoles contains water, sap, excretory product etc. In *Amoeba*, contractile vacuole is important for excretion.

Q. 13. Describe the structure of the following with the help of labelled diagrams.

(i) Nucleus (ii) Centrosome

[NCERT Ex. Q. 13, Page 103]

Ans. (i) Nucleus:

(a) The nucleus is a large organelle controlling all the activities of the eukaryotic cells.

(b) The nucleus is bounded by two membrane, which make the nuclear envelope.

(c) The outer and inner membranes are separated by a narrow space called perinuclear space.

(d) At some points, the nuclear envelope is interrupted by the presence of small structures called nuclear pores.

(e) Nucleolus is a rounded structure and is the site for ribosomal RNA synthesis.

(f) The space between the nuclear envelope and the nucleolus is filled with a transparent fluid called nucleoplasm.

(g) The nucleoplasm contains chromatin which is a DNA-protein complex.

(h) Nucleus is the seat of heredity.

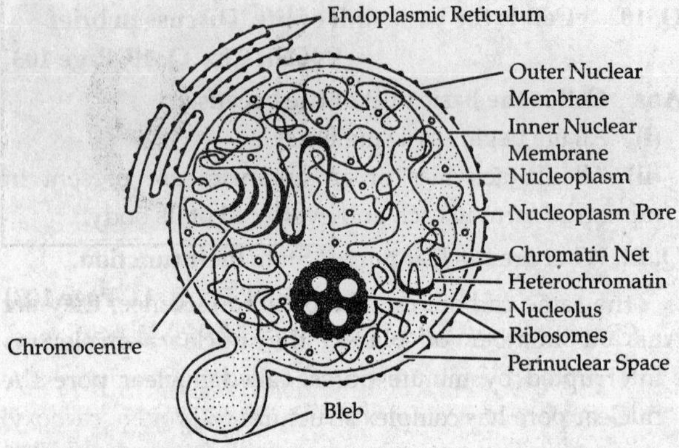

(ii) Centrosome:

(a) Centrosome is an organelle usually containing two cylindrical structures called centrioles.

(b) They are surrounded by amorphous pericentriolar materials.

(c) Both the centrioles in a centrosome lie perpendicular to each other in which each has an organisation like the cart wheel.

(d) They are made up of nine evenly spaced peripheral fibrils of tubulin.

(e) Each of the peripheral fibril is a triplet. The adjacent triplets are also linked.

(f) The central part of the centriole is also proteinaceous and called hub, which is connected with tubules of the peripheral triplets by radial spokes made of protein.

(g) The centrioles form the basal body of the cilia or flagella, and the spindle fibres that give rise to spindle apparatus during cell division in animal cells.

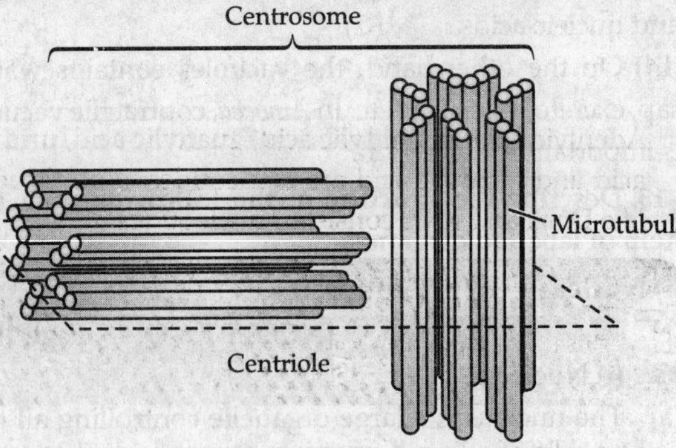

Q. 14. What is a centromere? How does the position of centromere form the basis of classification of chromosomes? Support your answer with a diagram showing the position of centromere on different types of chromosomes. **[NCERT Ex. Q. 14, Page 103]**

Ans. Centromere is the constriction present on the chromosomes, where chromatids are held together.

Chromosomes are divided into four types based on the position of centromere:

(i) Metacentric chromosome: The chromosome in which the centromere is present in the middle and divides the chromosome into two equal arms is known as a metacentric chromosome.

(ii) Sub-metacentric chromosome: The chromosome in which the centromere is slightly away from the middle region is known as a sub-metacentric chromosome. In this, one arm is slightly longer than the other.

(iii) Acrocentric chromosome: The chromosome in which the centromere is located close to one of the terminal ends is known as an acrocentric chromosome. In this, one arm is extremely long and the other is extremely short.

(iv) Telocentric chromosome: The chromosome in which the centromere is located at one of the terminal ends is known as a telocentric chromosome.

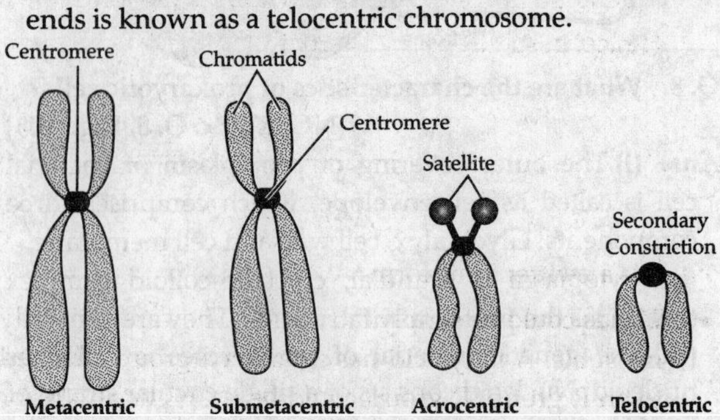

Types of chromosome

□□

CHAPTER 9

BIOMOLECULES

- Chemicals or molecules present in the living organism are known as **biomolecules**. Biomolecules are divided into two types- inorganic and organic.
- Inorganic biomolecules includes minerals, gases and water and organic biomolecules includes carbohydrates, fats, proteins, nucleic acids, vitamins, etc.
- Different biomolecules can be classified as aldehyde, ketones and aromatic compounds as chemical form and amino acids, nucleotides and fatty acids as biochemical forms.
- Except lipids, macromolecules are formed by polymerisation of sub-units called monomers.
- **Amino acids** are organic compounds containing an amino group and an acidic group as substituents on the same carbon, i.e., the α-carbon. Hence, they are called α-amino acids. They are substituted methanes.
- There are four substituent groups occupying the four valency positions. These are hydrogen, carboxyl group, amino group and a variable group designated as R group. Based on the nature of R group there are many amino acids but there are only twenty types which occur in proteins.
- Proteins are polymers of amino acids. Amino acids are linked by peptide bond formed by dehydration between COOH group of one amino acids and NH_3 group of next with the removal of H_2O.

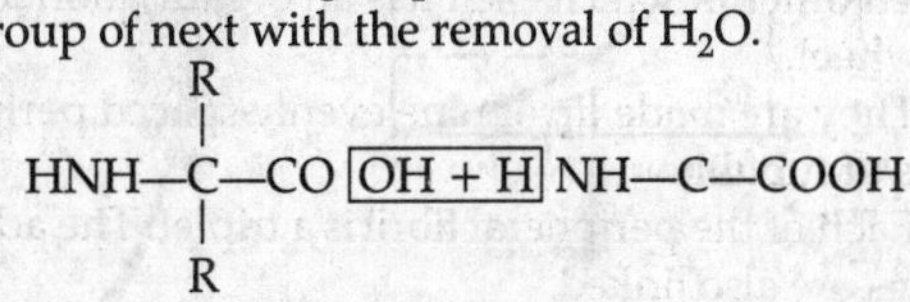

- A particular property of amino acids is the ionizable nature of $-NH_2$, and $-COOH$ groups. Hence, in solutions of different pHs the structure of amino acids changes.

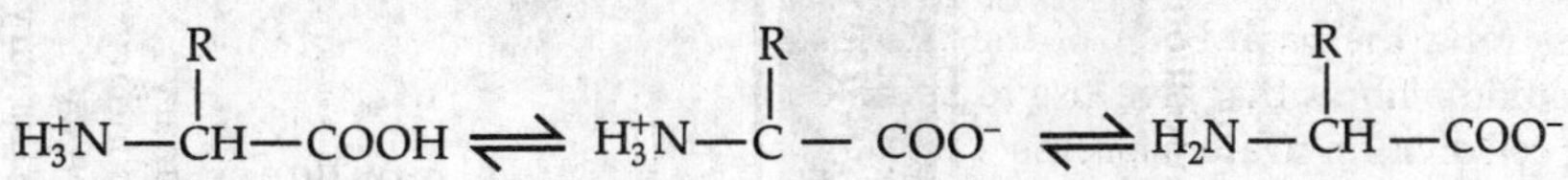

(A) (B) (C)

B is a zwitter ionic form

- **Lipids** could be simply fatty acids. They are generally insoluble. A fatty acid has a carboxyl group attached to an R group. R group could be $-CH_3$ or $-C_2H_5$ or higher number of $-CH_2$ groups. *For example,* Palmitic acid has 16 carbon. Another simple lipid is glycerol which is a trihydroxy propane. Fatty acids could be saturated or unsaturated.
- Many lipids have both glycerol and acids. Here the fatty acids are found esterified with glycerol. They can be monoglycerides, diglycerides and triglycerides. These are also called fats and oils based on melting point, i.e., gingelly oil.
- Some lipids have phosphorous and a phosphorylated organic compound in them. These are phospholipids and found in cell membrane, e.g., lecithin.

Nucleotides

- Living organisms have a number of carbon compounds in which heterocyclic rings can be found. Some of these are nitrogen bases-adenine, guanine, cytosine, uracil and thymine. When found attached to a sugar, they are called nucleosides. If a phosphate group is also found esterified to the sugar they are called nucleotides.
- Adenlyic acid, thymidylic acid, guanylic acid, uridylic acid and cytidylic acid are nucleotides. Nucleic acids like DNA and RNA consist of nucleotides only.

Primary and Secondary Metabolites

- The cells of a living organism are made of thousands of organic compound and in addition to this many molecules are formed during metabolism. The compounds which are produced in or required for metabolism are called metabolites. Metabolites are biomolecules involved in many cellular functions such as energy, stimulation, inhibition etc.
- **Primary metabolites** are those which are directly involved in physiological functions and helps in growth, reproduction and maturity, e.g., amino acids, saccharides, nitrogen bases etc.
- **Secondary metabolites** are those which are produced from the primary metabolites and are not directly involved in the physiological functions, e.g., alkaloids, flavonoids, rubber, essential oils, antibiotics, coloured pigments, scents, gums, spices etc.

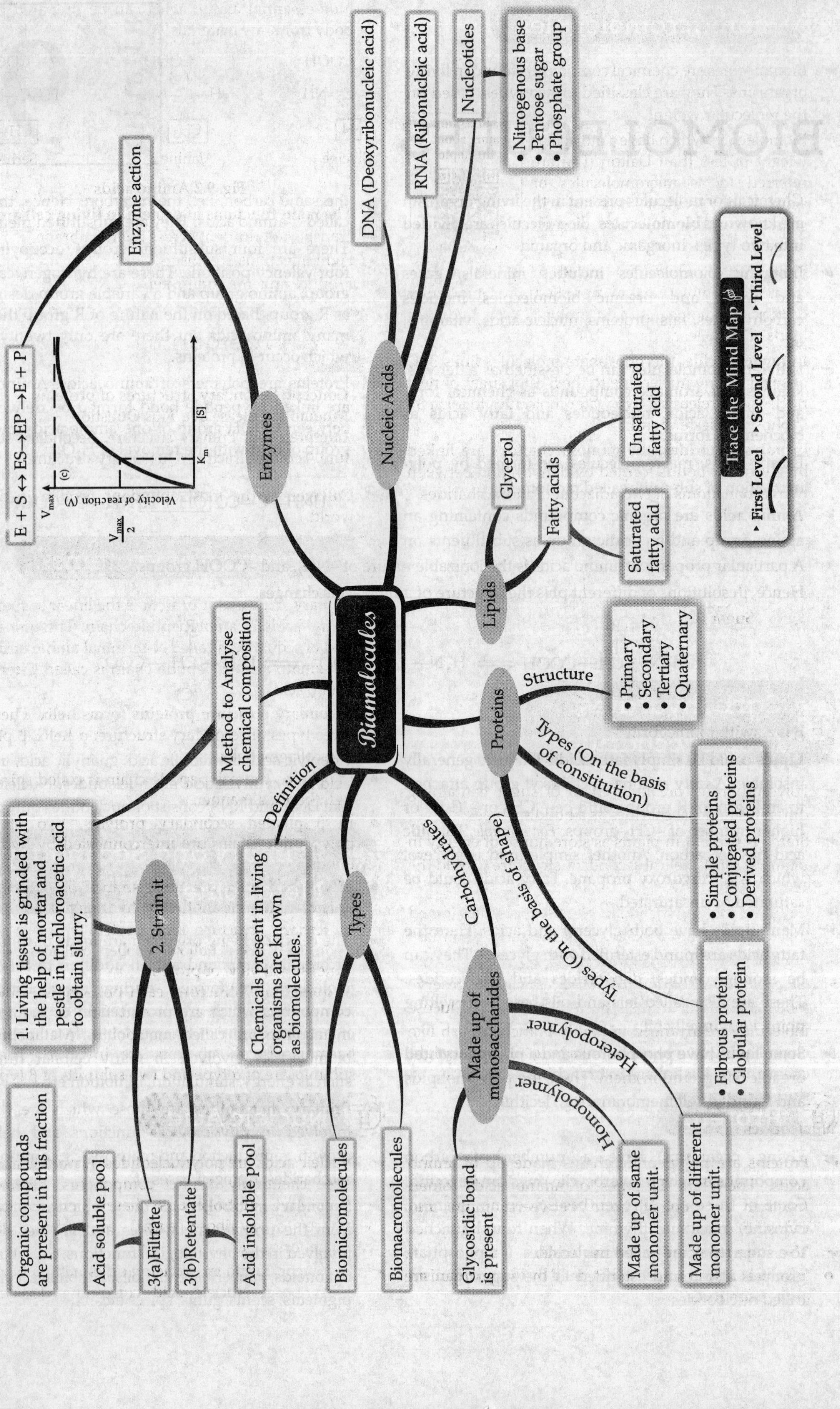
Biomolecules
Definition
Chemicals present in living organisms are known as biomolecules.
Types
Biomicromolecules
Biomacromolecules
Method to Analyse chemical composition
1. Living tissue is grinded with the help of mortar and pestle in trichloroacetic acid to obtain slurry.
2. Strain it
3(a)Filtrate
Acid soluble pool
Organic compounds are present in this fraction
3(b)Retentate
Acid insoluble pool
Enzymes
E + S ↔ ES→EP→E + P
Vmax
Vmax/2
Velocity of reaction (V)
Km
[S]
(c)
Enzyme action
Nucleic Acids
DNA (Deoxyribonucleic acid)
RNA (Ribonucleic acid)
Nucleotides
• Nitrogenous base
• Pentose sugar
• Phosphate group
Lipids
Glycerol
Fatty acids
Saturated fatty acid
Unsaturated fatty acid
Proteins
Structure
• Primary
• Secondary
• Tertiary
• Quaternary
Types (On the basis of constitution)
• Simple proteins
• Conjugated proteins
• Derived proteins
Types (On the basis of shape)
• Fibrous protein
• Globular protein
Carbohydrates
Made up of monosaccharides
Homopolymer
Heteropolymer
Glycosidic bond is present
Made up of same monomer unit.
Made up of different monomer unit.
Trace the Mind Map
First Level
Second Level
Third Level

Biomacromolecules

- Biomolecules are chemical compounds found in living organisms. They are classified in two types, based on the molecular weight.
- Biomolecules which have a molecular wieght of less than Dalton (Da) are referred to as micromolecules or simply biomolecules. These are acid soluble and their moleculaı weights range form 18 to 800 Da.

Scan to know more about this topic

Biomolecules

- Biomolecules which are found in the acid insoluble fraction are called macromolecules or biomacromolecules, e.g., proteins, carbohydrates, lipids and nuclei acids.
- In **nucleic acids**, the phosphate molecules links 3′ C of sugar of one nucleoside to the 5′ C of sugar of next nucleosides releasing two water molecules to form 3′-5′ phosphodiester bond.
- In **polysaccharides**, the monosaccharides are linked by glycosidic bonds formed by dehydration between two carbon atoms of two adjacent monosaccharides.

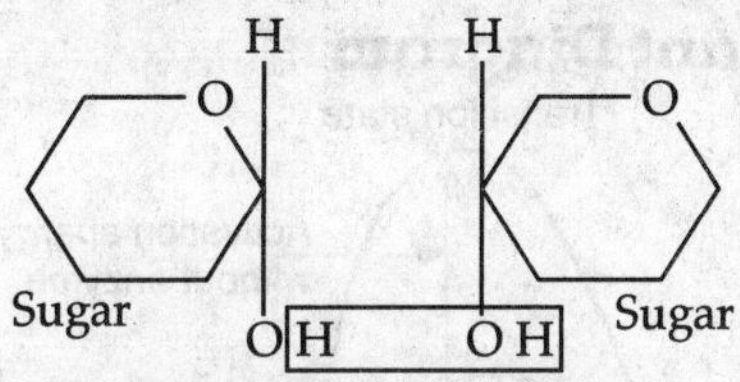

Fig. 9.1 Glycosidic bond

Carbohydrates (Polysaccharides)

- Polysaccharides are long chain of sugar containing different monosaccharides as a building block.
- Starch is present in plants as store house of energy in plants. It forms helical secondary structure to hold the 12 molecules.
- Cellulose molecules contain glucose molecules joined together by 1-4 β linkage. It is the most abundant organic molecules on earth.
- Glycogen is called animal starch as it is the reserve food materials for animals, bacteria and fungi. Glucose molecules are arranged in highly branched bush like chain having two types of linkage α, –1, 4 in straight chain and α, 1, 6 linkage in branching.

Protein

- Proteins are polypeptide chains made up of amino acids. There are 22 types of amino acids joined together by peptide bond between amino and carboxylic group.
- **There are two kinds of amino acids:**
  - **Essential amino acids** are obtained by living organism along with food.
  - **Non-essential amino acids** can be prepared by our body from raw materials.

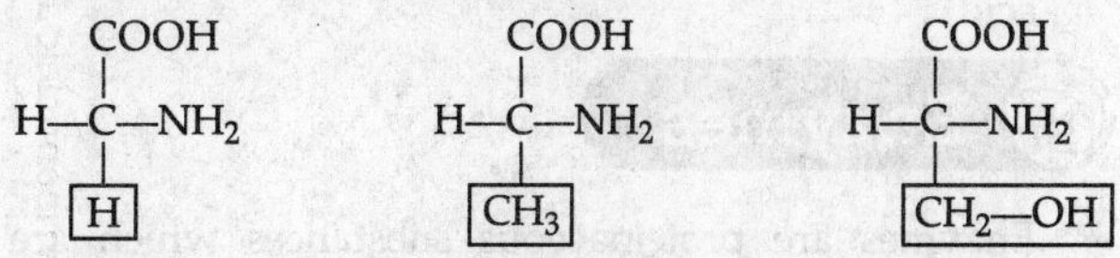

Glycine Alanine Serine

Fig. 9.2 Amino acids

- **The main functions of protein in living cell are:**
  - Transport of nutrient across the membrane.
  - Fight infectious organisms.
  - Produce enzyme and proteins.

Mnemonics

Concept: Secondary Structures of proteins
Mnemonic: Please See This Question
Interpretation: Primary structure, Secondary structure, Tertiary structure, Quaternary structure

- **Collagen** is the most abundant protein in animal world.

Structure of Proteins

- **Primary structure of protein** is the linear sequence of amino acids in a polypeptide chain. The first amino acid of sequence is called N-terminal amino acids and last amino acid of peptide chain is called C-terminal amino acids.
- **Secondary structure proteins** forms helix. There are three types of secondary structure: α helix, β pleated and collagen helix.
  - In α **helix**, the polypeptide chain is coiled spirally in right handed manner.
  - In β **pleated** secondary proteins, two of more polypeptide chains are interconnected by hydrogen bonds.
  - In **collagen** there are three strands or polypeptides coiled around one another by hydrogen bonds.
- In **tertiary structure** long protein chain is folded upon itself like a hollow woollen ball to give three dimensional view of protein.
- In **quaternary structure**, each polypeptide develops its own tertiary structure and function as subunit of protein. Example: Haemoglobin. In adult human haemoglobin, 4 sub-units are involved. The two subunits are of α type and two subunits of β types.

Nucleic Acid

- Nucleic acids are polynucleotides. A nucleic acid has three chemically distinct components: heterocyclic compound (nitrogenous base), polysaccharides (ribose/ deoxy-ribose sugar) and phosphate or phosphoric acid.
- The sugar found in nucleic acid is either ribose or deoxyribose. Nucleic acid containing deoxyribose

sugar is called DNA (Deoxyribonucleic acid) and those containing ribose sugars are called RNA (Ribonucleic acid).

Enzymes

- Enzymes are proteinaceous substances which are capable of catalyzing chemical reactions of biological origin without themselves undergoing any change, commonly called as biocatalysts.
- The nucleic acids that behave like enzymes are called **ribozymes**.
- The tertiary structure of protein has pockets or crevices into which substrate fit to catalyze the biochemical reactions.
- The major difference between inorganic and organic catalyst is that inorganic catalyst works effectively at high temperature and pressure but enzyme get damaged at high temperature. Thermal stability is an important quality of enzymes isolated from thermophilic organisms as these enzymes retain their catalytic power at high temperature is (upto 30°-90°C).

Scan to know more about this topic

Amino Acids and Lipids

- The external energy required to start a chemical reaction is called **activation energy**.

(i) The substrate binds to the active site of the enzyme.

(ii) This binding of the substrate induces the enzymes to alter its shape and fit more closely around the substrate.

(iii) The active site of the enzyme, now is in close proximity of the substrate breaks the chemical bonds of the substrate and an enzyme-product complex is formed.

(iv) The enzyme releases the products of the reaction and the free enzyme is ready to take up another molecule of the substrate.

Factors affecting Enzyme activity

- The activity of an enzyme is affected by a change in the conditions which can alter the tertiary structure of the protein. These include temperature, pH, change in substrate concentration or binding of specific chemicals that regulate its activity.
- **Temperature and pH:** Each enzyme shows its highest activity at a particular temperature and pH called the optimum temperature and optimum pH. Low temperature preserves the enzyme in a temporarily inactive state whereas high temperature destroys enzymatic activity because proteins are denatured by heat.
- **Concentration of Substrate:** With the increase in substrate concentration, the velocity of the enzymatic reaction rises at first and ultimately reaches the maximum velocity (V_{max}) which is not exceeded by any further rise in concentration of the substrate. This is because the enzyme molecules are fewer than the substrate molecules and after saturation of these molecules, there are no free enzyme molecules to bind with the additional substrate molecules.
- When the binding of the chemical shuts off enzyme activity, the process is called inhibition and the chemical is called an inhibitor.
- When the inhibitor closely resembles the substrate in its molecular structure and inhibits the activity of the enzyme, it is known as competitive inhibitor.

Co-factors:

- Three kinds of co-factors may be identified: prosthetic groups, co-enzymes and metal ion.
- Prosthetic groups are organic compound and tightly bound to the opoenzyme.
- Co-enzymes are also organic compounds but their association with openzyme is only transient, usually occuring during the course of catalysis.
- A number of enzymes require metal ions for their activity which from coordination bonds.
- Enzymes are classified into six classes, which are as follows:

(i) **Oxidoreductase:** These enzymes catalyse oxidation and reduction reactions.

(ii) **Transferase:** These enzymes catalyse the transfer of functional groups such as methyl or phosphate group.

(iii) **Hydrolases:** These enzymes catalyse the hydrolysis reactions.

(iv) **Ligases:** These enzymes catalyse the joining of two molecules by making a bond.

(v) **Isomerases:** These class of enzymes bring about the isomerisation reaction

(vi) **Lyases:** Lyases brings about lysis and cleavage of various bonds.

Important Diagram

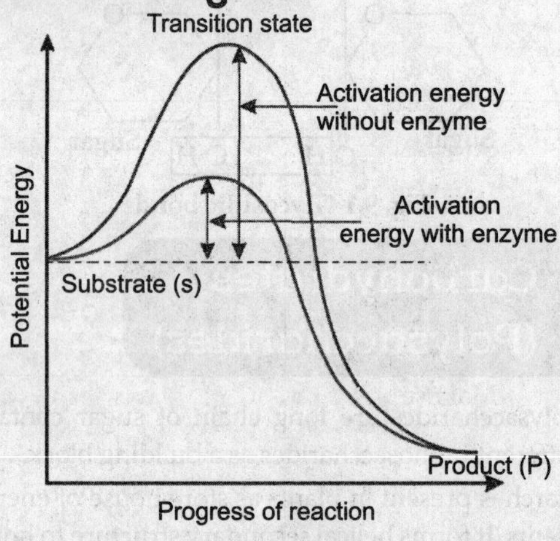

Activation energy requirement of non-catalysed and enzyme catalysed chemical reaction

Key Words

- **Biomicromolecules:** They are small sized simple chemicals that have low molecular weight (less than 1000 Da), higher solubility and simple conformation.
- **Biomacromolecules:** They are large sized complex chemicals that have high molecular weight (greater than 1000 Da, except lipids), low solubility and complex conformation.
- **Isoelectric point:** It is defined as the point at which a molecule exists as zwitter ion with no net charge.
- **Phospholipids (Phosphatides):** They are esters of fatty acids with glycerol containing an esterified phosphoric acid and a nitrogen base.
- **Primary structure of protein:** It is the linear sequence of amino acids in a polypeptide chain.

NCERT CORNER

Q. 1. What are macromolecules? Give examples? **[NCERT Ex. Q. 1, Page 119]**

Ans. Macromolecules are large sized complex chemicals that have high molecular weight, lower solubility and complex conformation. They usually produce colloidal complex. They belong to four classes of organic compounds–carbohydrates, lipids, proteins and nucleic acid.

Q. 2. What is meant by tertiary structure of proteins? **[NCERT Ex. Q. 2, Page 119]**

Ans. The complex three dimensional shape formed by the coiling and folding of helical polypeptide chain is known as tertiary structure of proteins. Such structures are held together by the weak bonds formed between various parts of the polypeptide chain.

Q. 3. Find and write down structures of 10 interesting small molecular weight biomolecules. Find if there is any industry which manufactures the compounds by isolation. Find out who are the buyers.[NCERT Ex. Q. 3, Page 119]

Ans. Name and structures of small molecular weight biomolecules:

Small molecular weight biomolecules	Structure
Insulin	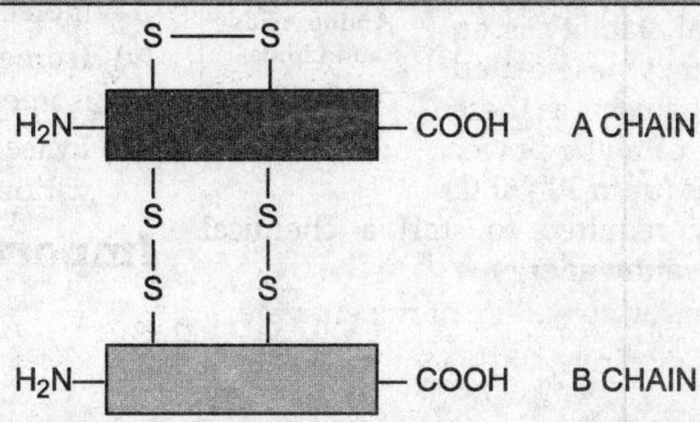
Sucrose	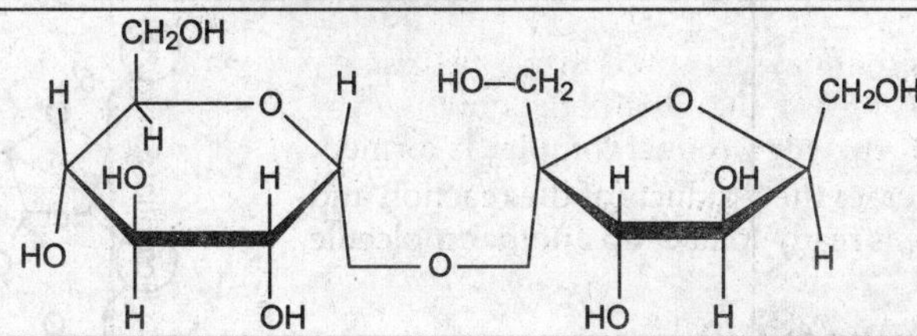
Maltose	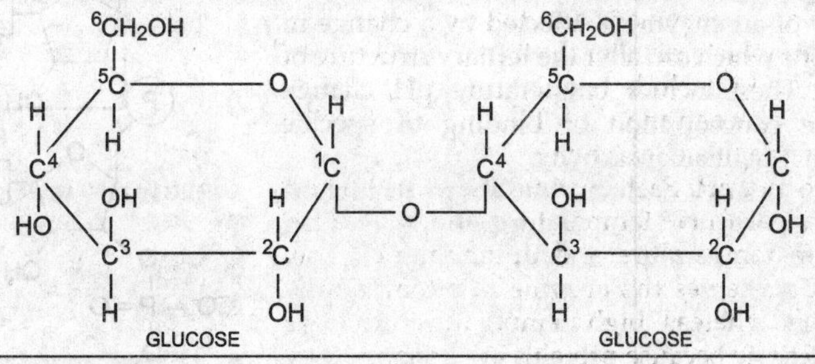
Lactose	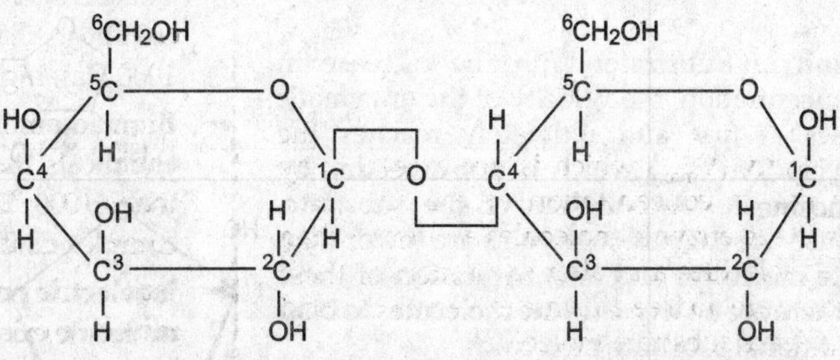

<table>
<tr><td>Ribose</td><td>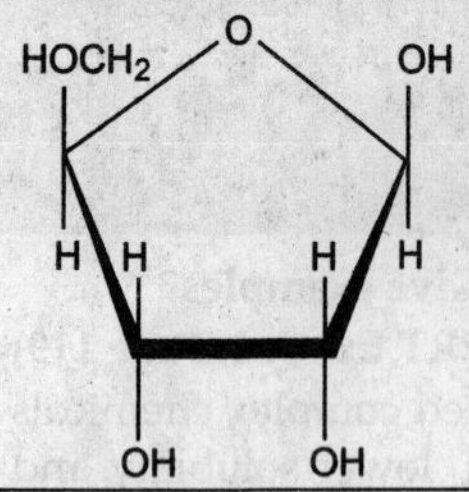
</td></tr>
<tr><td>DNA</td><td>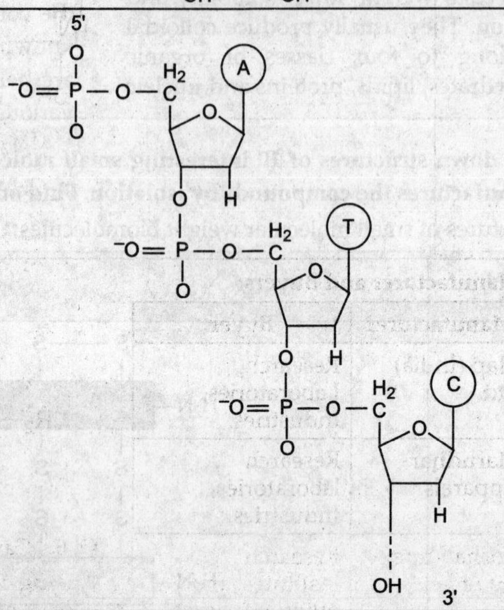
</td></tr>
<tr><td>RNA</td><td>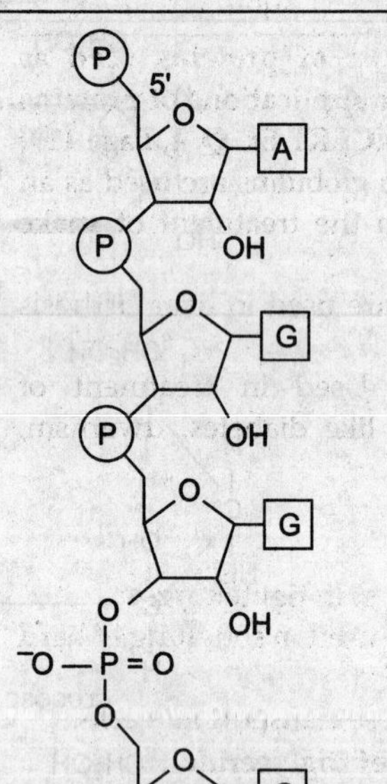
</td></tr>
<tr><td>Adenosine</td><td>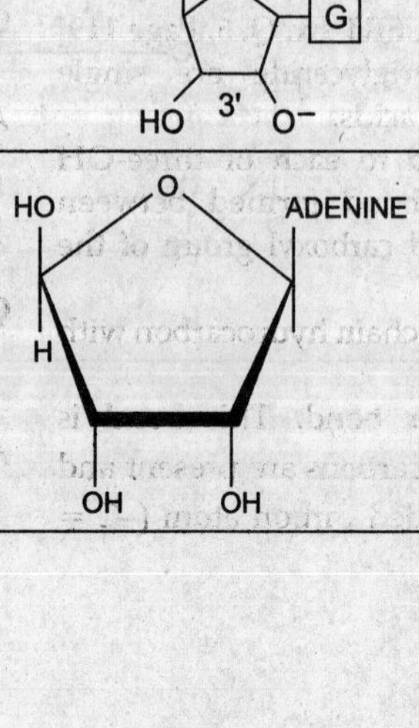
</td></tr>
</table>

Thymidine		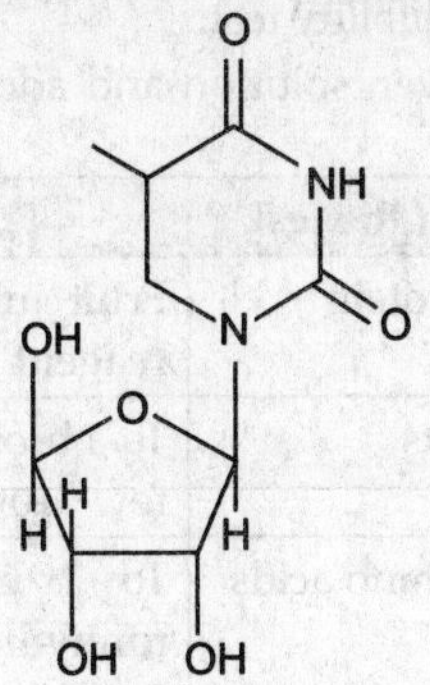
Glycerol		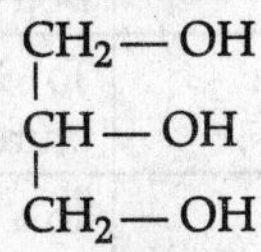

Compounds, their Manufacturer and Buyers:

Compound	Manufacturer	Buyer
Enzymes	Map (India) Ltd.	Research Laboratories, Industries.
Glucose	Marudhar Apparels.	Research laboratories, Industries.
Starch	Kosha Impex (P) Ltd.	Research institutes, and other industries.

Q. 4. Find out and make a list of proteins used as therapeutic agents. Find other applications of proteins (e.g., Cosmetics, etc.) [NCERT Ex. Q. 4, Page 119]

Ans. **(i) As antibodies:** Gamma globulins are used as an antibodies. These are used in the treatment of snake bite, tetanus, etc.

(ii) Human albumin: These are used in liver cirrhosis nephrotic syndrome.

(iii) Polypeptide hormones: Used in treatment of hormone deficiency disease, like diabetes, dwarfism, etc.

Other applications:

(i) Cosmetic uses:

(a) Egg protein is used for skin tightening.

(b) Keratolytic protein are used in softening of hard skin.

(ii) **Glut protein** enables glucose transport into cells.

Q. 5. Explain the composition of triglyceride. [NCERT Ex. Q. 5, Page 119]

Ans. (i) The components of triglyceride are single molecule of glycerol and 3 fatty acids.

(ii) One fatty acid is attached to each of three-OH groups of glycerol by ester bond formed between hydroxyl group of glycerol and carboxyl group of the fatty acid.

(iii) Fatty acids consist of a long chain hydrocarbon with a carboxylic group at one end.

(iv) Both of them form ester bond. This bond is saturated when single bonded carbons are present and unsaturated when double bonded carbon atom (–C = C–) are present.

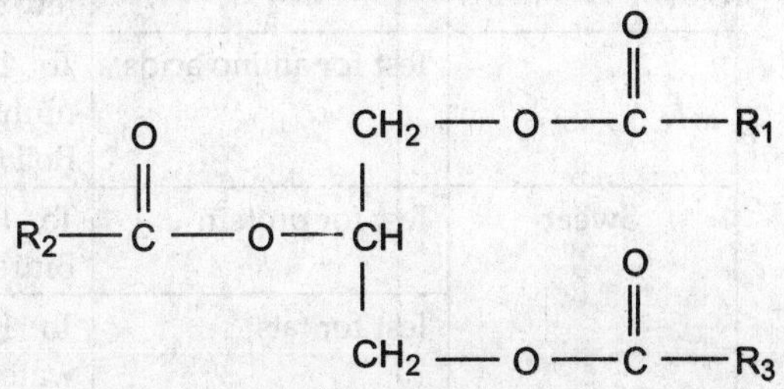

Q. 6. Can you attempt building models of biomolecules using commercially available atomic models (Ball and Stick models). [NCERT Ex. Q. 6, Page 119]

Ans. Ball and stick models can be used to describe the structure of biomolecules. It is the most fundamental model of representing bimolecular structures. In this model, the atoms are represented as balls while sticks represents the bond that holds the atoms. Double and triple bond are represented by springs that forms curved connection between the balls. The size and colour of various atoms are different and are depicted by the relative size of the balls.

Q. 7. Draw the structure of the amino acid, alanine. [NCERT Ex. Q. 7, Page 119]

Ans. **Alanine:** It is a neutral amino acid because it possesses one amino group and one carboxyl group (mono-amino mono carboxylic acid).

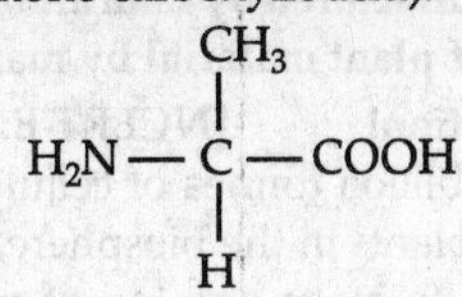

Q. 8. What are gums made of? Is fevicol different? [NCERT Ex. Q. 8, Page 119]

Ans. Gums are secondary metabolites. It is made by compounds present in plants, fungi and microbial cells. It is natural compound. Fevicol is different from gums. It is synthetic in nature.

Q. 9. Find out a qualitative test for proteins, fats and oils, amino acids and test any fruit juice, saliva, sweat and urine for them. [NCERT Ex. Q. 9, Page 119]

Ans. **Test for protein: Biuret's test:** Take a protein and add Biurets' reagent to it. The colour of reagent changes from light blue to purple.

Test for fats and oils: Grease or solubility test.

Test for amino acids: Take the given solution and add ninhydrin reagent to it. The colorless solution changes to pink, blue or purple depending on the amino acid.

Item	Name of the test	Procedure	Result	Inference
Fruit Juice	Test for protein	Fruit juice + Biuret's reagent	Color change from light blue to purple	Protein is present
	Test for fats	To a brown paper, add few drops of juice.	No translucent spot	Fats are absent or negligible
	Test for amino acids	To 1 ml juice, add ninhydrin reagent. Boil for 5 minutes	Colourless solution changes to pink, blue, or purple colour	Amino acids are present.
Saliva	Test for protein	To 1 ml saliva, add biuret's reagent.	Colour change from light blue to purple	Protein is present
	Test for fats	To a brown paper, add few drops of saliva	No translucent spot	Fats are absent
	Test for amino acids	To 1 ml saliva, add ninhydrin reagent. Boil for 5 minutes	Colourless solution changes to pink, blue, or purple colour	Amino acids are present.
Sweat	Test for protein	To 1 ml sweat, add Biuret's reagent	No colour change	Protein is absent.
	Test for fats	To 1 ml sweat, add water	Oily appearance	Fats are present
	Test for amino acids	To 1 ml sweat, add ninhydrin reagent. Boil for 5 minutes	No colour change	Amino acids are absent.
Urine	Test for protein	To 1 ml urine, add Biuret's reagent	Colour change from light blue to purple	Protein is present
	Test for fats	To few drops of sweat, add water	Little bit of oily appearance	Fats may be present
	Test for amino acids	To 1 ml urine, add ninhydrin reagent. Boil for 5 minutes	Colourless solution changes to pink, blue, or purple colour	Amino acids are present.

Q. 10. Find out how much cellulose is made by all the plants in the biosphere and compare it with how much of paper is manufactured by man and hence what is the consumption of plant material by man annually. What a loss of vegetation! [NCERT Ex. Q. 10, Page 119]

Ans. About 100 billion tonnes of cellulose are made per year by all the plants in the biosphere. It takes about 17 full grown tree to make one ton of paper. Since, trees are also used to fulfil other needs of man such as timber, food, medicines etc. Hence, it is difficult to calculate the consumption of plant material by man annually.

Q. 11. Describe the important properties of enzymes. [NCERT Ex. Q. 11, Page 119]

Ans. The properties of enzymes are:

(i) Enzyme are generally globular proteins. They may have additional inorganic or organic substance for their activity.

(ii) Being proteinaceous, the enzymes are giant molecules with a molecular weight of 6000 to 4,600,000.

(iii) Enzymes have colloidal nature. They are hydrophilic and form hydrosol in the free state.

(iv) Enzymes do not start a chemical reaction but increase the rate of chemical reaction. They do not change the equilibrium but bring about equilibrium very soon.

(v) The number of substrate molecules changed per second by a molecule or enzyme is called turnover number (K_{cat}). The rate of turn over number depends upon the efficiency of enzymes.

(vi) Enzyme are in no way transformed or used up in the chemical reaction but come out unchanged at the end of reaction.

(vii) All enzyme controlled reactions are reversible. Reversibility is dependent upon energy requirements, availability of reactants, concentration of products and pH.

(viii) Enzymes are highly specific in their action. For example, enzyme maltase acts on sugar maltose but not on lactose or sucrose. Different enzymes may act on the same substrate but give rise to different products.

□□

CELL CYCLE AND CELL DIVISION

CHAPTER 10

Cell Cycle

- The sequence of events by which a cell duplicates its genome, synthesises the other constituents of cells and eventually divides into two daughter cells is called **cell cycle**.
- DNA synthesis occurs in one specific stage of cell division but distribution of chromosome in cells occurs in complex series of events during cell division.
- Human cell divides once in approximately 24 hours, which may vary in different organisms. In yeasts it takes about 90 minutes to complete the cell division process.

Phases of Cell cycle

- Cell cycle is divided into two basic phases.

Interphase

- It is the phase between two successive M phases.
- Interphase lasts for 95% of a cell cycle. This phase is called as resting phase but during this period the cells prepare itself for nuclear division by cell growth.
- G_1 phase represents the interval between mitosis and initiation of DNA replication.
- Cell is continuously active and grows in size.
- During synthesis phase, replication or synthesis of DNA takes place and amount of DNA gets double per cell.
- During G_2 phase, protein is synthesised which is used for mitosis.
- In adult animals, some cells do not divide or may divide occasionally. The cells that do not divide further and exits the G_1 phase to enter an inactive stage is called **Quiescent Stage** (G_0) of cell cycle.
- In animals, mitotic division is present in only somatic diploid cells but in plants it is seen in both haploid and diploid cells.
- Mitotic cell division is also known as **equational division** because the numbers of chromosome remain same in parental and progeny cells.

M Phase

- When the actual cell division or mitosis occurs, it starts with karyokinesis (nuclear division) or separation of daughter of chromosome and end with cytokinesis or division of cell matrix (cytoplasm division).
- **Prophase** is the first phase of mitosis followed by G_2 phase. It involves following events:
  - Initiation of condensation of chromosomal materials.
  - Movement of centrioles towards opposite poles of the cell.
  - At the end of prophase, endoplasmic reticulum, nuclear membrane, golgi complex disappears.
- **Metaphase** starts with complete disappearance of nuclear membrane. It is the most suitable stage for the study of morphology of chromosomes. It involves:
  - Condensation of chromosomal materials into compact and distinct chromosomes made up of two sister chromatids attached with spindle fibres. Small disc-shaped structures at the surface of centromeres known as kinetochores serve as the sites of attachment of spindle fibres.
  - Chromosomes arrange at centre of cell called metaphase plate.
- **Anaphase** involves the
  - Splitting of each chromosome at centromere into two sister chromatids.
  - Two chromatids start moving towards opposite poles.
- **Telophase** is the last stage of mitosis. It involves following events:
  - Chromosomes reach at opposite poles and loose its identity as discrete unit.
  - Nuclear membrane reassembles around the chromosome clusters.
  - Nucleolus, Golgi complex and ER reappear.
- **Cytokinesis** is the division of cytoplasm of a cell after **karyokinesis** (division of chromosome) into two daughter cells. In animal cells, appearance of furrow in plasma membrane gradually deepens and joins to divide cytoplasm into two parts.
- In plants, cell wall formation starts at the centre and grows outwards to meet lateral walls. The formation of cell wall begins with formation of cell plate.

Significance of Mitosis

- Mitosis produces diploid daughter cells with identical genetic complement.
- It helps in repair of cells specially in lining of guts and blood cells.
- Meristematic division in apical and lateral cambium results in continuous growth of plants.

Scan to know more about this topic

Biomolecules

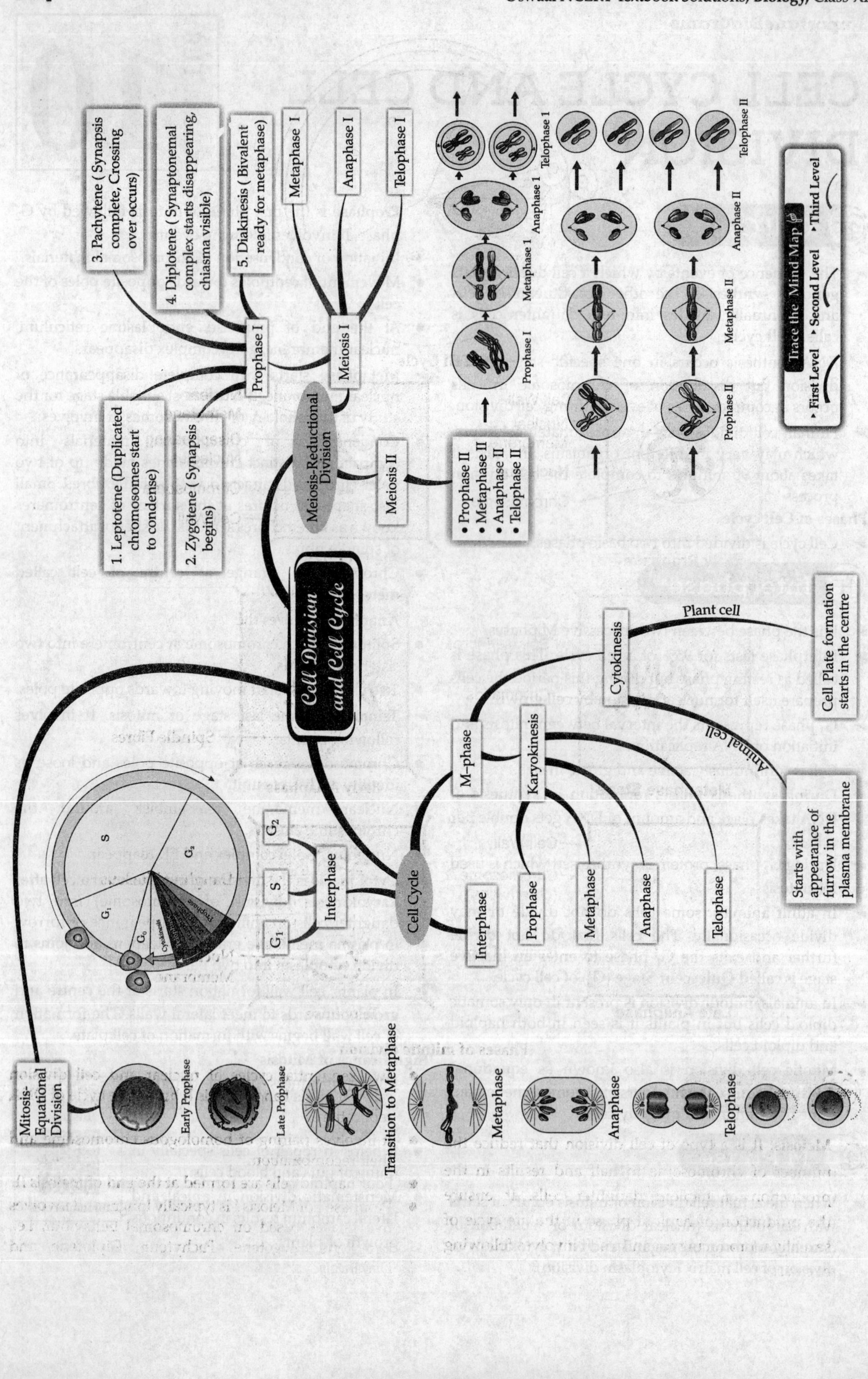
Cell Division and Cell Cycle
Meiosis-Reductional Division
Meiosis I
Prophase I
1. Leptotene (Duplicated chromosomes start to condense)
2. Zygotene (Synapsis begins)
3. Pachytene (Synapsis complete, Crossing over occurs)
4. Diplotene (Synaptonemal complex starts disappearing, chiasma visible)
5. Diakinesis (Bivalent ready for metaphase)
Metaphase I
Anaphase I
Telophase I
Meiosis II
• Prophase II
• Metaphase II
• Anaphase II
• Telophase II
Prophase I
Metaphase 1
Anaphase 1
Telophase 1
Prophase II
Metaphase II
Anaphase II
Telophase II
Trace the Mind Map
First Level
Second Level
Third Level
Cell Cycle
Interphase
G1
S
G2
M–phase
Karyokinesis
Cytokinesis
Plant cell
Animal cell
Cell Plate formation starts in the centre
Starts with appearance of furrow in the plasma membrane
Interphase
Prophase
Metaphase
Anaphase
Telophase
S
G2
G1
G0
Cytokinesis
Mitosis-Equational Division
Early Prophase
Late Prophase
Transition to Metaphase
Metaphase
Anaphase
Telophase

Important Diagrams

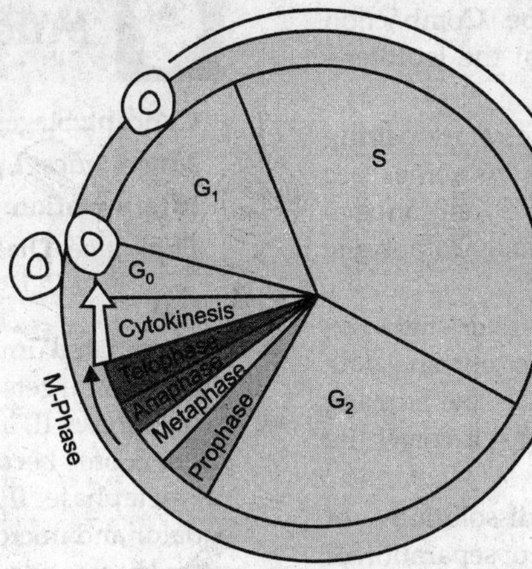

Cell Cycle

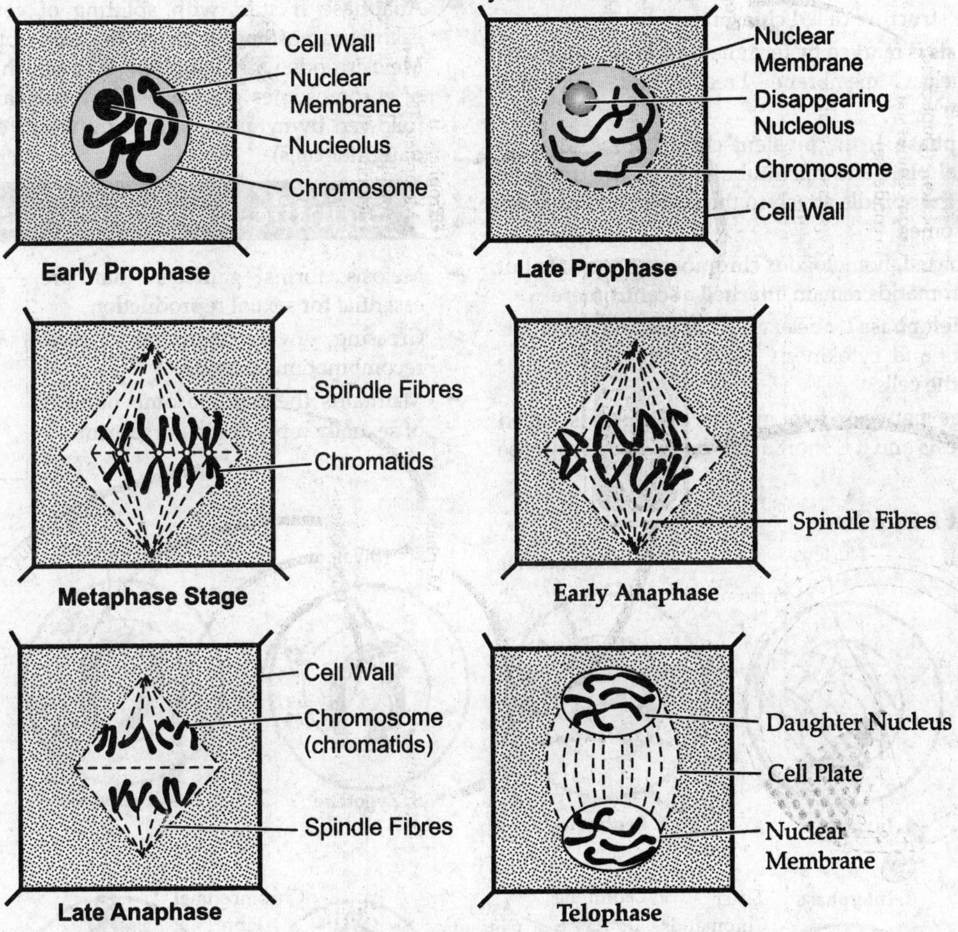

Phases of mitotic division

Meiosis

- **Meiosis:** It is a type of cell division that reduce the number of chromosome to half and results in the production of haploid daughter cells. It ensure the production of haploid phase in the life cycle of sexually reproducing organisms. It involves following events.

- Two sequential cycles of nuclear and cell division called meiosis I and meiosis II but single cycle of DNA replication.
- It involves pairing of homologous chromosome and their recombination.
- Four haploid cells are formed at the end of meiosis II.
- Prophase I of Meiosis I is typically longer and involves five phases based on chromosomal behaviour, i.e., Leptotene, Zygotene, Pachytene, Diplotene and Diakinesis.

- During **Leptotene,** the chromosome becomes distinct and visible under microscope. Compaction of chromosome continues throughout the leptotene phase.
- During **Zygotene** stage, chromosomes start pairing together **(synapsis).** The paired chromosomes are called **homologous chromosome**. Synaptonemal complex formed by a pair of homologous chromosome is called bivalent or a tetrad.
- During **Pachytene** stage, crossing over between non-sister chromatids of homologous chromosome occurs for exchange of genetic material. The crossing over is enzyme – mediated process which involves the enzyme recombinase.
- **Diplotene** is recognised by dissolution of synaptonemal complex and tendency of separation of bivalent except at the site of crossing over. This forms an X like structure called **chiasmata**.
- **Diakinesis** is marked by terminalisation of chiasmata. The nuclear membrane breaks and nucleolus disappear.
- **In metaphase I,** the bivalent chromosome align at equatorial plate and microtubules from the opposite poles of the spindle attach to the pair of homologous chromosomes.
- **In anaphase I,** homologous chromosome separate but sister chromatids remain attached at centromere.
- During **Telophase I**, nuclear membrane and nucleolus reappears and cytokinesis follows. This is called as dyad of the cells.
- The stage between two meiotic divisions is called **interkinesis** and it is short lived that follows Prophase II.

Mnemonics

Concept: Stages of Prophase I
Mnemonics: Limited Zoology Padao DiDi
Interpretation: Leptotene, Zygotene, Pachytene, Diplotene, Diakinesis

Meiosis II

- It is initiated immediately after cytokinesis before chromosome gets elongated.
- In prophase II, nuclear membrane disappears and chromosome becomes compact.
- At metaphase II stage, the chromosomes align at equator and microtubules attach with kinetochores of sister chromatids.
- Anaphase II start with splitting of centromere of each chromosome to move towards opposite poles. Meiosis ends with Telophase II in which two groups of chromosomes get enclosed by nuclear membrane followed by cytokinesis to form tetrad of cells (four daughter cells).

Significance of meiosis

- Meiosis forms gametes that are essential for sexual reproduction.
- Crossing over introduces new recombination of traits.
- Maintains the chromosome number of sexually reproducing organism.

Scan to know more about this topic
Meiosis

Important Diagrams

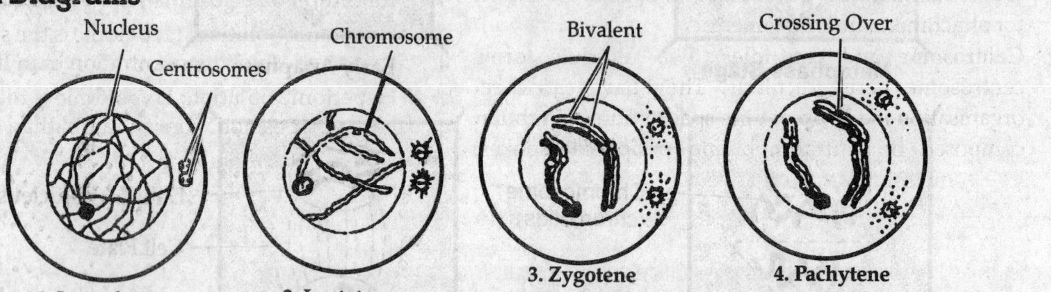

1. Interphase 2. Leptotene 3. Zygotene 4. Pachytene

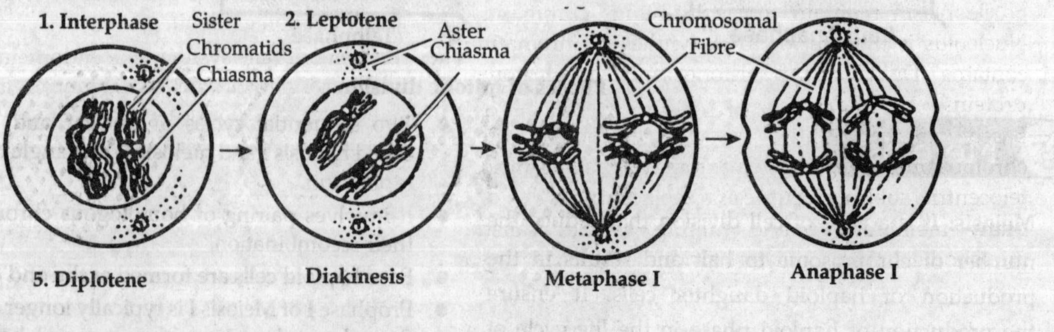

5. Diplotene Diakinesis Metaphase I Anaphase I

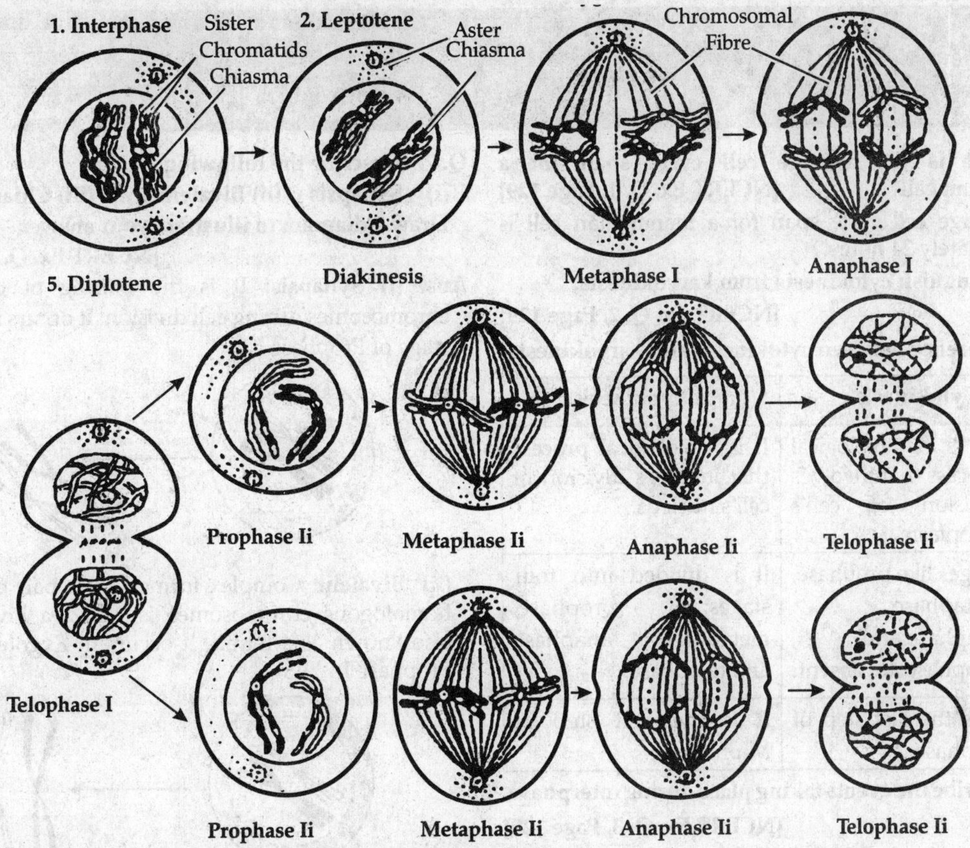

Stages in meiosis

Key Words

- **Cell cycle:** The sequence of events by which a cell duplicates its genome, synthesises other cell constituents, and eventually divides into two daughter cells is known as cell cycle.
- **Interphase:** The interval between two successive cell divisions is termed as Interphase.
- **S phase (Synthetic phase):** It is the stage during which DNA synthesis occurs.
- **G_0 or quiescent phase:** It is the stage wherein cells remain metabolically active, but do not proliferate unless called to do so.
- **Mitosis:** Mitosis is the process of cell division wherein the chromosomes replicate and get equally distributed into two daughter cells.
- **Cytokinesis:** It is the process in which the cell actually divides into two.
- **Synapsis:** The process of attachment of the homologous chromosomes to form a complex structure called synaptonemal complex is known as synapsis.
- **Crossing over:** Crossing over is the exchange of genetic material between two homologous chromosomes with the help of enzyme recombinase.
- **Chiasma:** The X-shaped, point of interchange and re-joining is known as chiasma.

NCERT CORNER

Q. 1. What is the average cell cycle span for a mammalian cell? **[NCERT Ex. Q. 1, Page 129]**

Ans. Average cell cycle span for a mammalian cell is approximately 24 hours.

Q. 2. Distinguish cytokinesis from karyokinesis. **[NCERT Ex. Q. 2, Page 129]**

Ans. Difference between cytokinesis and karyokinesis:

Cytokinesis	Karyokinesis
(i) It is a biological process that involves division of cell's cytoplasm.	It is a biological process that involves division of cell's nucleus.
(ii) Stages like prophase, metaphase, anaphase and telophase are absent.	It is divided into four stages: prophase, metaphase, anaphase and telophase.
(iii) It is the last step of M-phase	It is the first step of M-phase

Q. 3. Describe the events taking place during interphase. **[NCERT Ex. Q. 3, Page 129]**

Ans. It is the period during which the cell experiences growth and DNA replication in an orderly manner. **It is divided into 3 phases:** G_1 phase, S phase and G_2 phase.

Refer :Topic 1/LATQ, Q.1.

Q. 4. What is G_0 (quiescent phase) of cell cycle? **[NCERT Ex. Q. 4, Page 129]**

Ans. G_0 or quiescent phase is the stage wherein cells remain metabolically active, but do not proliferate unless called to do so. Such cells are used for replacing the cells lost during injury.

Q. 5. Why is mitosis called equational division? **[NCERT Ex. Q. 5, Page 129]**

Ans. Mitosis is the process of cell division wherein the chromosomes replicate and get equally distributed both quantitatively and qualitatively into two daughter cells. The chromosome number in each daughter cell is equal to that in the parent cell, i.e., diploid. Hence, mitosis is known as equational division.

Q. 6. Name the stage of cell cycle at which one of the following events occur:

(i) Chromosomes are moved to spindle equator.

(ii) Centromere splits and chromatids separate.

(iii) Pairing between homologous chromosomes takes place.

(iv) Crossing over between homologous chromosomes takes place. **[NCERT Ex. Q. 6, Page 130]**

Ans. (i) Metaphase

(ii) Anaphase

(iii) Zygotene of Prophase I Meiosis

(iv) Pachytene of Prophase I Meiosis

Q. 7. Describe the following:

(i) Synapsis (ii) Bivalent (iii) Chiasmata

Draw a diagram to illustrate your answer **[NCERT Ex. Q. 7, Page 130]**

Ans. (i) Synapsis: It is the pairing of homologous chromosomes during cell division. It occurs in Zygotene stage of Prophase I.

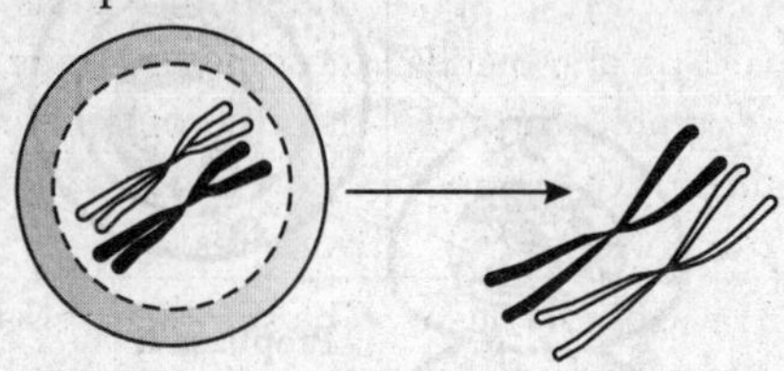

(ii) Bivalent: Complex formed by a pair of synapsed homologous chromosomes is called a bivalent. It is also known as a tetrad. It occurs in Zygotene stage of Prophase I.

(iii) Chiasmata: It is the point of crossing of two non-sister chromatids. It is X-shaped point of interchange of chromosomes. It is formed during diplotene stage of Prophase I.

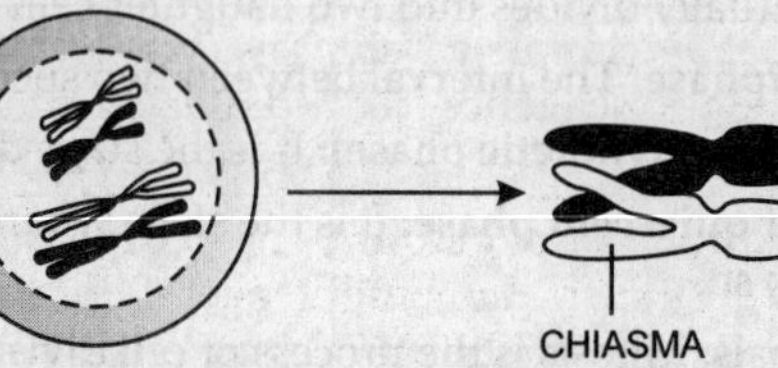

Q. 8. How does cytokinesis in plant cells differ from that in animal cells? **[NCERT Ex. Q. 8, Page 130]**

Ans.

S. No.	Cytokinesis in plant cell	Cytokinesis in animal cell
(i)	The division of the cytoplasm takes place by cell plate formation.	The division of the cytoplasm takes place by cleavage.
(ii)	Cell plate formation starts at the centre of the cell and grows outward, towards the lateral wall.	Cleavage starts at the periphery and then moves inward, dividing the cell into two parts.

Q. 9. Find examples where the four daughter cells from meiosis are equal in size and where they are found unequal in size. **[NCERT Ex. Q. 9, Page 130]**

Ans. The process of formation of sperms in human beings occurs by meiosis. It result in formation of four equal sized sperms (daughter cells). The process of formation of ovum in human beings occurs by meiosis. It results in formation of four daughter cells (one ovum and 2-3 small sized polar bodies), which are unequal in size.

Q. 10. Distinguish anaphase of mitosis from anaphase I of meiosis. **[NCERT Ex. Q. 10, Page 130]**

Ans.

S. No.	Anaphase of mitosis	Anaphase I of meiosis
(i)	Centromeres split and chromatids separate. Chromatids move to opposite poles.	The homologous chromosomes separate, while sister chromatids remain associated at their centromeres.
(ii)	The spindle usually persists during cytokinesis.	The spindle begins to degenerate soon after anaphase.

Q. 11. List the main differences between mitosis and meiosis. **[NCERT Ex. Q. 11, Page 130]**

S. No.	Mitosis	Meiosis
(i)	The cell divides only once and give rise to two daughter cell each being diploid. Mitosis occurs in all the somatic cells of the body.	The cell divides twice and give rise to four haploid cell. It occurs in the reproductive germ cells.
(ii)	It is completed in one sequence of stages.	The whole process is completed into two successive divisions.
(iii)	Prophase of mitosis is of short duration and is without substages.	The Prophase-I is of longer duration and completed in five sub stages: leptotene, zygotene, pachytene, diplotene and diakinesis.
(iv)	The homologous chromosome do not pair with each other i.e., synapsis is absent.	In meiosis-I, the homologous chromosomes (paternal and maternal) which are in single state form pairs.
(v)	Generally, no chiamata formation takes place. No crossing over takes place.	Chiasmata formation due to crossing over takes place in meiosis.
(vi)	Chromosome appears in two-stranded.	Chromosomes appears in tetrad stage.
(vii)	The centromere of each chromosome divides into two and thus the two chromatids of the chromosome become free from each other.	Centromere of the homologous chromosomes divides thus their chromatids do not become free in metaphase-I
(viii)	The two chromatids of each chromosome move towards the opposite poles of spindle.	In meiosis the two homologous chromosomes of each pair separate and move towards opposite poles of spindle during stage.
(ix)	The chromosome number in each daughter cell remains the same as in parent nucleus.	In meiosis, the chromosome number is reduced to half.

Q. 12. What is the significance of meiosis? **[NCERT Ex. Q. 12, Page 130]**

Ans. Significance of meiosis:

(i) Formation of gametes: Meiosis produces gametes that are essential for sexual reproduction.

(ii) Maintenance of chromosome number: Meiosis maintains the chromosome number constant in sexually reproducing organisms. It is essential since the chromosome number is doubled after fertilisation.

(iii) Introduction of variation: Meiosis introduces variation in the organisms due to crossing over and random distribution of paternal and maternal chromosomes.

(iv) Mutations: Chromosomal and genomic mutations can take place by irregularities of meiotic divisions. Some of the mutations may be advantageous to the organism and are perpetuated by natural selection.

(v) Genetic information: It switches on genetic information for the development of gametes or gametophyte and switches off the sporophytic information.

(vi) Evidence of basic relationship of organisms: Details of meiosis are essentially similar in the majority of organisms showing their basic similarities and relationship.

Q. 13. Discuss with your teacher about

(i) Haploid insects and lower plants where cell-division occurs, and

(ii) Some haploid cells in higher plants where cell-division does not occur. **[NCERT Ex. Q. 13, Page 130]**

Ans. (i) Drones (males) of honey bee and lower plants like *Chlamydomonas, Spirogyra,* etc. are haploids. In these animals, fertilisation is immediately followed by zygotic meiosis. This leads to production of haploid organisms. Such type of life cycle is called haplontic life cycle.

(ii) In some haploid cells in higher plants where cell division does not occur, the phenomenon of polyploidy can be observed. Polyploidy is a stage in which cells contain multiple pairs of chromosomes than the basic set. Polyploidy can be induced by applying colchicine to cell culture.

Q. 14. Can there be mitosis without DNA replication in 'S' phase? [NCERT Ex. Q. 14, Page 130]

Ans. No. Mitotic division cannot take place without DNA replication in S phase. During S phase, synthesis of DNA takes place. DNA replication maintains the chromosomal number in the daughter cells during mitosis.

Q. 15. Can there be DNA replication without cell division? [NCERT Ex. Q. 15, Page 130]

Ans. Yes. During cell division, the parent cell gets divided into two daughter cells. However, if there is repeated replication of DNA without any cell division, then this DNA keeps on accumulating inside the cell. This would increase the volume of the cell nucleus, thereby causing cell expansion. For example, in salivary gland of *Drosophila*, the chromosomes undergo repeated DNA duplication without cell division.

Q. 16. Analyse the events during every stage of cell cycle and notice how the following two parameters change

(i) Number of chromosomes (N) per cell

(ii) Amount of DNA content (C) per cell

[NCERT Ex. Q. 16, Page 130]

Ans. (i) (a) In G_1 phase, the number of chromosome (N) per cell remains same.

(b) In S or synthetic phase of cell cycle, DNA synthesis or the replication occurs. The amount of DNA per cell doubles. If it is 2C then it becomes 4C. There is no increase in chromosome number.

(c) Same above condition continues in G_2-phase.

(d) In M-phase the sister chromatids separate and move to different cells but the number of chromosomes remain same in mitosis.

(ii) (a) In G_1-Phase, the amount of DNA content (C) per cell remains same.

(b) In S-phase it is doubled due to DNA replication.

(c) It remains double in G_2-phase.

(d) It is halved in M-phase of cell cycle.

PHOTOSYNTHESIS IN HIGHER PLANTS

CHAPTER 11

Photosynthesis

- Photosynthesis is an enzyme regulated anabolic process of manufacturing organic compounds inside the chlorophyll containing cells from carbon dioxide and water with the help of sunlight as source of energy.

$$6CO_2 + 12H_2O \xrightarrow[\text{Chlorophyll}]{\text{Light}} C_6H_{12}O_6 + 6H_2O + 6O_2$$

- Photosynthesis is the basis of life on earth because it is the primary source of all food on earth and it is responsible for release of O_2 in the atmosphere.
- Chlorophyll, light and CO_2 is required for photosynthesis. It occurs only in green part of leaves in presence of light.
- Chloroplasts are green plastids which function as the site of photosynthesis in eukaryotic photoautotrophs. Inside the leaves, chloroplast is generally present in mesophyll cells along their walls.
- Within the chloroplast there is a membranous system consisting of grana, the stroma lamellae and the fluid stroma.
- The membrane system is responsible for synthesis of ATP and NADPH. In stroma enzymatic reactions incorporate CO_2 in plants leading to synthesis of sugar.
- The reaction in which light energy is absorbed by grana to synthesis ATP and NADPH is called light reaction. The later part of photosynthesis in which CO_2 is reduced to sugar, in which light is not necessary is called dark reaction.
- Maximum absorption by chlorophyll 'a' occurs in blue and red regions having higher rate of photosynthesis. So, chlorophyll 'a' is the chief pigment.
- Other thylakoid pigments like chlorophyll 'b' (yellow green), xanthophyll (yellow) and carotenoids (yellow to yellow-orange) are called accessory pigments that absorb light and transfer energy to chlorophyll 'a' and protect them from photo-oxidation.

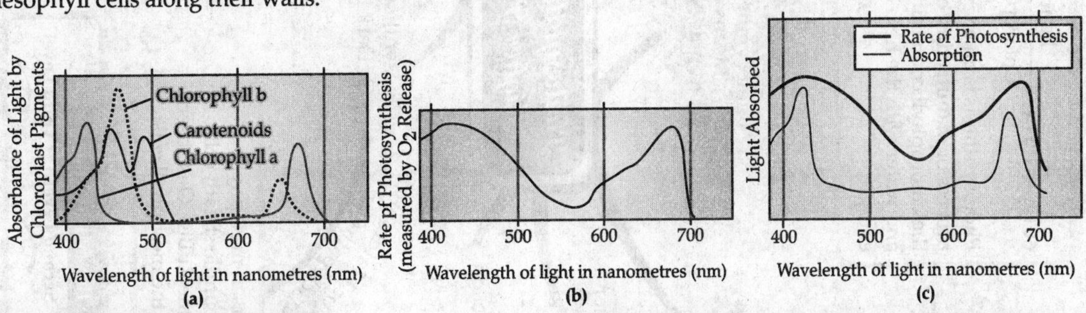

Light Reaction

- Light reaction (photochemical phase) includes :

(a) Light absorption
(b) Water splitting
(c) Oxygen release
(d) Formation of high energy chemical intermediates (ATP and NADPH).

- The pigments are organised into two discrete LHC (light harvesting complex) within Photosystem I and Photosystem II.
- LHC are made up of hundreds of pigment molecules containing all pigments (except single chlorophyll a molecules) also called antennae.
- The pigments in photosystem I and photosystem II absorb the lights of different wavelength.
- Single chlorophyll molecules make the reaction centre. In PS I, reaction centre has absorption peak at 700nm, hence called P700 and in PS II, reaction centre has absorption peak at 680 nm, so called P680.

The Electron Transport System

- Reaction centre of photosystem II absorbs light of 680 nm in red region and cause electron to become excited.
- These electrons are picked by an electron acceptor which passes the electron to electron transport system consisting of cytochromes.
- This movement of electrons is down hill in terms of redox potential scale.
- Electrons are passed through electron transport chain and passed on to the pigment of PS I. Electron in the PSI also get excited due to light of wavelength 700nm and is transferred to another acceptor molecule that has a higher redox potential.

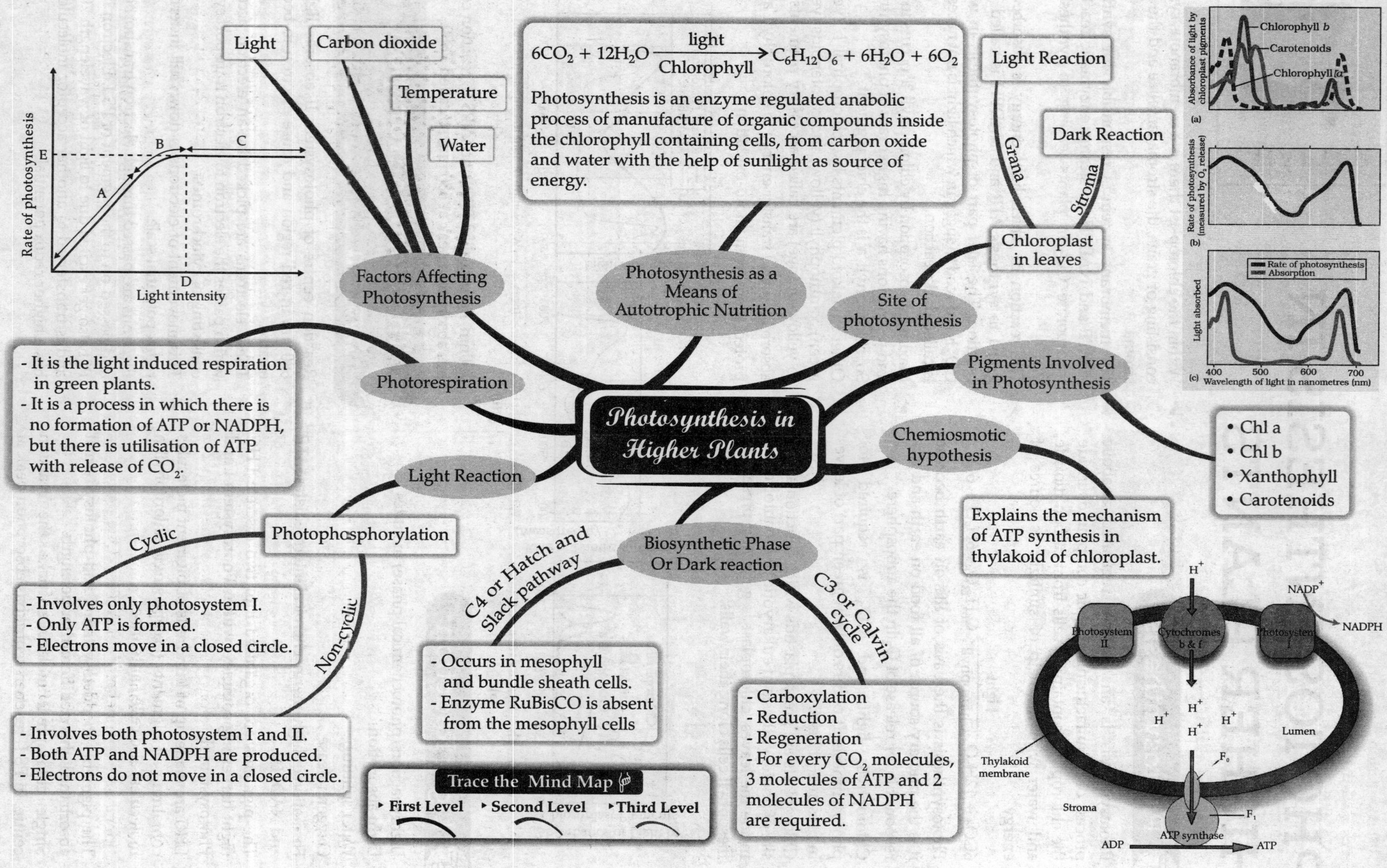
Photosynthesis in Higher Plants
Photosynthesis as a Means of Autotrophic Nutrition
6CO2 + 12H2O —light / Chlorophyll→ C6H12O6 + 6H2O + 6O2
Photosynthesis is an enzyme regulated anabolic process of manufacture of organic compounds inside the chlorophyll containing cells, from carbon oxide and water with the help of sunlight as source of energy.
Site of photosynthesis
Chloroplast in leaves
Grana
Light Reaction
Stroma
Dark Reaction
Pigments Involved in Photosynthesis
• Chl a
• Chl b
• Xanthophyll
• Carotenoids
Absorbance of light by chloroplast pigments
Chlorophyll b
Carotenoids
Chlorophyll a
(a)
Rate of photosynthesis (measured by O2 release)
(b)
Light absorbed
Rate of photosynthesis
Absorption
400 500 600 700
(c) Wavelength of light in nanometres (nm)
Chemiosmotic hypothesis
Explains the mechanism of ATP synthesis in thylakoid of chloroplast.
H+
NADP+
NADPH
Photosystem II
Cytochromes b & f
Photosystem I
Lumen
Thylakoid membrane
Stroma
F0
F1
ATP synthase
ADP
ATP
Biosynthetic Phase Or Dark reaction
C3 or Calvin cycle
- Carboxylation
- Reduction
- Regeneration
- For every CO2 molecules, 3 molecules of ATP and 2 molecules of NADPH are required.
C4 or Hatch and Slack pathway
- Occurs in mesophyll and bundle sheath cells.
- Enzyme RuBisCO is absent from the mesophyll cells
Light Reaction
Photophosphorylation
Cyclic
- Involves only photosystem I.
- Only ATP is formed.
- Electrons move in a closed circle.
Non-cyclic
- Involves both photosystem I and II.
- Both ATP and NADPH are produced.
- Electrons do not move in a closed circle.
Photorespiration
- It is the light induced respiration in green plants.
- It is a process in which there is no formation of ATP or NADPH, but there is utilisation of ATP with release of CO2.
Factors Affecting Photosynthesis
Light
Carbon dioxide
Temperature
Water
Rate of photosynthesis
Light intensity
A
B
C
D
E
Trace the Mind Map
First Level
Second Level
Third Level

- When electron passes in downhill direction, energy is released that reduce the ADP to ATP and $NADP^+$ to NADPH. The whole scheme of transfer of electron is called Z-scheme due to its shape.
- Photolysis of water release electrons that provide electron to PS II. Oxygen is released during photosynthesis due to this.

$$2H_2O \longrightarrow 4H^+ + O_2 + 4e^-$$

Cyclic and Non-cylicphoto-phosphorylation

- The process of synthesis of ATP from ADP and inorganic phosphate in the presence of light is known as photophosphorylation.
- When the two photosystems work in a series first PS II and then PS I, a process called non-cyclic photophosphorylation occurs. The two photosystems are connected through an electron transport chain.
- When only PS I is functional, the electron is circulated within the photosystem and the phosphorylation occurs due to cyclic flow of electrons.
- Cyclic photophosphorylation also occurs when only light of wavelength beyond 680 nm are available for excitation.

Chemiosmotic Hypothesis of ATP Formation

- This hypothesis was proposed by Mitchell in 1961. ATP synthesis is linked to development of proton gradient across the membrane of thylakoids and mitochondria.
- The process involved in the development of proton gradient across the membrane are :

(i) Splitting of water molecules occurs inside the thylakoid to produce hydrogen ion or proton.

(ii) As electron passes through the photosystem, protons are transported across the membrane because primary acceptor of electron is located towards the outer side of the membrane.

Scan to know more about this topic

Chemiosmotic Hypothesis

(iii) The NADP reductase enzyme is located on the stroma side of membrane. Electrons come out from the acceptor of electrons of PSI. Protons are necessary for reduction of $NADP^+$ to NADPH + H^+. These protons are also removed from the stroma. This creates proton gradient across the thylakoids membrane along with pH in the lumen.

(iv) Gradient is broken down due to movement of protons across the membrane to the stroma through trans-membrane channel of F_0 of ATPase. One part of this enzyme is embedded in membrane to form trans-membrane channel. The other portion is called F_1 that protrudes on the outer surface of thylakoid membrane which makes the energy packed ATP.

(v) ATP and NADPH produced due to movement of electron is used immediately to fix CO_2 to form sugar.

- The product of light reaction is used to drive the process leading to synthesis of sugar and is called biosynthetic phase of photosynthesis.

Calvin Cycle/C_3 cycle/Reductive Pentose Sugar Phosphate Pathway

- Melvin Calvin, Benson and their colleagues used radioactive ^{14}C and *Chlorella* and *Scenedesmus* algae to discover that first CO_2 fixation product is 3-carbon organic compound (3-phosphoglyceric acid) or PGA. Later on a new compound was discovered which contain 4- carbon called Oxaloacetic Acid (OAA). On the basis of number of carbon atoms in first stable product they are named as C_3 and C_4 pathway. C_3 cycle involves 3 steps :

• Carboxylation is the fixation of CO_2 into 3-phosphoglyceric acid (3-PGA). Carboxylation of RuBP occurs in presence of enzyme RuBP carboxylase (RuBisCO) which results in the formation of two molecules of 3-PGA.

• Reduction is series of reaction that leads to formation of glucose. Two molecules of ATP and two molecules of NADPH are required for reduction of one molecules of CO_2. Six turn of this cycle are required for removal of one molecule of glucose molecule from pathway.

• Regeneration is the generation of RuBP molecules for the continuation of cycle. This process require one molecules of ATP.

• For every molecules of CO_2 entering the Calvin cycle, 3 molecules of ATP and 2 molecules of NADPH is required. To make one molecules of glucose, 6 turns of cycle is completed.

In	Out
Six CO_2	One glucose
18 ATP	18 ADP
12 NADPH	12 NADP

C_4 pathway/Hatch Slack Pathway

- This pathway was worked out by Hatch and Slack (1965, 1967), mainly operational in plants growing in dry tropical region like Maize, Sugarcane, Sorghum, etc.
- In this pathway, first stable product is a 4-carbon compound, Oxaloacetic acid (OAA) so called as C_4 pathway. C_4 plants have Kranz Anatomy (vascular bundles are surrounded by bundle sheath cells arranged in wreath like manner), characterised by large number of chloroplast, thick wall, impervious to gases and absence of intercellular spaces.
- The primary CO_2 acceptor is a 3-carbon molecule (Phosphoenol pyruvate) present in mesophyll cells and enzyme involved is PEP carboxylase.

- OAA formed in mesophyll cell forms 4-carbon compound like malic acid or aspartic acid which is transported to bundle sheath cells.
- In bundle sheath cell, it is broken into CO_2 and a 3-carbon molecule. The 3-carbon molecule is returned back to mesophyll cells to form PEP.
- The CO_2 molecule released in bundle sheath cells enters the Calvin cycle, where enzyme RuBisCO is present that forms sugar.

Photorespiration

- It is the light dependent process of oxygenation of RuBP and release of carbon dioxide by photosynthetic organs of plants.
- Photorespiration decrease the rate of photosynthesis when oxygen concentration is increased from 2-3% to 21%.
- Presence of light and higher concentration of oxygen results the binding of RubisCO enzyme with O_2 to form phosphoglyceric acid and phosphoglycolate.

RuBisCO + $O_2 \longrightarrow$ PGA + phosphoglycolate

This pathway involves Chloroplast, Peroxisome and Mitochondria. Photorespiration does not occur in C_4 plants.

Factors affecting photosynthesis

(a) Light : As light intensity increases, the rate of photosynthesis also increases until light reaches saturation point.

(b) Carbon dioxide concentration : With increase in concentration of CO_2, rate of photosynthesis increase till the compensation point.

(c) Temperature : It does not influence the rate of photosynthesis directly but at higher temperature, enzyme activity is inhibited due to denaturation to affect the dark reaction.

(d) Water : Rate of photosynthesis do not increase proportionally as after saturation no more water is required during photosynthesis.

Principle of law of limiting factors states that if a chemical process is affected by more than one factor, then its rate could be determined by the factor which is nearest to its minimal value which directly affects the process if its quality is changed.

Important Diagram

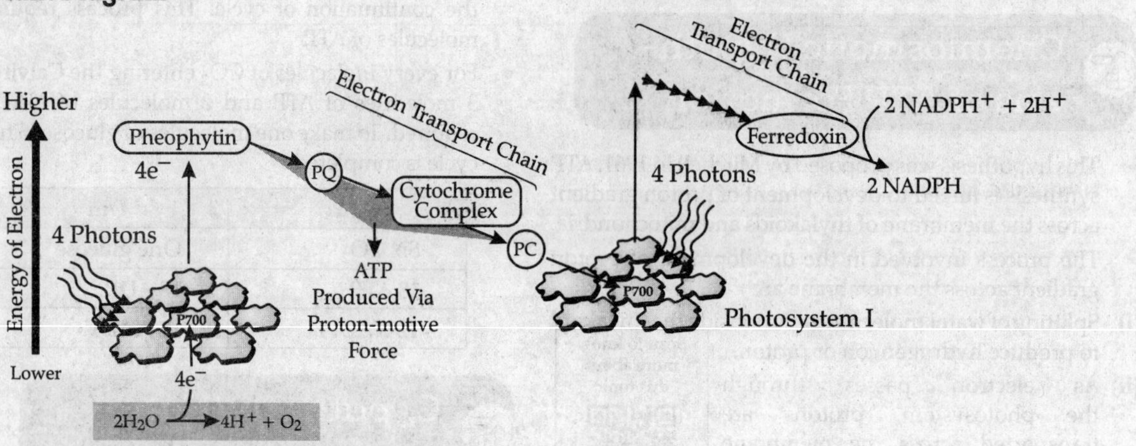

Non-cyclic photophosphorylation

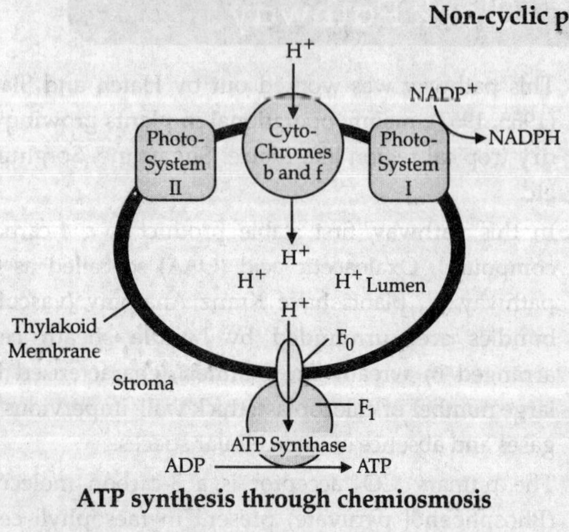

ATP synthesis through chemiosmosis

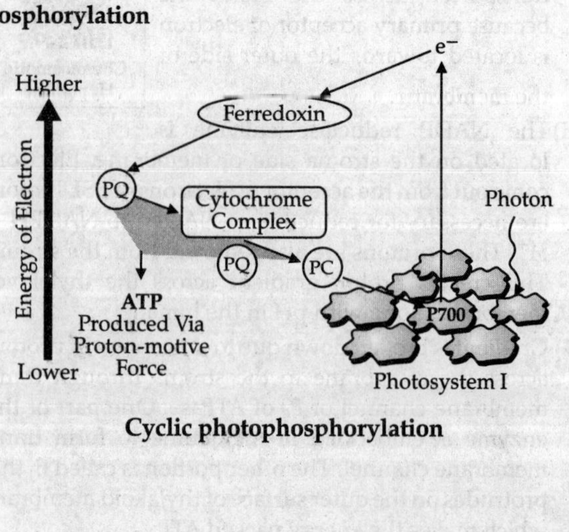

Cyclic photophosphorylation

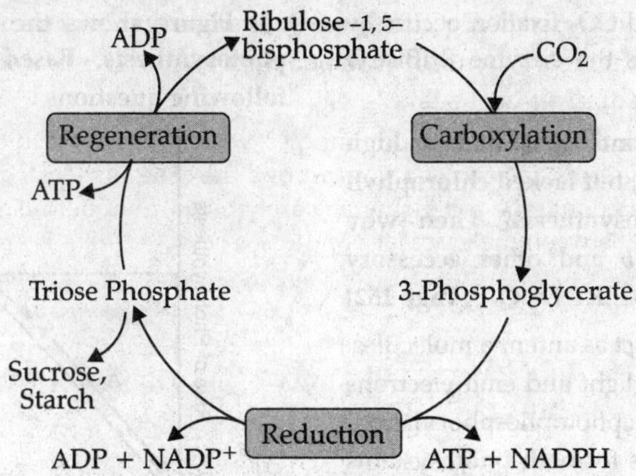

The Calvin Cycle

Key Words

- **Photosynthesis :** It is a physio-chemical process that involves production of organic compounds from inorganic molecules using light energy trapped by chlorophyll.
- **Pigments :** The pigments are chemicals which absorb light energy and convert it to chemical energy.
- **Absorption spectrum :** An absorption spectrum is the graph plotted against the fraction of light absorbed by the pigment.
- **Photolysis of water :** It is the process of splitting of water with release of oxygen and hydrogen.
- **Action spectrum :** Curve showing rate of photosynthesis at different wavelengths of light is called action spectrum.
- **Photophosphorylation :** It is the process of formation of high-energy chemicals (ATP and NADPH) in chloroplast in the presence of sunlight.
- **Photorespiration :** It is a process in which there is no formation of ATP or NADPH, but there is utilisation of ATP with release of CO_2.

NCERT CORNER

Q. 1. By looking at a plant externally can you tell whether a plant is C_3 or C_4? Why and how?

[NCERT Ex. Q. 1, Page 151]

Ans. One cannot distinguish whether a plant is C_3 or C_4 by observing its leaves and other morphological features externally.

Unlike, C_3 plants, the leaves of C_4 plants have a special anatomy called Kranz anatomy and this difference can only be observed at the cellular level.

For example, although wheat and maize are grasses, wheat is a C_3 plant while maize is a C_4 plant.

Q. 2. By looking at which internal structure of a plant can you tell whether a plant is C_3 or C_4? Explain.

[NCERT Ex. Q. 2, Page 151]

Ans. By seeing the V. S. of leaves, one of C_3 plant and the other of a C_4 plant.

(i) The C_4 plant leaves have Kranz anatomy.

(ii) The bundle sheath cells make several layers around the vascular bundles.

(iii) They possess large number of chloroplasts, thick cell wall impervious to gaseous exchange and there are no intercellular spaces e.g., maize and *Sorghum* leaves.

(iv) The chloroplasts in C_4 leaves are dimorphic.

(v) The C_3 plants do not have bundle sheath.

(vi) They possess one type of chloroplasts.

Q. 3. Even though a very few cells in a C_4 plant carry out the biosynthetic – Calvin pathway, yet they are highly productive. Can you discuss why?

[NCERT Ex. Q. 3, Page 151]

Ans. C_4 plants are highly productive as they have the mechanism for increasing the concentration of CO_2. The increase in CO_2 ensures that the enzyme RuBisCO does not act as an oxygenase, but as carboxylase. This prevents photorespiration and increases the rate of photosynthesis.

Q. 4. RuBisCO is an enzyme that acts both as a carboxylase and oxygenase. Why do you think RuBisCO carries out more carboxylation in C_4 plants?

[NCERT Ex. Q. 4, Page 152]

Ans. The enzyme RuBisCO is absent from the mesophyll cells of C_4 plants. It is present in the bundle sheath cells surrounding the vascular bundles. In C_4 plants, the Calvin cycle occurs in the bundle sheath cells. The primary CO_2 acceptor in the mesophyll cells is phosphoenol pyruvate- a three carbon compound. It is converted into the four carbon compound oxaloacetate. Oxaloacetate is further converted into malic acid. Malic acid is transported to the bundle sheath cells, where it undergoes decarboxylation and CO_2 fixation occurs by the calvin cycle. This prevents the enzyme RuBisCO from acting as an oxygenase.

Q. 5. Suppose there were plants that had a high concentration of chlorophyll *b*, but lacked chlorophyll *a*, would it carry out photosynthesis? Then why do plants have chlorophyll *b* and other accessory pigments? [NCERT Ex. Q. 5, Page 152]

Ans. Chlorophyll 'a' molecules act as antenna molecules. They get excited by absorbing light and emit electrons during cyclic and non-cyclic photophosphorylation. They form the reaction centres for both photosystems I and II. Therefore, chlorophyll 'a' is essential for photosynthesis.

Chlorophyll 'b' and other photosynthetic pigments such as carotenoids and xanthophylls, on the other hand act as accessory pigments. Their role is to absorb energy and transfer it to chlorophyll 'a'. Carotenoids and xanthophylls also protect the chlorophyll molecule from photo-oxidation.

If any plant lack chlorophyll 'a' and has high concentration of chlorophyll 'b', then this plant would not undergo photosynthesis.

Q. 6. Why is the colour of a leaf kept in the dark is frequently yellow, or pale green? Which pigment do you think is more stable? [NCERT Ex. Q. 6, Page 152]

Ans. The production of chlorophyll pigment essential for photosynthesis is directly proportional to the amount of light available. In the absence of the light, the production of chlorophyll-a molecule stops and they get broken slowly. This changes the colour of leaf gradually to light green. During the process, the xanthophylls and carotenoid pigments become predominant, causing the leaf to become yellow. These pigments are more stable as light is not essential for their production. They are always present in plants.

Q. 7. Look at leaves of the same plant on the shady side and compare it with the leaves on the sunny side. Or, compare the potted plants kept in the sunlight with those in the shade. Which of them has leaves that are darker green? Why? [NCERT Ex. Q. 7, Page 152]

Ans. Light is the limiting factor for photosynthesis. Leaves get lesser light for photosynthesis when they are in shade. Therefore, the leaves or plants in shade perform lesser photosynthesis as compared to leaves or plants kept in sunlight.

In order to increase the rate of photosynthesis, the leaves present in shade have more chlorophyll pigments. This increase in chlorophyll content increases the amount of light absorbed by the leaves, which in turn increases the rate of photosynthesis. Therefore, leaves or plants in shade are greener than the leaves or plants kept in sun.

Q. 8. Figure shows the effect of light on the rate of photosynthesis. Based on the graph, answer the following questions :

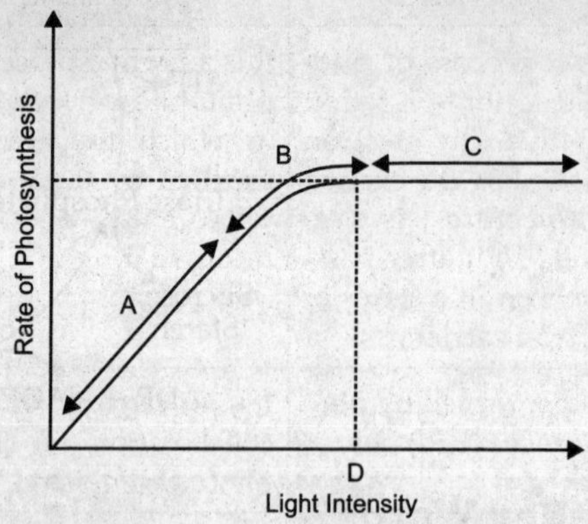

(i) At which point/s (A, B or C) in the curve is light a limiting factor?
(ii) What could be the limiting factor/s in region A?
(iii) What do C and D represent on the curve?
[NCERT Ex. Q. 8, Page 152]

Ans. (i) At higher light intensities, the rate of photosynthesis becomes limiting. Light is limiting in A and 50% of B.

(ii) Light.

(iii) C is saturation of light. Here, the rate of photosynthesis is not increased by increasing intensity of light.

D represent intensity of light at which same factor may be limiting.

Q. 9. Give comparison between the following :
(i) C_3 and C_4 pathways.
(ii) Cyclic and non-cyclic photophosphorylation.
(iii) Anatomy of leaf in C_3 and C_4 plants.
[NCERT Ex. Q. 9, Page 152]

Ans. (i)

S.No.	C_3 Plants	C_4 Plants
(i)	Photosynthesis occurs in mesophyll tissues.	Photosynthesis occurs both in mesophyll and bundle sheath cells.
(ii)	The carbon dioxide acceptor is RuBisCO.	The carbon dioxide acceptor is PEP carboxylase.
(iii)	Kranz anatomy is absent.	Kranz anatomy is present.
(iv)	The 1st stable compound formed is 3C compound called 3 Phosphoglyceric acid (PGA).	The 1st stable compound is carbon oxaloacetic acid (OAA).
(v)	The optimum temperature is 20-25°C.	The optimum temperature is 35 – 44°C.
(vi)	Photorespiratory loss is high.	Photorespiration does not take place.

(ii)

S. No.	Cyclic photophosphorylation	Non-cyclic photophosphorylation
(i)	It is a process of photophosphorylation in which an electron expelled by the excited photo-centre is returned to it after passing through a series of electron carriers .	It is a normal process of photophosphorylation- in which the electron expelled by the excited photocentre does not return to it.
(ii)	It is performed by photosystem I (PS I) only.	It is carried out in collaboration of both photosystem I and II.
(iii)	It synthesises only ATP.	Non-cyclic Photophosphorylation is not only connected with ATP synthesis but also production of NADPH.

(iii)

C_3 leaves	C_4 leaves
RuBisCO is present in mesophyll cells.	RuBisCO is present in bundle sheath cells.
Bundle sheath cells are absent.	Bundle sheath cells are present.
The first stable product produced is 3- phosphoglycerate- a 3C compound.	The first stable product produced is oxaloacetic acid- a 4C compound.
In C_3 leaves, photorespiration takes place.	In C_4 leaves, photorespiration does not occur.

□□

CHAPTER 12

RESPIRATION IN PLANTS

- Respiration is an energy releasing enzymatically controlled catabolic process which involves a step-wise oxidative breakdown of food substance inside living cells.

$$C_6H_{12}O_6 + 6O_2 \longrightarrow 6CO_2 + 6H_2O + \text{Energy}$$

- Living organism require energy for all activities like absorption, movement, reproduction or even breathing
- Energy is obtained from oxidation of food during respiration.
- **Cellular respiration** is the mechanism of breaking down of food materials within the cell to release energy for synthesis of ATP.
- Breaking down of complex molecules takes place to produce energy in cytoplasm and in the mitochondria.
- Breaking down of C-C bond of complex compounds through oxidation within the cells leading to release of considerable amount of energy is called respiration. The compounds that get oxidised is called respiratory substrates.
- Energy released during oxidation is not used directly but utilised in synthesis of ATP, which is broken down when energy is required. Therefore, ATP is called energy currency of cells.
- The process of respiration requires oxygen. In plants, oxygen is taken in by stomata, lenticels and root hairs.
- Plants can get along without respiratory organs because:
  - Each plant part takes care of its own gas-exchange needs.
  - Plants do not present great demands for gas exchange.
  - Distance that gases must diffuse in large plant is not large.
  - During photosynthesis, O_2 is released in leaves and diffused to other part of leaves.
  - Most cells of a plant have at least a part of their surface in contact with air.
  - There is loose packing of parenchyma cells in network of air spaces.
- During the process of respiration, oxygen is utilised and carbon dioxide and water is released along with energy molecules in form of ATP.
- **Aerobic Respiration** is an enzymatically controlled release of energy in a step wise catabolic process of complete oxidation of organic food into carbon dioxide and water with oxygen acting as terminal oxidant.

Glycolysis

- The scheme of glycolysis is given by Gustav Embden, Otto Meyerhof, and J. Parnas. It is also called as **EMP pathway**.
- Glycolysis is the partial oxidation of glucose or similar hexose sugar into two molecules of pyruvic acid through a series of enzyme mediated reaction releasing some ATP and NADH. It occurs in cytoplasm.
- In plants, glucose is derived from sucrose or from storage carbohydrates. Sucrose is converted into glucose and fructose by enzyme invertase.
- Glycolysis starts with phosphorylation of glucose in presence of enzyme hexokinase to form glucose-6-phosphate. One molecules of ATP is used in this process.
- In next step, glucose-6-phosphate is converted into fructose-6-phosphate, catalyzed by enzyme phosphohexose isomerase.
- Fructose-6-phosphate uses another molecules of ATP to form fructose-1-6 bisphosphate in presence of enzyme phosphofructokinase.
- In glycolysis, two molecules of ATP are consumed during double phosphorylation of glucose to fructose 1,6 bisphosphate. Two molecules of NADPH are formed at the time of oxidation of glyceraldehyde 3-phosphate to 1,3 biphosphoglycerate. Each NADH is equivalent to 3ATP, so that net gain in glycolysis is 8 ATP.
- 3-phosphoglycerate produces phosphoenol pyruvate and further. Phosphoenol pyruvate is converted into pyruvic acid.
- Pyruvic acid is the key product of glycolysis, further breakdown of pyruvic acid depends upon the need of the cell.
- In animal cells, like muscles during exercise, when oxygen is insufficient for aerobic respiration, pyruvic acid is reduced to Lactic acid by enzyme lactate dehydrogenase due to reduction by $NADH_2$.

Fermentation

- Fermentation takes place unaeorbic conditions in many prokaryotes and unicellular eukaryotes for the complete oxidation of glucose to CO_2 and H_2O, organisms adopt Kreb's cycle which is also called as aerobic respiration.
  - In fermentation by yeast, pyruvic acid is converted to ethanol and CO_2. The enzyme involved is pyruvic acid decarboxylase and alcohol dehydrogenase.

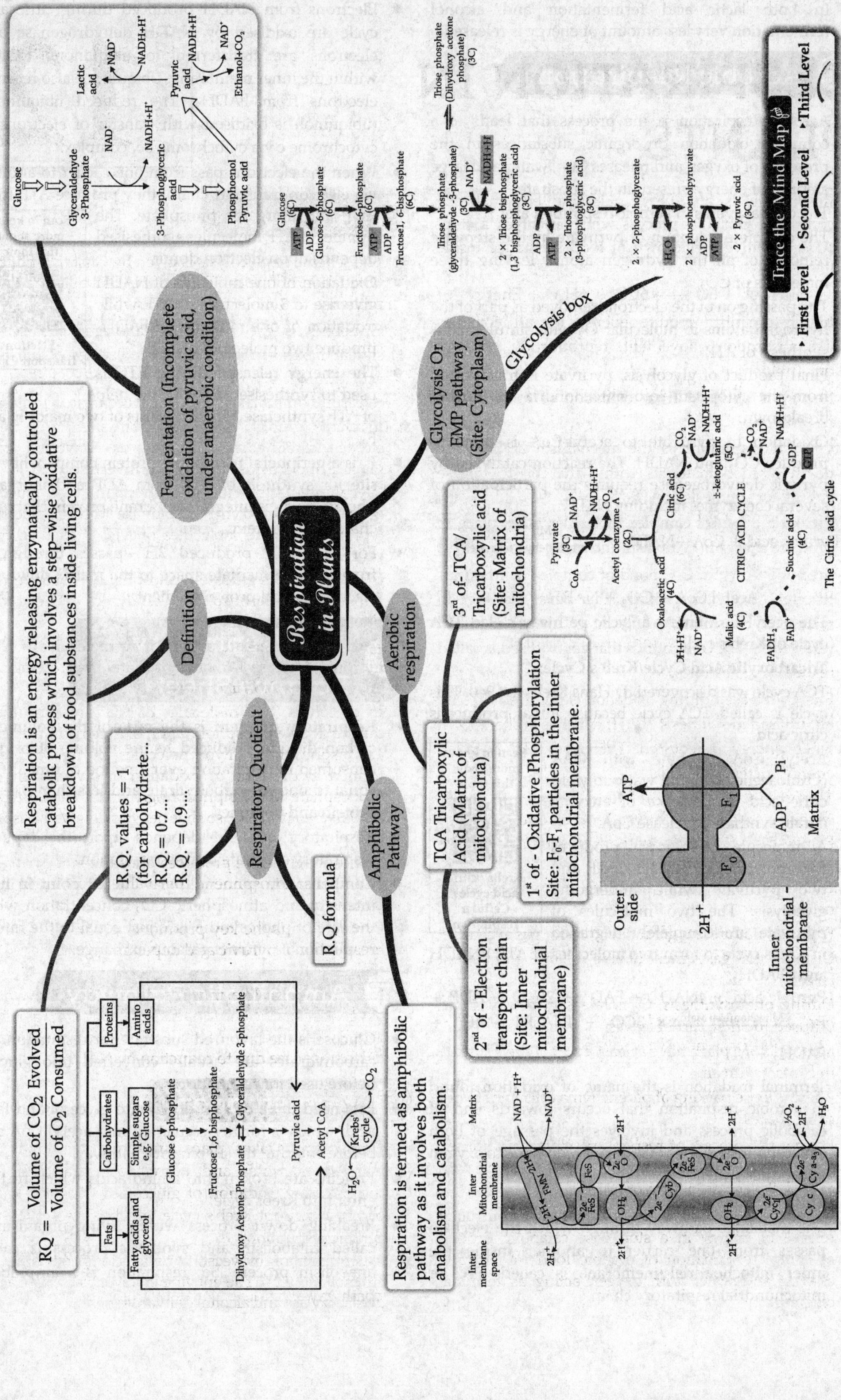
Respiration in Plants
Definition
Respiration is an energy releasing enzymatically controlled catabolic process which involves a step–wise oxidative breakdown of food substances inside living cells.
Fermentation (Incomplete oxidation of pyruvic acid, under anaerobic condition)
Glycolysis Or EMP pathway (Site: Cytoplasm)
Glycolysis box
Aerobic respiration
3rd of- TCA/ Tricarboxylic acid (Site: Matrix of mitochondria)
The Citric acid cycle
TCA Tricarboxylic Acid (Matrix of mitochondria)
1st of - Oxidative Phosphorylation Site: F0-F1 particles in the inner mitochondrial membrane.
2nd of - Electron transport chain (Site: Inner mitochondrial membrane)
Respiratory Quotient
R.Q. values = 1 (for carbohydrate... R.Q. = 0.7... R.Q. = 0.9....
R.Q formula
RQ = Volume of CO2 Evolved / Volume of O2 Consumed
Amphibolic Pathway
Respiration is termed as amphibolic pathway as it involves both anabolism and catabolism.
Trace the Mind Map
First Level
Second Level
Third Level

- In both lactic acid fermentation and alcohol fermentation very less amount of energy is released.

Aerobic Respiration

- Aerobic Respiration is the process that leads to a complete oxidation of organic substances in the presence of oxygen and releases CO_2, water and large amount of energy present in the substrate.
- The crucial events in aerobic respiration are:

(i) The complete oxidation of pyruvate by the stepwise removal of all the hydrogen atoms, leaving three molecules of CO_2.

(ii) The passing on of the electrons removed as part of the hydrogen atoms to molecular O_2 with simultaneous synthesis of ATP.

- Final product of glycolysis, pyruvate is transported from the cytoplasm into mitochondria for further breakdown.
- Oxidation of pyruvate to acetyl-CoA is done to produce CO_2 and NADH. The reaction catalyzed by pyruvic dehydrogenase requires the participation of several coenzymes including NAD^+.

$$\text{Pyruvic acid} + \text{CoA} + NAD^+ \xrightarrow[\text{Pyruvate dehydrogenase}]{Mg^{2+}} \text{Acetyl CoA} + CO_2 + NADH + H^+$$

- The acetyl CoA enters a cyclic pathway called TCA cycle or Kreb's cycle.
- **Tricarboxylic Acid Cycle/Kreb's Cycle:**
- TCA cycle was discovered by Hans Krebs in 1940. This cycle is called TCA cycle because initial product is citric acid.
- Acetyl CoA combine with OAA (Oxaloacetic acid) and water to yield citric acid in presence of enzyme citrate synthase to release CoA.

Scan to know more about this topic
Krebs / citric acid cycle / Cellular respiration

- A molecule of glucose produces two molecules of NADH, 2ATP and two pyruvate while undergoing glycolysis. The two molecules of pyruvate are completely degraded in Krebs cycle to form two molecules of ATP, 8NADH and $2FADH_2$.

$$\text{Pyruvic acid} + 4NAD^+ + FAD^+ + 2H_2O + ADP + Pi \xrightarrow{\text{Mitochondrial Matrix}} 3CO_2 + 4NADH + 4H^+ + FADH_2 + ATP$$

- Terminal oxidation is the name of oxidation found in aerobic respiration that occurs towards end of catabolic process and involves the passage of both electrons and protons of reduced coenzyme to oxygen to produce water.
- **Electron Transport Chain**
- The metabolic pathway through which the electron passes from one carrier to another inside the inner mitochondrial membrane is called ETC or mitochondrial respiratory chain.
- Electrons from NADH produced during citric acid cycle are oxidised by NADH dehydrogenase and electrons are transferred to ubiquinone located within the inner membrane. Ubiquinone also receives electrons from $FADH_2$. The reduced ubiquinone (ubiquinol) is oxidised with transfer of electrons to cytochrome c via cytochrome bc_1 complex.
- When the electrons pass from one carrier to another via electron transport chain, they produce ATP from ADP and inorganic phosphate. The number of ATP molecules synthesised depends upon electron donor.
- Oxidation of one molecule of NADH give rise to 3 molecules of ATP, while oxidation of one molecule of $FADH_2$ produce two molecules of ATP.

Scan to know more about this topic
Electron Transport Chain

- The energy released during ETC is used to synthesise ATP with the help of ATP synthetase, which consists of two major F_1 and F_0.
- F_1 is a peripheral membrane protein complex having site for synthesis of ATP from ADP and inorganic phosphate. F_0 is integral membrane protein that form channel for protein.
- For each ATP produced $2H^+$ passes through F_0 from the intermediate space to the matrix down the electrochemical proton gradient.

The Respiratory Balance Sheet

- **Respiratory quotient** is the ratio of the volume of carbon dioxide produced to the volume of oxygen consumed in respiration over a period of time. RQ is equal to one for carbohydrate and less than one for protein and peptones.
- Respiratory quotient depends upon the type of respiratory substrate during respiration.
- Compensation point is that value or point in light intensity and atmospheric CO_2 concentration when the rate of photosynthesis is just equal to the rate of respiration *i.e.*, no net gaseous exchange.

Amphibolic Pathway

- Glucose is the favoured substrate for respiration. All carbohydrates are usually converted into glucose before used for respiration.
- Fats need to be broken down into glycerol and fatty acid, which is further converted into acetyl CoA and before entering the respiratory pathway.
- Proteins are broken into amino acids which further enter into Krebs cycle.
- Breaking down process within living organism is called catabolism and synthesis process is called anabolism process. So, respiration is a amphibolic pathway.

Key Words

- **Electron transport system:** The metabolic pathway, through which the electron passes from one carrier to another, is called electron transport system.
- **Oxidative phosphorylation:** Phosphorylation that takes place in presence of oxygen is called oxidative phosphorylation.
- **Respiratory quotient:** Respiratory quotient or respiratory ratio is the ratio of the volume of CO_2 evolved to the volume of O_2 consumed during respiration.

NCERT CORNER

Q. 1. Differentiate between
(i) Respiration and Combustion
(ii) Glycolysis and Krebs cycle
(iii) Aerobic respiration and Fermentation
[NCERT Ex. Q. 1, Page 165]

Ans. (i) Difference between respiration and combustion:

Respiration	Combustion
(i) It is a biochemical process that occurs in living cells.	It is a physicochemical process that does not take place in living cells.
(ii) ATP is generated.	ATP is not generated.
(iii) Enzymes are required.	Enzymes are not required.
(iv) It is biologically controlled process.	It is an uncontrolled process.

(ii) Differences between glycolysis and krebs cycle:

Glycolysis	Krebs cycle
(i) It is a linear pathway, which occurs in the cell cytoplasm.	It is a cyclic process, which occurs in mitochondrial matrix.
(ii) It occurs in both aerobic and anaerobic respiration.	It occurs in aerobic respiration.
(iii) It generates $2NADH_2$ and 2ATP molecules on the breakdown of one glucose molecule.	It produces 6 $NADH_2$, $FADH_2$, and 2 ATP molecules on the breakdown of the two acetyl CoA molecules.

(iii) Differences between aerobic respiration and fermentation:

Aerobic respiration	Anaerobic respiration (Fermentation)
(i) It occurs in the presence of oxygen.	Fermentation occurs in the absence of oxygen.
(ii) The process takes place in cytoplasm and mitochondria.	It occurs in cytoplasm.
(iii) The end products are carbon dioxide and water.	The end products are ethyl alcohol and carbon dioxide.
(iv) In this, complete oxidation of the respiratory substrate takes place.	In this, incomplete oxidation of respiratory substrate takes place.
(v) During the process, about 36 ATP molecules are produced.	During the process, only 2 ATP molecules are produced.

Q. 2. What are respiratory substrates? Name the most common respiratory substrate.
[NCERT Ex. Q. 2, Page 165]

Ans. The organic substances which can be catabolised in the living cells to release energy are called respiratory substrates. The most common respiratory substrate is glucose.

Q. 3. Give the schematic representation of glycolysis?
[NCERT Ex. Q. 3, Page 165]

Ans.

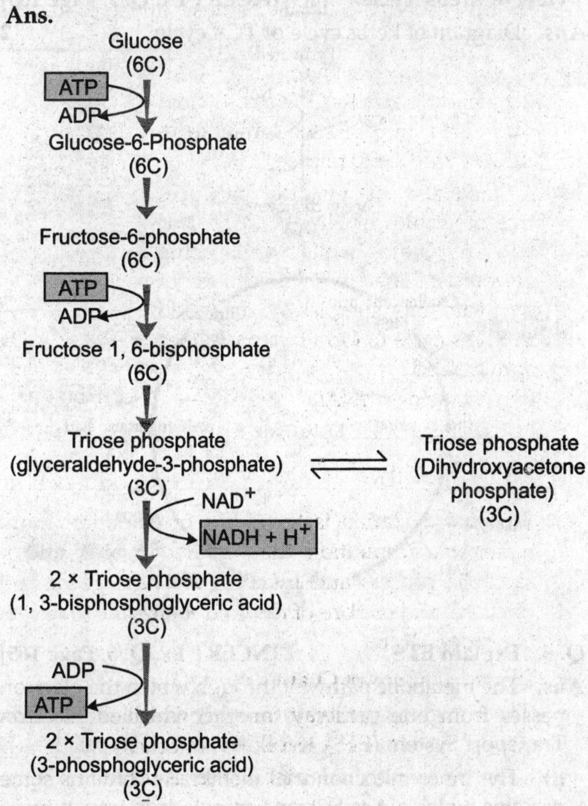

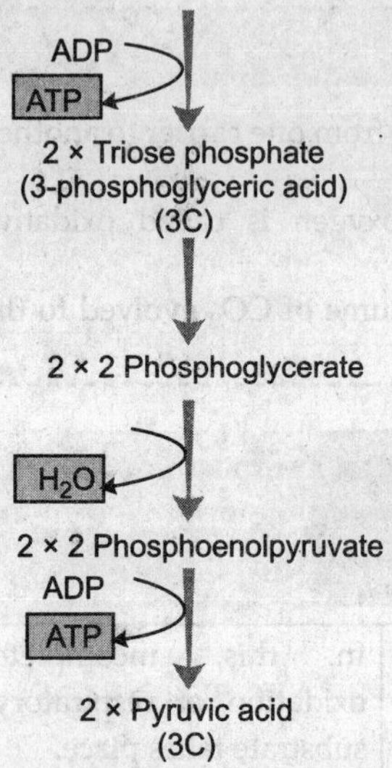

Q. 4. What are the main steps in aerobic respiration? Where does it take place? [NCERT Ex. Q. 4, Page 165]

Ans. Main steps in aerobic respiration are:

Main steps in aerobic respiration	Site of occurrence
Glycolysis	Cytoplasm
Krebs cycle	Matrix of mitochondria.
Electron transport chain.	Inner mitochondrial membrane.
Oxidative phosphorylation.	F_0-F_1 particles in the inner mitochondrial membrane.

It takes place in cytoplasm and mitochondria.

Q. 5. Give the schematic representation of an overall view of krebs' cycle. [A I] [NCERT Ex. Q. 5, Page 165]

Ans. Diagram of kerbs cycle or TCA cycle: **2**

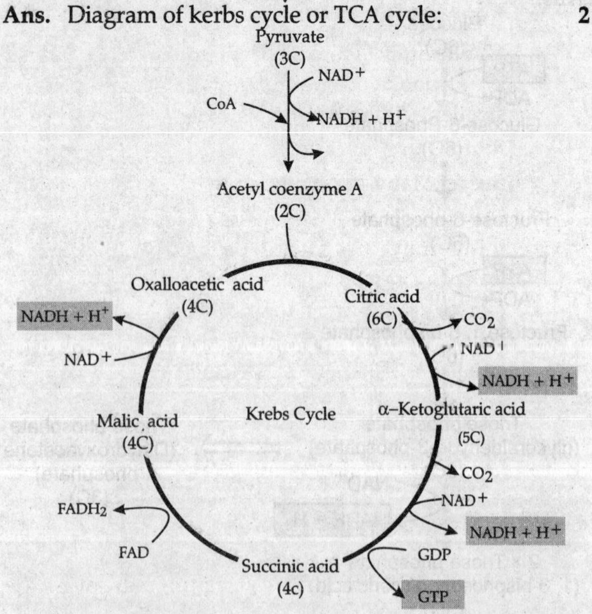

Q. 6. Explain ETS. [NCERT Ex. Q. 6, Page 165]

Ans. The metabolic pathway through which the electron passes from one carrier to another is called Electron Transport System (ETS). It follows several steps:

(i) The inner mitochondrial membrane contains some proteins which act as H^+ ions and electron transporting enzymes which are arranged in ordered manner in a specific series called electron transport chain.

(ii) These enzymes take part in the passage of electrons from a substance to its ultimate acceptor.

(iii) The electron carriers include flavins, iron-sulphur complexes, quinones and cytochromes.

(iv) The glucose molecule is completely oxidised by the end of the citric acid cycle, but energy is not released unless NADH and $FADH_2$ are oxidised through ETS.

(v) Electrons from NADH are oxidised by an NADH dehydrogenase (complex I) and electrons are then transferred to ubiquinone which also receives reducing equivalents via $FADH_2$ that is produced during oxidation of succinate, through succinate dehydrogenase (complex II).

(vi) The reduced ubiquinone is then oxidised with the transfer of electrons to cytochrome *c* via cytochrome bc_1 complex (complex III)

(vii) Cytochrome-*c* is a small protein attached to the outer surface of inner membrane and acts as a mobile carrier for transfer of electrons between complex III and IV.

(viii) Complex IV refers to cytochrome *c* oxidase complex containing cytochrome *a* and a_3 and two copper centers.

(ix) When the electrons pass from one carrier to another in ETS, they are coupled to ATP synthetase (complex V) for the production of ATP from ADP and inorganic phosphate.

(x) The number of ATP molecule synthesised depends on nature of the electrons donor.

(xi) Oxidation of one molecule of NADH gives rise to 3 molecules of ATP, while one molecule of $FADH_2$ yields 2 molecules of ATP.

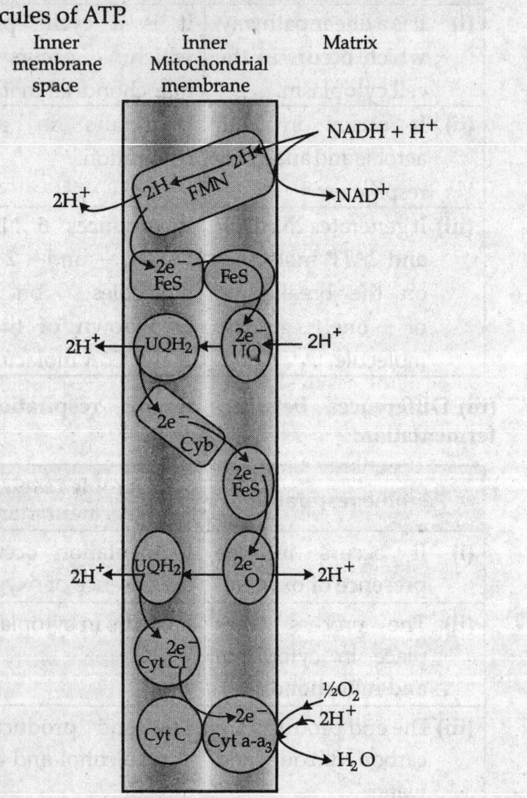

Q. 7. Distinguish between the following:
(i) Aerobic respiration and anaerobic respiration
(ii) Glycolysis and fermentation
(iii) Glycolysis and citric acid cycle
[NCERT Ex. Q. 7, Page 165]

Ans. (i)

Aerobic Respiration	Anaerobic Respiration
(i) It uses oxygen forbreaking the respiratory material into simpler substances.	Oxygen is not used in the breakdown of respiratory substrate.
(ii) Respiratory material is completely oxidised.	Respiratory material is incompletely broken.
(iii) It involves electron transport.	Electron transport is absent.

(ii)

Glycolysis	Fermentation
(i) It is the first step of respiration which occurs without requirement of oxygen and is common to both aerobic and anaerobic modes of respiration.	It is a type of anaerobic respiration which does not require oxygen.
(ii) Pyruvic acid is produced as its end product.	Ethanol or lactic acid is produced as its end product.

(iii) Refer to NCERT Corner/ Q1 (ii).

Q. 8. What are the assumptions made during the calculation of net gain of ATP?
[NCERT Ex. Q. 8, Page 165]

Ans. Assumption:

(i) There is a sequential, orderly pathway functioning with one substrate forming the next via glycolysis, Krebs's cycle and ETS.

(ii) NADH synthesised in glycolysis is transferred into mitochondria and undergoes oxidative phosphorylation.

(iii) None of intermediates in pathway are used to make any other compound.

(iv) Only glucose is being respired. No other alternative substrate enters in the pathway at any intermediate stage.

Q. 9. Discuss "The respiratory pathway is an amphibolic pathway." [NCERT Ex. Q. 9, Page 165]

Ans. (i) Respiration is a catabolic process as during respiration, various substrates are broken down for deriving energy. Carbohydrates are broken down into glucose before entering respiratory pathway.

(ii) Fats get converted into fatty acids and glycerol whereas fatty acids get converted into acetyl CoA before entering the respiration.

(iii) Similarly, proteins are converted into amino acids, which enter respiration after deamination.

(iv) During synthesis of fatty acids, acetyl CoA is withdrawn from respiratory pathway. Similarly respiratory substrates get withdrawn.

(v) Thus, respiration is also involved in anabolism.

Q.10. Define RQ. What is its value for fats?
[NCERT Ex. Q. 10, Page 165]

Ans. Respiratory quotient (RQ) is the ratio of the volume of carbon dioxide produced to the volume of oxygen consumed in respiration over a period of time.

RQ is more than one for fats.

Q.11. What is oxidative phosphorylation?
[NCERT Ex. Q. 11, Page 165]

Ans. Oxidative phosphorylation:

(i) The formation of ATP by linking ADP and Pi inorganic phosphate during aerobic respiration is called oxidative phosphorylation ADP + Pi $\rightarrow$ ATP

(ii) Because of proton gradient, the protons return to the matrix. The energy released by the flow of protons down the gradient is utilised in synthesising ATP.

(iii) Due to transport of two electrons from NADH (by the electron transport chain) three pairs of protons are simultaneously to the outer compartment.

As a result of this, from one pair of protons which returns to the matrix through inner membrane particles one high energy ATP bond is produced.

(iv) The oxidative phosphorylation produces 3 ATP molecules per molecule of NADH oxidised.

(v) The FADH donates its electrons down the chain. Its oxidation produce 2 ATP molecules.

Q.12. What is the significance of step-wise release of energy in respiration? [NCERT Ex. Q. 12, Page 165]

Ans. Step wise metabolism serves several purposes:

(i) The step wise release of chemical bond energy enables the cell to utilise a relatively higher proportion of energy in ATP synthesis.

(ii) It minimises the wastage of energy.

(iii) It keeps the temperature of the cell low to prevent its burning.

(iv) The activities of enzymes for different steps of respiration can be enhanced or inhibited by specific compounds.

(v) The intermediates of respiratory pathway can be used for the synthesis of other biomolecules.

□□

CHAPTER 13

PLANT GROWTH AND DEVELOPMENT

- Root, stem, leaves, flower, fruits and seeds arise in orderly manner in plants.
- Plants complete their vegetative phase to move into reproductive phase in which flowers and fruits are formed for continuation of life cycle of plant.
- Development is the sum of two processes: **growth** and **differentiation.** Intrinsic and extrinsic factors control the process of growth and development in plants.

Growth

- **Growth** is a permanent or irreversible increase in dry weight, size, mass or volume of cell, organ or organism. It is internal or intrinsic in living beings.
- In plant, growth is accomplished by cell division, increase in cell number and cell enlargement. So, growth is a quantitative phenomenon which can be measured in relation to time.
- Plant growth is generally indeterminate due to capacity of unlimited growth throughout the life. Meristem tissues is present at certain locality of plant body.
- The plant growth in which new cells are always being added to plant body due to meristem is called open form of growth.
- Root apical meristem and shoot apical meristem are responsible for primary **growth** and **elongation** of plant body along the axis.
- **Intercalary meristem** located at nodes produce buds and new branches in plants.
- Secondary growth in plants is the function of lateral meristem i.e., vascular cambium and cork cambium.

Scan to know more about this topic

Plant growth and development

Phases of plant growth

- **Meristematic phase** is also called as the phase of cell formation or cell division. It occurs at root apex, shoot apex and other region having meristematic tissue. The cells in this region are rich in protoplasm and possess large conspicuous nuclei. Their cell walls is thin and cellulosic with abundant plasmodesmatal connection.
- **Phase of Elongation:** Newly formed cells produced in the meristematic phase undergo enlargement. Increased vacuolation and new cell wall deposition are the other characteristics of the cells in this phase.
- Cell enlargement occurs in all direction with maximum elongation in conducting tissues and fibres.
- **Phase of maturation:** The enlarged cells develops into special or particular type of cells by undergoing structural and physiological differentiation.
- **Growth Rate:** Increase in growth per unit time is called growth rate. Growth rate may be arithmetic or geometrical.
- Quantitative comparison between the growth of living system can be made by:

I. Measurement and comparison of total growth per unit time is called the absolute rate.

II. The growth of given system per unit time expressed on a common basis is called relative growth rate.

Condition for growth

- Necessary condition for growth includes water, oxygen and essential elements. Water is required for cell enlargement and maintaining turgidity. Water also provide medium for enzymatic conditions.
- Optimal temperature and other environmental conditions are also essential for growth of the plant.

Differentiation, Dedifferentiation and Redifferentiation

- Cells produced by apical meristem and cambium differentiate to become specialised to perform specific function. This act of maturation is called **differentiation.**
- The living differentiated cells that have lost ability of division can regain the capacity of division. This phenomenon is called **dedifferentiation.** For example interfascicular cambium and cork cambium.
- Dedifferentiated cells mature and lose the capacity of cell division again to perform specific functions. This process is called **redifferentiation.**

Development

- It is the sequence of events that occur in the life history of cell, organ or organism which includes seed germination, growth, differentiation, maturation, flowering, seed formation and senescence.
- Different structures develop in different phases of growth as well as in response to environment. The ability to change under the influence of internal or external stimuli is called **plasticity**. Heterophylly is the example of plasticity as in lark spur and butter cup.
- Development in plants is under the control of intrinsic and extrinsic factors.

Important Diagram

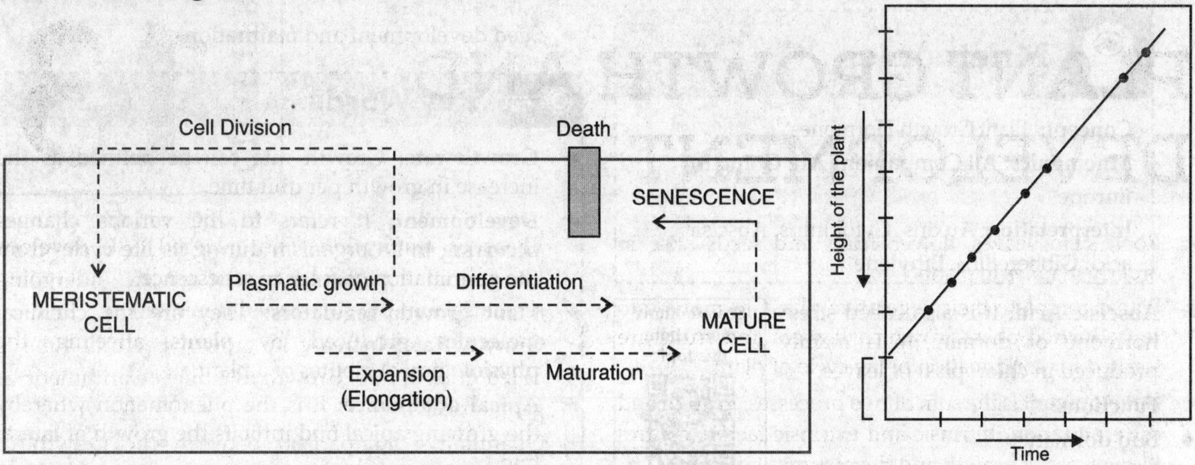

Sequence of development process in plant cell

Plant Growth Regulators

- Plant growth regulators are the chemicals that regulate the growth and development of plants. They are also known as plant growth hormones.
- PGRs are broadly divided into two groups on the basis of their functions. One group of PGRs are involved in growth promoting activities such as cell division, cell enlargement, pattern formation, flowering, fruiting and seed formation. These are called plant growth promoters, e.g., auxins, gibberellins and cytokinins, ABA, Ethylene.
- The PGR's of the other group act as plant growth inhibitors. Plant growth inhibitors are involved in various growth inhibiting activities such as dormancy and abscission. They also play an important role in plant responses to wounds and stresses of biotic and abiotic origin, e.g., abscisic acid. Ethylene, could fit either of the group, but it is largely a plant inhibitor.
- Auxin was isolated by **F.W. Went** from tips of coleoptiles of oat seedlings.
- The 'bakane disease' of rice seedlings is caused by fungal pathogen *Gibberella fujikuroi*. E. Kurosawa found that this disease is caused due to presence of Gibberellin.
- **Skoog and Miller** identified and crystallised the cytokinesis promoting active substance called kinetin.
- Three independent researches reported the purification and chemical characterisation of three different kinds of inhibitors: Inhibitor B, Abscission II and Dormin. Later, it was found that all the three were chemically identical and named abscissic acid (ABA). Cousins in 1960, confirmed the release of a volatile substance from ripened oranges that hastened the ripening of unripened bananas. Later it was identified as ethylene.
- **Auxin** was first isolated from human urine. It is commonly indole-3-acetic acid (IAA). It is generally produced at stem and root apex and migrate to its site of action.
- Auxins like IAA and IBA (indole butyric acid) have been isolated from plants. NAA (naphthalene acetic acid) and 2,4-D (2,4-dichlorophenoxyacetic) are synthetic auxins.

Functions:

- Cell enlargement
- Apical dominance
- Cell division and controls xylem differentiation
- Inhibition of abscission
- Induce parthenocarpy

- **Gibberellins:** These are promotery PGR found in more than 100 forms named as GA_1, GA_2, GA_3.... GA_{100}. The most common one is GA_3 (Gibberellic acid).

Functions:

- Cell elongation
- Breaking of dormancy
- Early maturity
- Seed germination
- Promotes bolting (internode elongation) in plants.

Scan to know more about this topic

Gibberellins

- **Cytokinins:** This plant growth hormone is basic in nature. Most common forms includes kinetin, zeatin etc. They are mainly synthesised in root apices, developing shoot-buds, with rosette habit young fruits, etc.

Functions:

- Cell division and cell differentiation.
- Essential for tissue culture.
- Overcome apical dominance.
- Promote nutrient mobilisation thereby delaying leaf senescence.

Scan to know more about this topic

Cytokinins

- **Ethylene :** It is a gaseous hormone which stimulates transverse or isodiametric growth but retards the longitudinal one. It is one of the most widely used PGR in agriculture.

Functions:

- Inhibition of longitudinal growth.
- Fruit ripening (The increase in the rate of respiration during ripening is known as respiratory climatic).
- Promotes senescence and abscission.
- Promote apical dominance.

- Breaks seed and bud dormancy.

Mnemonics

Concept: Plant Growth Hormones

Mnemonics: All Companions Are Going to Europe

Interpretation: Auxins, Cytokinins, Abscisic acid, Gibberellins, Ethylene

- **Abscisic Acid:** It is also called stress hormone or dormin. It is mainly produced in chloroplast of leaves.

Scan to know more about this topic

Abscisic acid

Functions:

- Bud dormancy
- Leaf senescence
- Induce parthenocarpy
- Seed development and maturation

Key Words

- **Growth rate:** Growth rate can be defined as the increase in growth per unit time.
- **Development:** It refers to the various changes occurring in an organism during its life cycle- from the germination of seeds to senescence.
- **Plant growth regulators:** They are the chemical molecules produced by plants affecting the physiological attributes of a plant.
- **Apical dominance:** It is the phenomenon whereby the growing apical bud inhibits the growth of lateral bud.

NCERT CORNER

Q. 1. Define growth, differentiation, development, dedifferentiation, re-differentiation, determinate growth, and meristem and growth rate.

[NCERT Ex. Q. 1, Page 179]

Ans. **(i) Growth:** Growth is defined as a permanent or irreversible increase in dry weight, size, mass or volume of a cell, organ or organism.

(ii) Differentiation: Differentiation is a permanent localised qualitative change in size, biochemistry, structure and function of cells, tissues or organs.

(iii) Development: It is the sequence of events that occurs in the life history of a cell, organ or organism which includes growth, differentiation, maturation, and senescence.

(iv) Dedifferentiation: The sum of events that bestow the regaining capacity in differentiated cells to divide once again are termed as dedifferentiation.

(v) Redifferentiation: The product of dedifferentiated cells or tissues which lose the ability to divide are called redifferentiated cells or tissues and this event is called as redifferentiation.

(vi) Determinate growth: It refers to the limited growth. It occurs in certain regions of a plant.

(vii) Meristem: The meristem refers to the cells that remain dividing. It is located at root and shoot tips.

(viii) Growth rate: Increased growth per unit time is known as growth rate.

Q. 2. Why is not any one parameter good enough to demonstrate growth throughout the life of a flowering plant? **[NCERT Ex. Q. 2, Page 179]**

Ans. In plants, growth is said to have taken place when the amount of protoplasm increases. Measuring the growth of protoplasm involves many parameters such as the weight of the fresh tissue sample, the weight of the dry tissue sample, the differences in length, area, volume, and cell number measured during the growth period. Thus, measuring the growth of plants using only one parameter does not provide enough information and hence, is insufficient for demonstrating growth.

Q. 3. Describe briefly:

(i) Arithmetic growth

(ii) Geometric growth

(iii) Sigmoid growth curve

(iv) Absolute and relative growth rates.

[NCERT Ex. Q. 3, Page 179]

Ans. **(i) Arithmetic growth:** In arithmetic growth, one of the daughter cells continues to divide, while the other differentiates into maturity following mitotic cell division. The rate of growth is constant and increase in growth occurs in arithmetic progression, i.e., 2,4,6,8,10,..

Example: Elongation of roots at a constant rate.

(ii) Geometric growth : In geometric growth, growth is slow in the initial stages (lag phase) whereas rapid during the later stages (log or exponential phase). The daughter cells formed as a result of mitosis retain the ability to divide, but slow down due to limited supply of nutrients. The size or number increases in multiplicative fashion, i.e., 2,4,6,8,16,32,..

(iii) Sigmoid growth curve: It is an S-shaped graph produced on plotting growth of living organisms in their natural environment against time. This curve is divided into three phases: lag phase, log phase or exponential phase of rapid growth, and stationary phase.

Exponential growth can be expressed as:

$$W_1 = W_0 e^{rt}$$

where,

W_1 = Final size

W_0 = Initial size

r = Growth rate

t = Time of growth

e = Base of natural logarithms

(iv) Absolute growth rate refers to the measurement and comparison of total growth per unit time whereas relative growth rate refers to the growth of a given system per unit time, expressed on a common basis.

Q. 4. List five main groups of natural plant growth regulators. Write a note on discovery, physiological functions and agricultural / horticultural applications of any one of them. [NCERT Ex. Q. 4, Page 179]

Ans.

S. No.	Plant Growth regulator (s)	Discovery	Important functions/Application
(i)	Auxins e.g., 2AA, 2BA, NAA and 2, 4D	Discovered by F.W. Went (1928) from coleoptile of *Avena sativa.*	They promote stem growth by cell elongation. They initiate formation of lateral roots.
(ii)	Gibberellin e.g., GA_1, GA_2 and GA_3.	Yabuta and Sumiki (1938) isolated crystalline gibberellin from the fungus.	They promote stem growth of the internodes by cell elongation and break seed dormancy. They are involved in germination of seeds. GA_3 is used to speed up malting in brewing industry.
(iii)	Cytokinins e.g., Zeatin	Letham (1963) isolated naturally occurring cytokinin in pure crystalline form from immature maize seeds.	They interact with auxins in apical meristem but promote lateral bud growth. It is necessary for cytokinesis. It retards senescence (Richmond-Lang Effect). It induces femaleness in flowers.
(iv)	Abscisic acid (ABA) e.g., Dormin.	Addicott and co-workers (1964) isolated abscisic acid from immature cotton fruits.	It inhibits cell division and growth in stem and root. It promotes dormancy in both buds and seeds.
(v)	Ethylene, a gaseous hormone. ($CH_2 = CH_2$)	Crocker (1935) isolated from ripened fruits.	Ethylene inhibits growth of stem and root. It induces fruit ripening, fruit and leaf fall (abscission).

Q. 5. Why is abscisic acid also known as stress hormone? [NCERT Ex. Q. 5, Page 179]

Ans. Abscisic acid is also called as stress hormone because it induces various responses in plants against stress conditions like drought, water logging and other adverse environmental conditions. It is produced in many parts of the plants but more abundantly inside the chloroplasts of green cells. It increases the tolerance of plants towards various stresses. It induces the closure of stomata during water stress. It promotes seed dormancy and ensures seed germination during favourable conditions.

Q. 6. 'Both growth and differentiation in higher plants are open'. Comment. [NCERT Ex. Q. 6, Page 179]

Ans. Plants retain the capacity for unlimited growth throughout the life due to the presence of meristems at certain locations in their body. The cells of such meristems have the capacity to divide and self-perpetuate. The product however, soon loses the capacity to divide and such cells make up plant body. This form of growth where in new cells are always being added to the plant body by the activity of the meristem is called the open form of growth. The cells divided from root apical and shoot apical meristems and cambium differentiate the mature cells to perform specific functions. It is called differentiation.

Differentiation in plants is open because cells/ tissues arising out of the same meristems have different structures at maturity. The final structure at maturity of cell tissue is also determined by the location of the cell within.

Q. 7. Both a short day plant and a long day plant can produce flower simultaneously in a given place. Explain. [NCERT Ex. Q. 7, Page 179]

Ans. The flowering response in short-day plants and long-day plants is dependent on the durations for which these plants are exposed to light. The short-day plant and long-day plant can flower at the same place, provided they have been given an adequate photoperiod.

Q. 8. Which one of the plant growth regulators would you use if you are asked to:
(i) Induce rooting in a twig
(ii) Quickly ripen a fruit
(iii) Delay leaf senescence
(iv) Induce growth in axillary buds
(v) 'Bolt' a rosette plant
(vi) Induce immediate stomatal closure in leaves.
[NCERT Ex. Q. 8, Page 179]

Ans. (i) Induce rooting in a twig- Auxins
(ii) Quickly ripen a fruit- Ethylene
(iii) Delay leaf senescence- Cytokinins
(iv) Induce growth in axillary buds- Cytokinins
(v) 'Bolt' a rosette plant- Gibberellin
(vi) Induce immediate stomatal closure in leaves- Abscisic acid

Q. 9. Would a defoliated plant respond to photoperiodic cycle? Why? [NCERT Ex. Q. 9, Page 179]

Ans. No, a plant that has lost its leaves will not respond to the photoperiodic cycle. It is because, the photoperiodic stimulus is picked up only by the leaves in plants so that, the hormone required for flowering can be produced. Therefore, in the absence of leaves, i.e, in a defoliated plant light perception would not occur, i.e., the plant would not respond to light.

Q.10. What would be expected to happen if:
(i) GA_3 is applied to rice seedlings
(ii) Dividing cells stop differentiating
(iii) A rotten fruit gets mixed with unripe fruits
(iv) You forget to add cytokinin to the culture medium.
[NCERT Ex. Q. 10, Page 180]

Ans. (i) Rice seedlings will exhibit internode elongation and increase in height.
(ii) Undifferentiated mass of cells is formed.
(iii) Ethylene produced from the rotten fruits will hasten the ripening of the unripe fruits.
(iv) Cell division, growth and differentiation will not be observed.

□□

CHAPTER 14

BREATHING AND EXCHANGE OF GASES

- The process of exchange of O_2 from the atmosphere with CO_2 produced by the cell is called breathing. It occurs in two stages: Inspiration and Expiration. During inspiration, air enters the lungs from atmosphere and during expiration air leaves the lungs.

Respiratory organs

- Mechanism of breathing varies in different organisms according to their body structure and habitat.

Respiratory organs	Organisms
Entire body surface	Sponges, Coelenterate, flat-worms
Skin	Earthworm
Tracheal system	Insects
Gills	Pisces, aquatic arthropods and molluscs
Lungs	Amphibians, mammals

Human Respiratory System

- Human respiratory system consists of a pair of nostrils, pharynx, larynx, bronchi and bronchioles that finally terminates into alveoli.
- Nasal chamber open into pharynx that leads to larynx. Larynx contains voice box (sound box) that help in sound production.
- The trachea, primary, secondary and tertiary bronchi and initial bronchioles are supported by incomplete cartilaginous rings to prevent collapsing in absence of air.
- Each bronchiole terminates into a irregular walled, vascularised bag like structure called alveoli.
- The branching network of bronchi, bronchioles and alveoli collectively forms the lungs.
- Two lungs are covered with double layered pleura having pleural fluid between them to reduce the friction on the lung surface.
- Alveoli is the site of actual diffusion of O_2 and CO_2 between blood and atmospheric air.

Scan to know more about this topic

Human Respiration

Steps of Respiration

- Breathing in which oxygen rich atmospheric air is diffused in and CO_2 rich alveolar air is diffused out.
- Diffusion of gases across alveolar membrane.
- Transport of gases by blood.
- Diffusion of O_2 and CO_2 between blood and tissues.
- Utilisation of O_2 by cells to obtain energy and release of CO_2 (cellular respiration).

Mechanism of Breathing

- Breathing involves inspiration and expiration. During inspiration, atmospheric air is drawn in and during expiration, alveolar air is released out.
- Movement of air in and out takes place due to difference in pressure gradient. Inspiration occurs when pressure inside the lung is less and expiration occurs when pressure is more in lungs than outside.
- The diaphragm and external and internal intercostal muscles between the ribs help in developing pressure gradient due to change in volume.
- The contraction of intercostal muscles lifts the ribs and sternum causing an increase in volume of thoracic cavity that results in the decrease in pressure than the atmospheric pressure to cause inspiration.
- Relaxation of the diaphragm and intercostal muscles reduce the thoracic volume and increase the pressure to cause expiration.
- The volume of air involved in breathing movements is estimated by using spirometer for clinical assessment of pulmonary functions.

Scan to know more about this topic

Mechanism of Breathing

Important Diagram

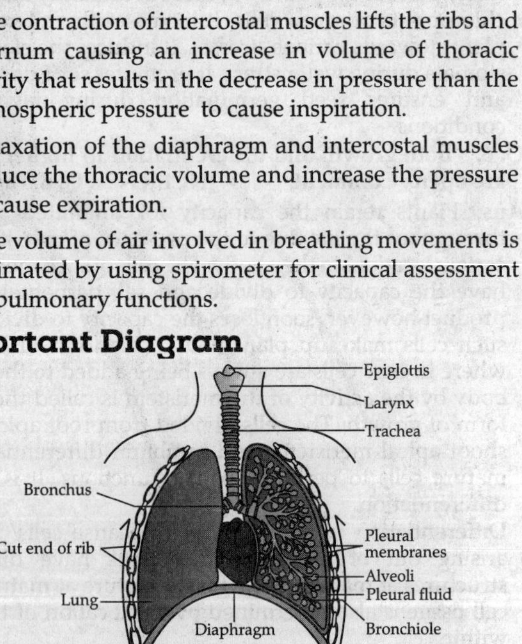

Human Respiratory System

Respiratory Volume and Capacities

- **Tidal Volume (TV):** Volume of air inspired or expired during a normal respiration. It is about 500 mL in healthy man.
- **Inspiratory Reserve Volume (IRV):** Additional volume of air a person can inspire by forceful inspiration. It is about 2500 mL to 3000 mL.

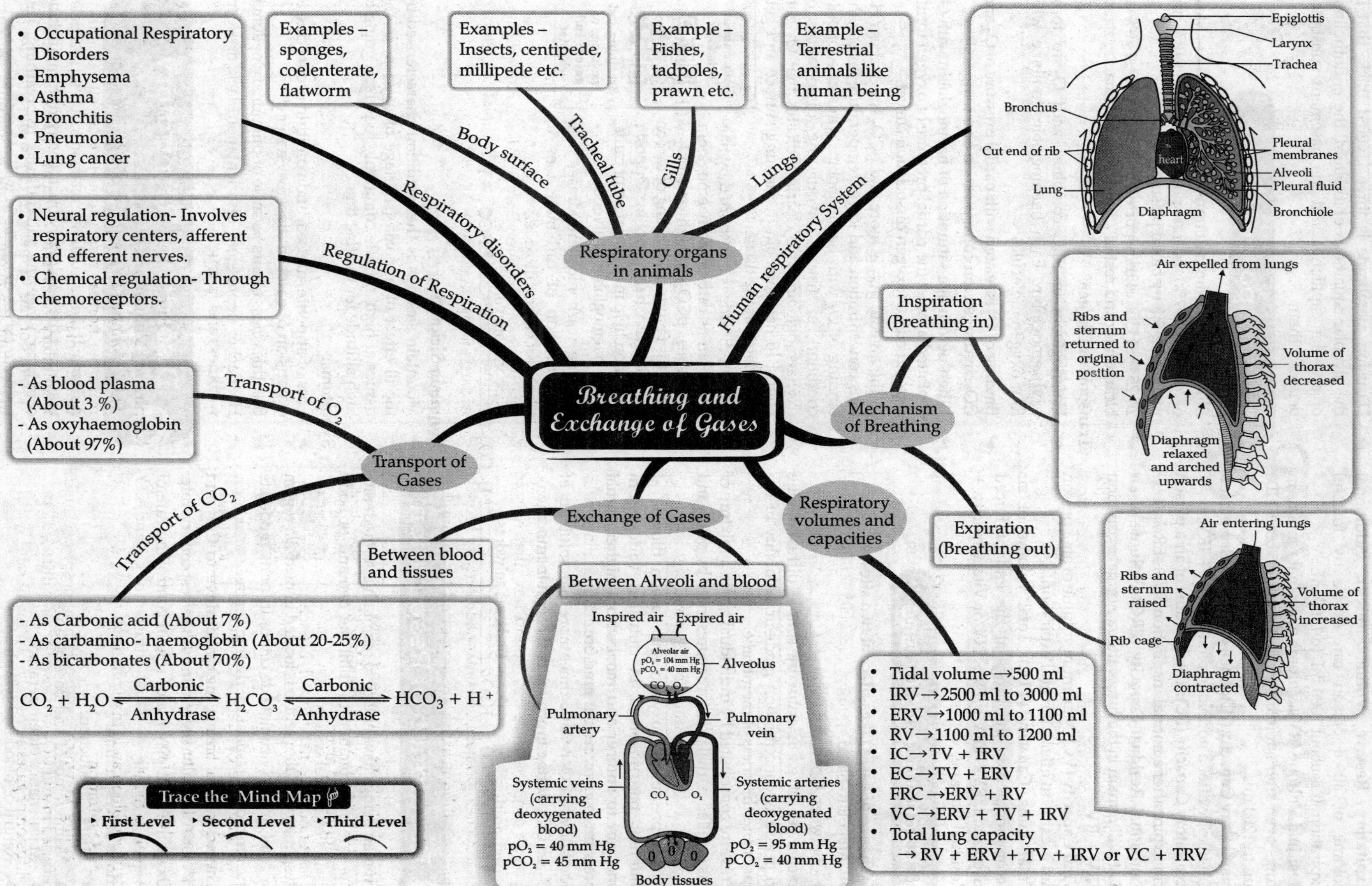
Breathing and Exchange of Gases
Respiratory organs in animals
Body surface
Examples – sponges, coelenterate, flatworm
Tracheal tube
Examples – Insects, centipede, millipede etc.
Gills
Example – Fishes, tadpoles, prawn etc.
Lungs
Example – Terrestrial animals like human being
Human respiratory System
Epiglottis
Larynx
Trachea
Bronchus
Cut end of rib
Lung
heart
Diaphragm
Pleural membranes
Alveoli
Pleural fluid
Bronchiole
Respiratory disorders
• Occupational Respiratory Disorders
• Emphysema
• Asthma
• Bronchitis
• Pneumonia
• Lung cancer
Regulation of Respiration
• Neural regulation- Involves respiratory centers, afferent and efferent nerves.
• Chemical regulation- Through chemoreceptors.
Mechanism of Breathing
Inspiration (Breathing in)
Air expelled from lungs
Ribs and sternum returned to original position
Volume of thorax decreased
Diaphragm relaxed and arched upwards
Expiration (Breathing out)
Air entering lungs
Ribs and sternum raised
Volume of thorax increased
Rib cage
Diaphragm contracted
Transport of Gases
Transport of O_2
- As blood plasma (About 3 %)
- As oxyhaemoglobin (About 97%)
Transport of CO_2
- As Carbonic acid (About 7%)
- As carbamino- haemoglobin (About 20-25%)
- As bicarbonates (About 70%)
$CO_2 + H_2O \underset{\text{Anhydrase}}{\overset{\text{Carbonic}}{\rightleftharpoons}} H_2CO_3 \underset{\text{Anhydrase}}{\overset{\text{Carbonic}}{\rightleftharpoons}} HCO_3 + H^+$
Exchange of Gases
Between blood and tissues
Between Alveoli and blood
Inspired air
Expired air
Alveolar air
pO_2 = 104 mm Hg
pCO_2 = 40 mm Hg
Alveolus
CO_2 O_2
Pulmonary artery
Pulmonary vein
CO_2 O_2
Systemic veins (carrying deoxygenated blood)
pO_2 = 40 mm Hg
pCO_2 = 45 mm Hg
Systemic arteries (carrying deoxygenated blood)
pO_2 = 95 mm Hg
pCO_2 = 40 mm Hg
Body tissues
Respiratory volumes and capacities
• Tidal volume →500 ml
• IRV→2500 ml to 3000 ml
• ERV →1000 ml to 1100 ml
• RV→1100 ml to 1200 ml
• IC→TV + IRV
• EC→TV + ERV
• FRC →ERV + RV
• VC→ERV + TV + IRV
• Total lung capacity → RV + ERV + TV + IRV or VC + TRV
Trace the Mind Map
First Level
Second Level
Third Level

- **Expiratory Reserve Volume (ERV):** Additional volume of air a person can expire by forceful expiration. It is about 1000 mL to 1100 mL.
- **Residual Volume (RV):** Volume of air that remains in lungs even after a forcible expiration. It is about 1100 mL to 1200 mL.
- **Inspiratory Capacity (IC):** Total volume of air a person can inspire after a normal expiration. TV + IRV
- **Expiratory Capacity (EC):** Total volume of air a person can expire after a normal inspiration TV + ERV
- **Functional Residual Capacity (FRC):** Volume of air that will remain in the lungs after a normal expiration ERV + RV
- **Vital Capacity (VC):** Maximum volume of air a person can breathe in after a forceful expiration.
- **Total Lung Capacity (TLC):** Total volume of air accommodated in the lungs at the end of forced inspiration. RV+ ERV+ TV+ IRV or Vital capacity + Residual Volume.

Exchange of Gases

- **Exchange of gases takes place at two sites:**
  - Alveoli to blood.
  - Between blood and tissues.
- Exchanges of gases occur by simple diffusion due to pressure/ concentration gradient, solubility of the gases and thickness of membrane.
- Pressure contributed by individual gas in a mixture of gas is called partial pressure represented by pCO_2 and pO_2.
- Partial pressure of oxygen and carbon dioxide at different part involved in diffusion varies from one part to another and moves from higher partial pressure to lower partial pressure.
- Solubility of CO_2 is 20-25 times more than solubility of O_2, so CO_2 diffuse much faster through membrane.
- Diffusion membrane is three layered thick, that is the alveolar squamous epithelium, the endothelium of alveolar capillaries and the basement substance between them.

Transport of Gases

- Blood is the medium of transport of CO_2 and O_2. Most of oxygen (97%) is transported through RBC and remaining 3% by blood plasma.
- 20-25% of CO_2 is transported by RBC and rest 70% as bicarbonate and rest of 7% by blood plasma.

Transport of Oxygen

- Haemoglobin in RBC combines with O_2 to form oxyhaemoglobin. Each haemoglobin combine with four oxygen molecules.
- Binding of O_2 is related with partial pressure of O_2 and CO_2, hydrogen ion concentration and temperature.
- When percentage saturation of haemoglobin with O_2 is plotted against the partial pressure of oxygen forms sigmoid curve (oxygen dissociation curve).
- In the alveoli, pO_2 is more and pCO_2 is less. Less H^+ ions concentration and lower temperature favour the binding of O_2 with haemoglobin. whereas, opposite condition in tissues favour the dissociation of oxyhaemoglobin. This clearly indicates that O_2 gets bound to haemoglobin in the lung surface and gets dissociated at the tissue.
- Carbon dioxide is transported by haemoglobin as carbamino-haemoglobin. In tissues, pCO_2 is high and pO_2 is less. This favour the binding of carbon dioxide with haemoglobin. Opposite condition help in dissociation of carbamino- haemoglobin in alveoli.
- Enzyme carbonic anhydrase help in formation of carbonate ions to transport carbon dioxide.

Scan to know more about this topic

Breathing and exchange of gases : Full chapter

$$CO_2 + H_2O \xrightleftharpoons{\text{Carbonic anhydrase}} H_2CO_3 \xrightleftharpoons{\text{Carbonic anhydrase}} HCO_3^- + H^+$$

Regulation of Respiration

- Human beings have ability to maintain and moderate the rate of respiration to fulfil the demand of body tissues by neural system.
- Respiratory rhythm centre is located in medulla region of hind brain. Pneumotaxic centre in pons moderate the function of respiratory rhythm centre.
- Chemosensitive area is highly sensitive to CO_2 and H^+ ions that ultimately control the respiratory rate. Oxygen do not play major role in controlling rate of respiration.

Functions of Respiration:

- Energy production.
- Maintenance of acid-base balance.
- Maintenance of temperature
- Return of blood and lymph.

Mountain Sickness:

- Mountain sickness is the condition characterised by the ill effect of hypoxia (shortage of oxygen) in the tissues at high altitude commonly to person going to high altitude for the first time.

Symptoms:

- Loss of appetite, nausea, and vomiting occurs due to expansion of gases in digestive system.
- Breathlessness occurs because of pulmonary oedema.
- Headache, depression, disorientation, lack of sleep, weakness and fatigue.

Disorder of Respiratory System

- **Asthma:** It is due to allergic reaction to foreign particles that affect the respiratory tract. The symptoms include coughing, wheezing and difficulty in breathing. This is due to excess of mucus in wall of respiratory tract.

- **Emphysema:** It is the inflation or abnormal distension of the bronchioles or alveolar sacs of lungs. This occurs due to destroying of septa between alveoli because of smoking and inhalation of other smokes. The exhalation becomes difficult and lung remains inflated.
- **Occupational Respiratory Disorders:** Occurs due to occupation of individual. This is caused by inhalation of gas, fumes or dust present in surrounding of work place. This includes Silicosis, Asbestosis due to exposure of silica and asbestos. The symptom includes proliferation of fibrous connective tissue of upper part of lung causing inflammation.
- **Pneumonia:** It is acute infection or inflammation of the alveoli of the lungs due to bacterium *Streptococcus pneumoniae.* Alveoli become acutely inflamed and most of air space of the alveoli is filled with fluid and dead white blood corpuscles limiting gaseous exchange.

Key Words

Concept: Respiratory System
Mnemonics: Adam and Eve are Over Powered
Interpretation: Asthma, Emphysema Occupation respiratory disorders, Pneumonia

NCERT CORNER

Q. 1. Define vital capacity. What is its significance ? **[NCERT Ex. Q. 1, Page 192]**

Ans. **Vital capacity** is the maximum volume of air a person can breathe in after a forced expiration. The greater the vital capacity, more is energy available to body. $VC = TV + IRV + ERV = 500 + 2500$ to $3000 + 1000$ to $1500 = 4000$ to 5000 ml.

Significance of VC: Vital capacities show the strength of our inspiration and expiration. Sports or mountain dwellers have higher vital capacity. Young persons, possess more vital capacity than older person. Males show higher vital capacity than the females. Hence, VC differs with the activities of a person.

Q. 2. State the volume of air remaining in the lungs after a normal breathing. **[NCERT Ex. Q. 2, Page 192]**

Ans. The volume of air remaining in the lungs after a normal expiration is functional residual capacity (FRC). It includes expiratory reserve volume (ERV) and residual volume (RV).

Since, $FRC = ERV + RV$
$= 1500 + 1500$
$= 3000$ mL

Thus, the functional residual capacity of the human lungs is 2500 to 3000 mL.

Q. 3. Diffusion of gases occurs in the alveolar region only and not in the other parts of respiratory system. Why? **[NCERT Ex. Q. 3, Page 192]**

Ans. The alveoli have very thin walls consisting of squamous epithelium. The alveolar wall is also provided with an extensive network of blood. But other parts are lined by thick lining which does not allow exchange of gases.

Q. 4. What are the major transport mechanisms for CO_2? Explain. **[NCERT Ex. Q. 4, Page 192]**

Ans. **Transport of CO_2: (i)** In the dissolved state Because of its high solubility, about 7% CO_2 gets dissolved in the blood plasma and is carried in solution to the lungs.

(ii) In the form of bicarbonates: The dissolved CO_2 in the blood reacts with water to form carbonic acid. This reaction occurs rapidly inside the RBCs due to the presence of the enzyme carbonic anhydrase.

$$CO_2 + H_2O \xrightleftharpoons{\text{Carbonic anhydrase}} H_2CO_3$$

$$H_2CO_3 \xrightleftharpoons{\text{Carbonic anhydrase}} H^+ + HCO_3^-$$

Most of the bicarbonate ions (HCO_3^-) formed within RBCs diffuse out into the blood plasma along a concentration gradient. About 70% of CO_2 is carried as bicarbonates.

(iii) As carbaminohemoglobin: About 20-25% of CO_2 is transported in combination with amino radicals (NH_2) of haemoglobin.

Q. 5. What will be the pO_2 and pCO_2 in the atmospheric air compared to those in the alveolar air ?

(i) pO_2 lesser, pCO_2 higher
(ii) pO_2 higher, pCO_2 lesser
(iii) pO_2 higher, pCO_2 higher
(iv) pO_2 lesser, pCO_2 lesser **[NCERT Ex. Q. 5, Page 192]**

Ans. (ii) pO_2 higher, pCO_2 lesser.

The partial pressure of oxygen in atmospheric air is more than that of oxygen in alveolar air. In atmospheric air PO_2 is about 159 mm Hg. In alveolar air, it is about 104 mm Hg. The PCO_2 in atmospheric air is lesser than that of PCO_2 in alveolar air. In atmospheric air, PCO_2 is about 0.3 mm Hg and in alveolar air it is about 40 mm Hg.

Q. 6. Explain the process of inspiration under normal conditions. **[NCERT Ex. Q. 6, Page 192]**

Ans. During breathing,

(i) The contraction of intercostal muscles raise the ribs upwards and outwards.

(ii) The diaphragm becomes flattened, on contraction.

(iii) The contraction movements result in increasing the volume of thoracic cavity and lowering the pressure inside the lungs.

(iv) To equalise this pressure, air from outside is rushed into the lungs during inspiration.

Q. 7. How is respiration regulated ?

[NCERT Ex. Q. 7, Page 192]

Ans. **(i)** Respiration is controlled by a 'respiratory centre' located in the floor of the medulla oblongata of the brain.

(ii) The pneumotaxic center present in the pons region of the brain can alter the function performed by the respiratory rhythm center by signalling to reduce the inspiration rate.

(iii) The chemosensitive region present near the respiratory center is sensitive to carbon dioxide and hydrogen ions. Increase in these substances activates this centre and signals the rhythmic centre to change the rate of expiration for eliminating these compounds.

(iv) The receptors present in the carotid artery and aortic arch detect the levels of carbon dioxide and hydrogen ions in the blood. As the levels of carbon dioxide increases, the respiratory centre send nerve impulses for necessary changes.

Q. 8. What is the effect of pCO_2 on oxygen transport?

[NCERT Ex. Q. 8, Page 192]

Ans. High pCO_2 favours the dissociation of oxyhaemoglobin to release oxygen, thus decreasing the transport of oxygen by blood.

Q. 9. What happens to the respiratory process in a man going up a hill? **[NCERT Ex. Q. 9, Page 192]**

Ans. **(i)** With the increase in height one feels difficulty in breathing due to considerable decrease in the oxygen in the air.

(ii) Consequently, the alveolar pO_2 reduces and oxygen cannot be diffused into the blood.

(iii) Thus, the process of oxygenation of blood progressively gets decreased to such an extent that the person feel mountain sickness thus, the rate of breathing is increased.

Q.10. What is the site of gaseous exchange in an insect?

[NCERT Ex. Q. 10, Page 192]

Ans. In insects, the gaseous exchange occurs through network of tube called tracheal system. There are small openings on the sides of the insect's body, known as spiracles, through which oxygen rich air moves in. The spiracles are connected to the network of tubes. From the spiracles, oxygen enters the tracheae. From here, the oxygen diffuses into the cells of the body.

Q.11. Define oxygen dissociation curve. Can you suggest any reason for its sigmoidal pattern ?

[NCERT Ex. Q. 11, Page 192]

Ans. **O_2 dissociation curve:** The relationship between the partial pressure of oxygen (pO_2) and percentage saturation of the haemoglobin with oxygen is graphically illustrated by a curve called oxygen dissociation curve. The sigmoid shape of the dissociation curve is because of the binding of oxygen for haemoglobin. As the first oxygen molecule binds to haemoglobin, it increases the affinity for the second molecule of oxygen to bind. Subsequently, haemoglobin attracts more oxygen.

Q.12. Have you heard about hypoxia? Try to gather information about it, and discuss with your friends.

[NCERT Ex. Q. 12, Page 192]

Ans. Hypoxia is a condition of oxygen shortage in the tissues. It is of two kinds:

(i) Artificial hypoxia and

(ii) Anaemic hypoxia.

(i) Artificial hypoxia is the result of shortage of O_2 in air at high altitudes. It causes mountain sickness and results into headache, dizziness, nausea, vomiting, mental fatigue and breathlessness.

(ii) Anaemic hypoxia results due to reduced O_2 capacity of blood due to less content of Hb or carbon monoxide poisoning.

Q.13. Distinguish between

(i) IRV and ERV

(ii) Inspiratory capacity and expiratory capacity.

(iii) Vital capacity and total lung capacity.

[NCERT Ex. Q. 13, Page 192]

Ans. **(i)** Differences between IRV and ERV:

S. No.	IRV	ERV
(i)	It is about 2500-3000 ml of air.	It is about 1,000 ml to 1100 ml.
(ii)	It is the volume of air a person can inspire by forcible inspiration.	It is the volume of air a person can expire by forcible expiration.

(ii) Differences between Inspiratory capacity and expiratory capacity:

S. No.	Inspiratory Capacity	Expiratory Capacity
(i)	It is designated as IC.	It is designated as EC.
(ii)	$IC = TV + IRS$	$EC = TV + ERV$
(iii)	It refers to the total volume of air a person can inspire after normal expiration.	It is the total volume of air, a person may expire after a normal inspiration.

(iii) Differences between vital capacity and total lung capacity:

S. No.	Vital Capacity	Total lung Capacity
(i)	The maximum volume of air a person can breathe in after a forced expiration.	Total volume of air accommodated in the lungs at the end of a forced inspiration.
(ii)	This includes ERV, TV and IRV.	This is includes RV, ERV, TV and IRV or vital capacity + residual volume.

Q. 14. What is Tidal volume? Find out the Tidal volume (approximate value) for a healthy human in an hour.

[NCERT Ex. Q. 14, Page 192]

Ans. Tidal volume is the volume of air inspired or expired during normal respiration. It is about 6000 to 8000 mL of air per minute.

Tidal volume for a healthy human in an hour can be calculated as:

Tidal volume= 6000 to 8000 mL/minute.

Tidal volume in an hour = 6000 to 8000 mL × 60 min = 3.6×10^5 mL to 4.8×10^5 mL.

CHAPTER 15

BODY FLUIDS AND CIRCULATION

- Body fluids are the medium of transport of nutrients, oxygen and other important substance in the body.

Blood

- Blood is the most commonly used body fluid in most of the higher organisms. Lymph also transports certain substances like protein and fats.
- Blood is a mobile connective tissue composed of a fluid matrix plasma and the cells, the blood corpuscles. It forms about 30-35% of the extracellular fluid. It is slightly alkaline fluid having pH 7.4.
- Plasma is straw coloured viscous fluid that constitutes 55% of blood volume. It consists of 90-92% water, 6-8% protein (fibrinogens, albumins and globulins), glucose, amino acids and small amount of minerals like Na^+, Mg^{++}, Ca^{++}, HCO_3^-. Cl^-, etc.
- Erythrocytes, leucocytes and platelets are collectively called formed elements.
- Erythrocytes are most abundant cells in human body. Total blood count of RBCs is 4-5.5 million per mm^3 of blood which is slightly less in females due to menstruation. It is formed in the red bone marrow. They have life span of 120 days.
- Nucleus is absent in mammalian RBCs which are biconcave in shape.
- Every 100 ml of blood contain 12-16 gm of haemoglobin.
- RBCs are destroyed in spleen (graveyard of RBCs).

Mnemonics

Concept: Types of WBCs
Mnemonic: Nine **L**ittle **M**onkey **E**ating **B**ananas
Interpretation: Neutrophils, Lymphocytes Monocytes, Eosinophils, Basophils.

- Leucocytes or WBCs are colourless due to absence of haemoglobin. 6000-8000 per mm^3 of blood of WBCs are present.
- Neutrophils are most abundant and basophils are least abundant WBCs. Monocytes and neutrophils are phagocytic cells which destroy foreign organisms.
- Basophils secrete histamine, serotonin and heparin that are involved in inflammatory reactions.
- Eosinophils resist infection and allergic reactions. B and T lymphocytes are responsible for immune response of the body.
- Thrombocytes or platelets are cell fragments produced from megakaryocytes in bone marrow. Blood normally contains 150000-350000 platelets per mm^3 of blood. Platelets are involved in clotting or coagulation of blood in case of injuries.
- **Blood Groups:** Blood of human beings differ in certain aspects although it appears same in all individuals. Two main types of grouping are ABO and Rh.
- ABO grouping is based on presence or absence of two surface antigens on RBC, antigen A and antigen B. The plasma of an individual also contains two antibodies produced in response of antigens.

Blood Group	Antigens on RBCs	Antibodies in Plasma	Donor's Group
A	A	anti-B	A, O
B	B	anti-A	B, O
AB	A, B	nil	AB, A, B, O
O	nil	anti-A, B	O

- During blood transfusion, blood of donor has to be matched with blood of recipients to avoid clumping of RBCs.
- Group 'O' blood can be donated to any individual with any blood group, so it is called universal donor.
- Person with 'AB' blood group can receive blood from any person of any group, so it is called universal recipient.

Scan to know more about this topic

Blood Groups

- **Rh grouping:** Rh antigen (similar to antigen present in Rhesus monkey) are observed on surface of RBCs of majority of individuals (about 80%). Such people are called Rh positive (Rh^+). The person in which this antigen is absent are called Rh negative (Rh^-).
- **Erythroblastosis foetalis:** If father blood is Rh^+ and mother blood is Rh^-, the foetus blood will be Rh^+. During the delivery of first child there is a possibility of exposure of mother blood with foetus blood to develop antibodies in mother blood. In subsequent pregnancy, the mother blood can leak into foetus blood that destroys the foetal RBC. This case is called erythroblastosis foetalis.

Coagulation of blood (Blood Clotting)

- When an injury is caused to a blood vessel bleeding starts which is stopped by a process called blood clotting. An injury or trauma stimulates the platelets in the blood to release certain factors that activate the mechanism of coagulation. Calcium and vitamin K play important role in blood clotting.

Lymph

- During flow of blood through capillaries, some water soluble molecules move out in the space between cells of tissues. This fluid released out is called interstitial

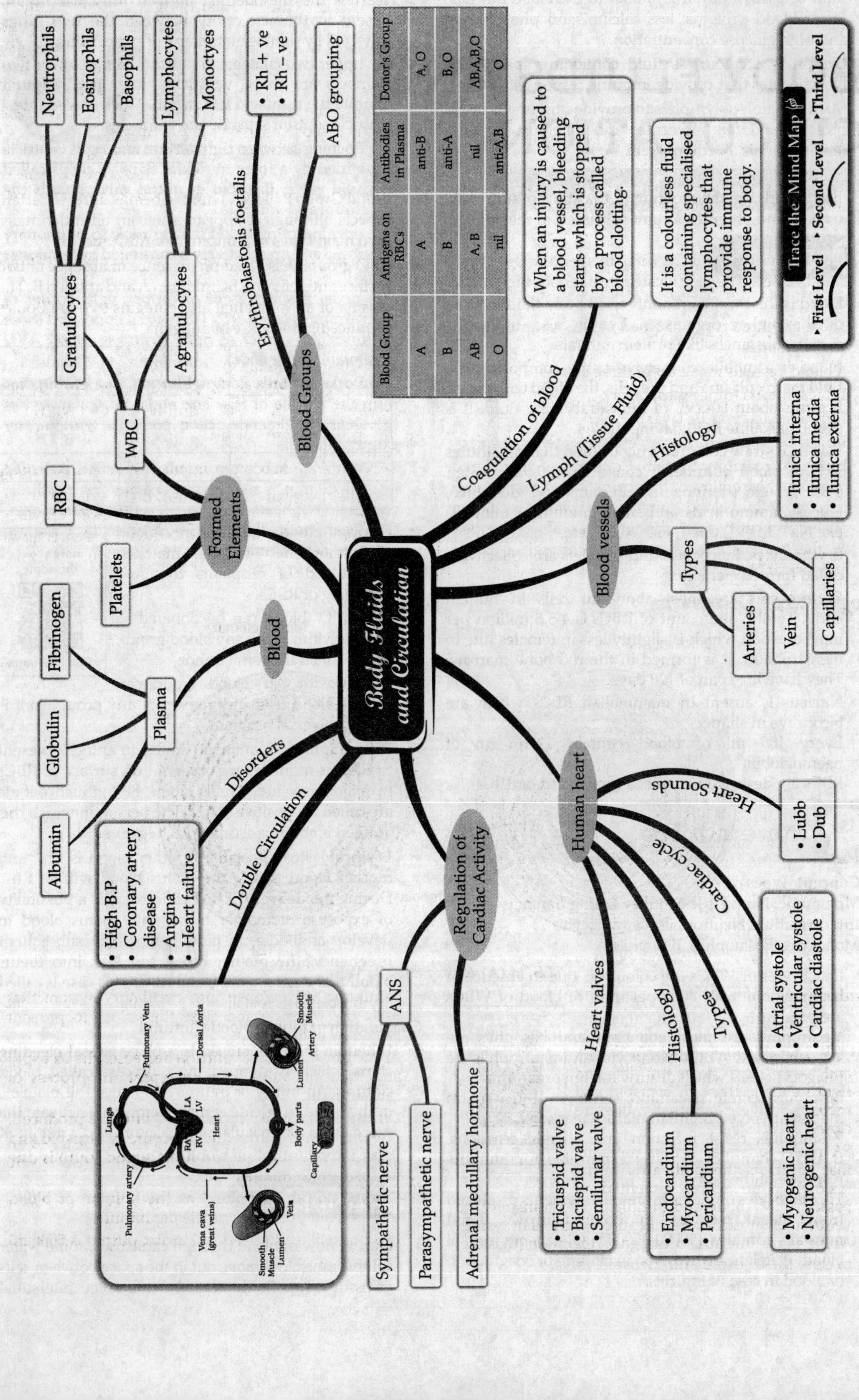

Blood Group	Antigens on RBCs	Antibodies in Plasma	Donor's Group
A	A	anti-B	A, O
B	B	anti-A	B, O
AB	A, B	nil	AB,A,B,O
O	nil	anti-A,B	O

fluid or tissue fluid. It is similar to the blood but has fewer blood proteins, less calcium and phosphorus and high glucose concentration.

- Lymph is a colourless fluid containing specialised lymphocytes that provide immune response to body.
- Main function of lymph is to provide immunity, carry proteins and fats molecules and transport oxygen, food materials, hormones, etc.

Circulatory Pathways

Blood vessels

- Blood moves around the body in special tubes called blood vessels. They are located throughout the human body.
- There are three types of blood vessels: arteries, veins and capillaries.
- A blood vessel is made up of three layers:
  - Tunica interna (inner most layer).
  - Tunica media (middle layer).
  - Tunica externa or Tunica adventitia (outermost layer)
- **Human Circulatory System:** Consists of 4-chambered muscular heart, closed, branching blood vessels and circulatory fluid blood. Annelids and chordates have a closed circulatory system in which the blood pumped by the heart is always circulated through a closed network of blood vessels.

- Heart is the mesodermal derived muscular organ, present in thoracic cavity between the two lungs protected by double membrane of pericardium.
- The upper two chamber is called atria and lower two chambers are called ventricles. Inter-atrial septum separate the right and left atrium. Thick walled inter-ventricle septum separate the ventricles.
- The opening between right atrium and right ventricle is guarded by a three muscular flaps or cusps called tricuspid valve. Bicuspid or mitral valve guards the left atrium and ventricle.
- The opening of right and left ventricle to pulmonary artery and aorta respectively is controlled by semilunar valve.
- The nodal tissue present on upper right corner of right atrium is called SAN (sino-atrial node) and those on lower left corner of right atrium is called AVN (atrio-ventricular node).
- The Purkinje fibres along with right and left bundles form the bundle of His. The nodal musculature has the ability to generate action potential without any external stimuli.
- SAN generate maximum number of action potential i.e., 70-75 min^{-1} and is responsible for rhythmic contraction of heart. Therefore it is called pacemaker. Our heart normally beats 70-75 times in a minute (average 72 beats min^{-1})

Important Diagram

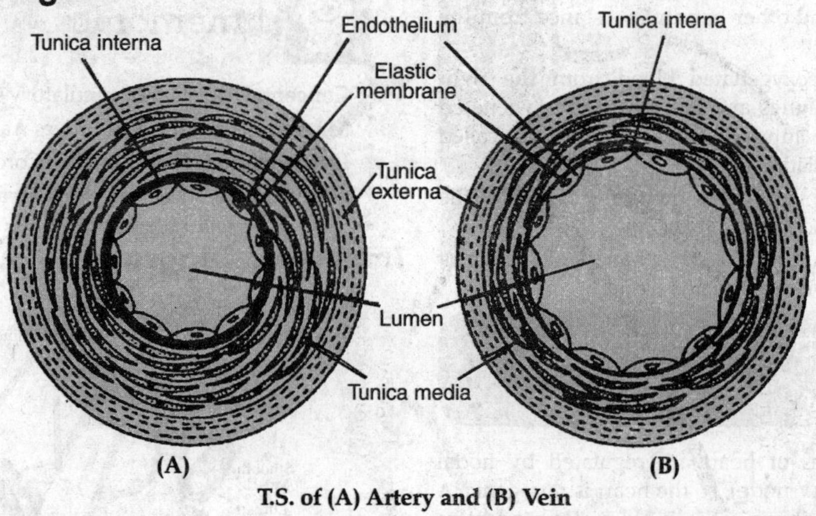

T.S. of (A) Artery and (B) Vein

Cardiac Cycle

Scan to know more about this topic

Human Heart

- To begin with, all four chambers are in relaxed state called joint diastole. The blood from pulmonary vein and vena cava flows to left and right ventricle through bicuspid and tricuspid valve. Semilunar valves are closed at this stage.
- SA node generates action potential that contracts the both atria (atrial systole). The action potential is passed to AV node and bundle of HIS transmit it to ventricular musculature to cause ventricular systole. At the same time atria undergoes relaxation (diastole) to close the bicuspid and tricuspid valve.
- Semilunar valves open into circulatory system that relax the ventricle and close the valves to prevent back flow of blood.
- As the pressure inside ventricle decreases the bicuspid and tricuspid valve open to repeat the process of cardiac cycle.
- During each cardiac cycle two sounds are produced. The first sound (lub) is due to closure of bicuspid and tricuspid valve and second heart sound (dub) is due to closure of semilunar valve.
- Cardiac output is defined as the volume of blood pumped out by each ventricle per minute.
- In a normal healthy person, cardiac output is 5000 ml or 5 L on an average.

- ECG (Electrocardiograph) is a graphical representation of electrical activity of heart during cardiac cycle. The electrocardiograph machine is used to obtain electrocardiogram. The patient is connected to three electrical leads to wrists and left ankle.
- The P-wave represents the electrical excitation of atria (depolarisation) which leads to contraction of atria.
- The QRS-wave represents the depolarisation of ventricles, which initiates the ventricular contraction.
- The T-wave represents the return of ventricle from excited to normal state (repolarisation).
- The end of T-wave marks the end of systole. Counting the number of QRS complex in given period of time determine the heartbeat rate.

Double Circulation

- Flow of same blood twice through the heart once in oxygenated form and other in deoxygenated form is called double circulation. It includes systematic and pulmonary circulation.
- Systemic circulation includes flow of oxygenated blood from the left ventricle to all parts of body and deoxygenated blood from various body parts enters into the right atrium. All systemic circulation starts form aorta and ends at superior vena cava, inferior vena cava or coronary sinus to right atrium.
- The systemic system provides oxygen, nutrients and other substance to the tissues of different body parts and take CO_2 and other harmful substance from the body parts.
- The flow of deoxygenated blood from the right ventricle to the lungs and the return of oxygenated blood from the lung to the left atrium is called pulmonary circulation.
- Two pulmonary veins from each lung transport the oxygenated blood to the left atrium.
- Double circulation reduces the chances of mixing of oxygenated and deoxygenated blood.

Regulation of Cardiac Activity

- Normal activities of heart are regulated by nodal tissue (SA and AV node), so the heart is myogenic. A special neural centre in medulla oblongata moderates the cardiac function by ANS. Sympathetic nerve increase the rate of heart beat and parasympathetic nerve of ANS decreases the rate of heart beat. Adrenal medullary hormone also increases the cardiac output.

Disorder of Circulatory System

(a) **Hypertension (high blood pressure):** Blood pressure higher than (120/80). 120 mm Hg is the systolic that is pumping pressure and 80 mm Hg is the diastole, resting pressure. High blood pressure leads to heart disease and affect vital organs like brain and kidney.

(b) **Coronary Artery Disease (CAD):** Commonly known as atherosclerosis that affects the blood vessels that supply blood to heart muscles due to deposition of fat, calcium, cholesterol that makes the arteries lumen narrower.

(c) **Angina also called angina pectoris:** Acute chest pain due to less supply of oxygen to heart muscles. It may occur in elderly male and female. It occurs due to restricted blood flow.

(d) **Heart failure:** In this, heart does not pump enough blood to meet the requirement of body. It is also known as congestive heart failure because congestion of lung is one of its symptoms. Heart failure is different from heart attack (heart muscle is damaged by inadequate blood supply) and cardiac arrest (when heart stops beating).

Mnemonics

Concept: Disorders of circulatory system.

Mnemonic: High Court orders Aa gaye Hai

Interpretation: Hypertension, Coronary artery disease, Angina pectoris, Heart Failure.

Important Diagram

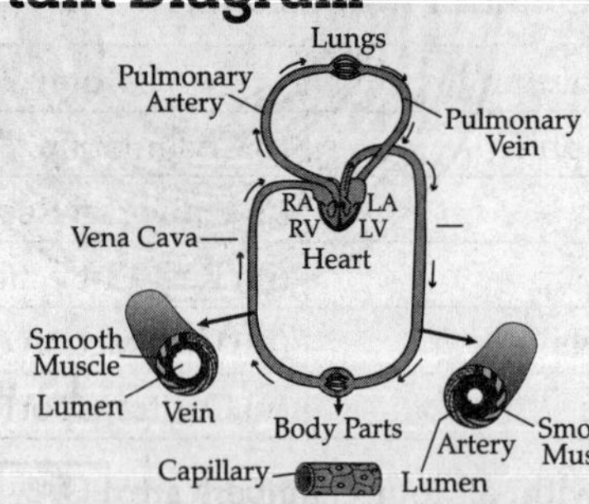

Double circulation in Humans

Key Words

- **Blood:** Red colour fluid connective tissue, composed of a fluid, plasma and the cells, the blood corpuscles.
- **Lymph node:** Small, oval or bean shaped structures located along the length of lymphatic vessels.
- **Plasma:** Pale, straw coloured fluid, occupying about one half of total blood volume.
- **Cardiac cycle:** Sequence of events that occur during single heart beat is called cardiac cycle.
- **Systemic circulation:** Circulation of blood between heart and body is called systemic circulation.
- **Cardiac output:** Amount of blood pumped by heart per minute is called cardiac output.
- **Pulse rate:** Number of times the heart beats in a minute is known as pulse rate.

NCERT CORNER

Q. 1. Name the components of the formed elements in the blood and mention one major function of each of them. **[NCERT Ex. Q. 1, Page 204]**

Ans. Components of formed elements are:

(i) Erythrocytes or Red Blood Cells (RBC): These cells contain a red colour pigment called haemoglobin. It is the haemoglobin that carries oxygen and transports it to all parts of the body. There are about 4-6 million RBCs per mm^3 of blood.

(ii) Leucocytes or White Blood Cells (WBC): They have a major role to play in defence system of body. It is divided into two main categories:

(a) Granulocytes: It is of three types: Neutrophils, basophils, and eosinophils. Neutrophils are phagocytic cells that protect the body against various infecting agents. Eosinophils are associated with allergic reactions while basophils are involved in inflammatory responses.

(b) Agranulocytes: It is of two types: Lymphocytes and monocytes. Lymphocytes generate immune responses against infecting agents while monocytes are phagocytic in nature.

(iii) Platelets (Thrombocytes): Platelets release blood clotting chemicals at the site of injury. These chemical form a clot and prevent further bleeding.

Q. 2. What is the importance of plasma proteins? **[NCERT Ex. Q. 2, Page 204]**

Ans. Plasma proteins includes fibrinogen, globulin and albumin

(i) Fibrinogen: It plays a role in the clotting of blood.

(ii) Globulin: It protects the body against infectious agents. It acts as antibodies.

(iii) Albumin: It helps in maintaining the fluid volume within the vascular space. It also regulates the blood pressure.

Q. 3. Match Column I with Column II:

Column I	Column II
(a) Eosinophils	(i) Coagulation
(b) RBC	(ii) Universal Recipient
(c) AB Group	(iii) Resist Infections
(d) Platelets	(iv) Contraction of Heart
(e) Systole	(v) Gas transport

[NCERT Ex. Q. 3, Page 204]

Ans.

Column I	Column II
(a) Eosinophils	(iii) Resist infections
(b) RBC	(v) Gas transport
(c) AB Group	(ii) Universal Recipient
(d) Platelets	(i) Coagulation
(e) Systole	(iv) Contraction of Heart

Q. 4. Why do we consider blood as a connective tissue? **[NCERT Ex. Q. 4, Page 204]**

Ans. Blood is considered as a type of connective tissue because:

(i) Like the other connective tissues, blood is mesodermal in origin.

(ii) It connects the body systems, transports oxygen and nutrients to all the parts of the body, and removes the waste products. Blood has an extra-cellular matrix called plasma, with red blood cells, white blood cells, and platelets floating in it.

Q. 5. What is the difference between lymph and blood? **[NCERT Ex. Q. 5, Page 204]**

Ans. Difference between Lymph and Blood:

	Blood	Lymph
(i)	It is a red-coloured fluid that contains RBCs.	It is a colourless fluid that does not contain RBCs.
(ii)	It contains plasma, RBCs, WBCs, and platelets.	It contains plasma, and lesser number of WBCs.
(iii)	It is involved in circulation of oxygen and carbon dioxide.	It helps in body defence and is a part of immune system.
(iv)	Its plasma has proteins, calcium, and phosphorus.	Its plasma has fewer proteins, and less calcium and phosphorus.
(v)	It transports materials towards and away from the tissue.	It transports materials from the body cell to the blood vice versa.
(vi)	The flow of blood in the blood vessels is fast.	The flow of lymph is slow.

Q. 6. What is meant by double circulation? What is its significance? **[NCERT Ex. Q. 6, Page 204]**

Ans. A mechanism in which blood circulates twice through the heart in one complete cycle is known as double circulation. Systemic circulation and pulmonary circulation are two pathways in which the blood flows in double circulation.

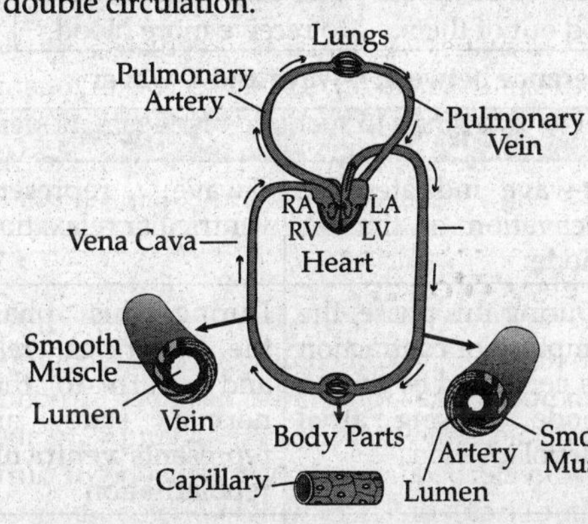

(i) The pulmonary circulation begins by pumping of deoxygenated blood by right ventricle. It is carried to the lungs and then it returns to left atrium as oxygenated blood.

(ii) The systemic circulation begins with pumping of oxygenated blood by the left ventricle to aorta. It is carried to all body tissues and deoxygenated blood from there is collected by the veins and then returned to the right auricle of heart.

(iii) Blood circulates twice, hence it is called double circulation.

Importance: The deoxygenated and oxygenated blood remain separated and do not mix.

Q. 7. Write the differences between:
(i) Blood and Lymph
(ii) Open and closed system of circulation
(iii) Systole and Diastole
(iv) P- wave and T-wave [NCERT Ex. Q. 7, Page 204]

Ans. (i) Differences between Blood and lymph: For answer, refer to NCERT CORNER/ Q 5

(ii) Differences between Open and Closed system of circulation:

Open circulatory system	Closed circulatory system
In this type of circulatory system, the hemolymph directly bathes the organs and tissues	In the closed circulatory system, blood circulates within closed vessels.
In an open circulatory system, gases are not transported.	In a closed circulatory system, gases are transported.
In an open circulatory system blood flow is slow.	Blood flow is fast in the closed circulatory system.
Present in mollusks and arthropods.	Present in annelids and vertebrates.

(iii) Differences between systole and diastole:

Systole	Diastole
Contraction of the heart chambers to drive blood into the aorta and the pulmonary artery is systole.	Relaxation of the heart chambers between two contractions is diastole. During diastole, the chambers are filled with blood.
Systole decreases the volume of the heart chambers and forces the blood out of them.	Diastole brings the heart chambers back into their original sizes to receive more blood.

(iv) Difference between P-wave and T-wave:

S. No.	P-wave	T-wave
(i)	P-wave indicates the activation of the SA node.	T-wave represents ventricular relaxation.
(ii)	During this phase, the impulse of contraction is generated by the SA node, causing atrial depolarisation.	During this phase, the ventricles relax and return to their normal state and represents ventricular repolarisation.
(iii)	It is of atrial origin.	It is of ventricular origin.

Q. 8. Describe the evolutionary change in the pattern of heart among the vertebrates.
[NCERT Ex. Q. 8, Page 204]

Ans. The evolution of the heart is based on the separation of oxygenated blood from deoxygenated blood for efficient oxygen transport. In fishes, the heart was like a hollow tube. They had only two chambers in its heart – one auricle and one ventricle. This evolved into the four-chambered heart in mammals.

Q. 9. Why do we call our heart myogenic?
[NCERT Ex. Q. 9, Page 204]

Ans. Human heart is myogenic as the contraction is initiated by a special modified heart muscle known as sino-atrial node (SA node). It is located in the right atrium. The SA node has the inherent power of generating a wave of contraction and controlling the heartbeat. Hence, it is known as the pacemaker.

Q.10. Sino-atrial node is called the pacemaker of our heart. Why? [NCERT Ex. Q. 10, Page 204]

Ans. The heart beat is originated at sino-atrial node. Since the SA node is responsible for initiating and maintaining the rhythmic contractile activity of the heart, it is called the pacemaker.

Q.11. What is the significance of atrio-ventricular node and atrio-ventricular bundle in the functioning of heart? [NCERT Ex. Q. 11, Page 204]

Ans. Significance of AV Node and AV Bundle in the functioning of Heart:

(i) AV node is a nodal tissue located in the lower left corner of right atrium very close to atrio-ventricular septum.

(ii) AV bundle continues from AV node and passes through the atrio-ventricular septum and emerges on the top of the inter-ventricular septum and; divides into 2 branches; left and right bundle of His. These bundles send branches and form minute fibres called Purkinje fibres throughout the muscle of ventricles on both sides.

(iii) AV node is also auto excitable like SA node. It has ability to generate action potential without any external stimuli. The AV node picks up the wave of contraction originated by SA node.

Q.12. Define a cardiac cycle and the cardiac output.
[NCERT Ex. Q. 12, Page 204]

Ans. Cardiac cycle: It is defined as the complete cycle of events in the heart from the beginning of one heart beat to the beginning of the next.

Cardiac output: It is the volume of blood pumped out by each ventricle per minute, i.e., stroke volume × heart rate

Q.13. Explain heart sounds.[NCERT Ex. Q. 13, Page 204]

Ans. The beating of heart produces characteristic sounds which can be heard by placing the ear against the chest or by using stethoscope. In a normal person, two sounds are produced per heartbeat.

(i) First sound: This is caused partly by the closure of the bicuspid and tricuspid valves and partly by the contraction of the muscles in the ventricles. The first sound, 'lubb' is low pitched, not very loud and of long duration.

(ii) **Second sound:** This is caused by the closure of the semilunar valves and marks the end of ventricular systole. The second 'dub' is highly pitched, louder, sharper and shorter in duration.

Q.14. Draw a standard ECG and explain the different segments in it. [NCERT Ex. Q. 14, Page 204]

Ans. ECG is graphic record of the electric current produced by the excitation of the cardiac muscles.

The instrument used to record the change is an electrocardiograph.

Components: (i) A normal electrocardiogram (ECG) is composed of a P-wave, a QRS wave (complex) and a T-wave.

(ii) The letters are arbitrarily selected and do not stand for any particular words.

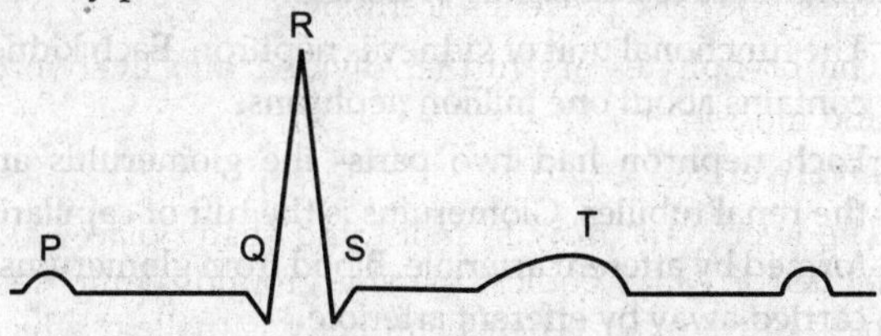

Diagrammatic presentation of a standard ECG

(iii) The P wave is a small upward wave that indicates the depolarisation of the atria. It is caused by the activation of SA node.

(iv) The QRS wave (complex) begins after a fraction of second of the P wave. It represents ventricular depolarisation (ventricular contraction). It is caused by the impulses of the contraction from AV node through the bundle of His and Purkinje fibres and marks the beginning of the systole.

(v) The T-wave is a dome-shaped which indicates ventricular repolarisation (ventricular relaxation).

The potential generated by the recovery of the ventricle from the depolarisation state is called the repolarisation wave.

(vi) Normal P-R interval is 0.12 to 0.2 sec. Normal QRS complex duration is 0.12 sec. Normal Q-T interval is 0.4 sec. The important of ECG is that it give accurate information about the heart. Therefore, ECG is of great diagnostic value in cardiac diseases.

□□

EXCRETORY PRODUCTS AND THEIR ELIMINATION

CHAPTER 16

Mode of Excretion

- Elimination of metabolic waste products from the animal body to regulate the composition of body fluids and tissues is called excretion. These waste products includes ammonia, uric acid, urea, carbon dioxide and ions like Na^+, K^+, Cl^- and phosphates and sulphate.
- Ammonia is the most toxic and **uric acid** is the least toxic. The process of removing ammonia is called **ammonotelism** and organisms that excrete ammonia are called **ammonotelic** (bony fishes, aquatic amphibians and insects).
- The organisms that release urea as nitrogenous wastes are called **ureotelic** (mammals, terrestrial amphibians).
- The organism that excretes uric acid are called **urecotelic** (reptiles, birds and land snails).
- Protonephridia or flame cells are the excretory structures in Platyhelminthes (e.g., *Planaria*), some annelids and the cephalochordata (e.g., *Amphioxus*).
- Nephridia are the excretory structures of earth worms and other annelids.
- Malpighian tubules are the excretory structures of most of the insects for example-Cockroaches.
- Antennal glands or green glands perform the excretory function in crustaceans like prawns.

Human Excretory System

- ► Human excretory system consists of
- A pair of kidneys
- A pair of ureters
- A urinary bladder
- A urethra
- ► **Kidneys** are reddish brown bean shaped structure situated between last thoracic and lumbar vertebra.

Scan to know more about this topic

Ammonotelism

- ► Each has a notch on its inner side called hilum through which ureter, blood vessels and nerves enter.
- ► Inside the hilum is a broad funnel shaped space called renal pelvis with projection called calyces.
- ► Inside the kidney are two zone- outer cortex and inner medulla. Medulla is divided into medullary pyramids projecting into calyx.
- ► Cortex extends between medullary pyramids as renal column called **Columns of Bertini**.
- ► The functional unit of kidney is nephron. Each kidney contains about one million nephrons.
- ► Each nephron had two parts- the glomerulus and the renal tubules. Glomerulus is the tuft of capillaries formed by afferent arteriole. Blood from glomerulus is carried away by efferent arteriole.
- ► Renal tubules starts with Bowman's capsule and continue with tubular parts divided into proximal convoluted tubules, Henle's loop and distal convoluted tubule.
- ► The malpighian tubules, PCT and DCT of nephron are situated in cortical region whereas loops of Henle's into medulla.

Urine formation

- Urine formation includes three processes Glomerular filtration, reabsorption and secretion.
- The first step in urine formation is the filtration of blood, which is carried out by the glomerulus and is called glomerular filtration.
- The amount of the filtrate formed by the kidneys per minute is called glomerular filtration rate (GFR), which is approximately 125 mL/minute i.e., 180 litres per day, in a healthy individual.
- Nearby 99 percent of the filtrate is reabsorbed by the renal tubules and this process is called reabsorption.
- Tubular secretion is also an important step in urine formation as it helps in the maintenance of ionic and acid base balance of body fluids.

Function of Tubules

- **Proximal Convoluted Tubules (PCT):** All the important nutrients, 70-80% electrolytes and water are reabsorbed.
- **Henle's Loop:** Maintains high osmolarity of medullary interstitial fluid.
- **Distal Convoluted Tubules (DCT):** Conditional reabsorption of Na^+ and water. Maintain pH and sodium- potassium balance.
- **Collecting Duct:** Large amount of water is reabsorbed to produce concentrated urine.

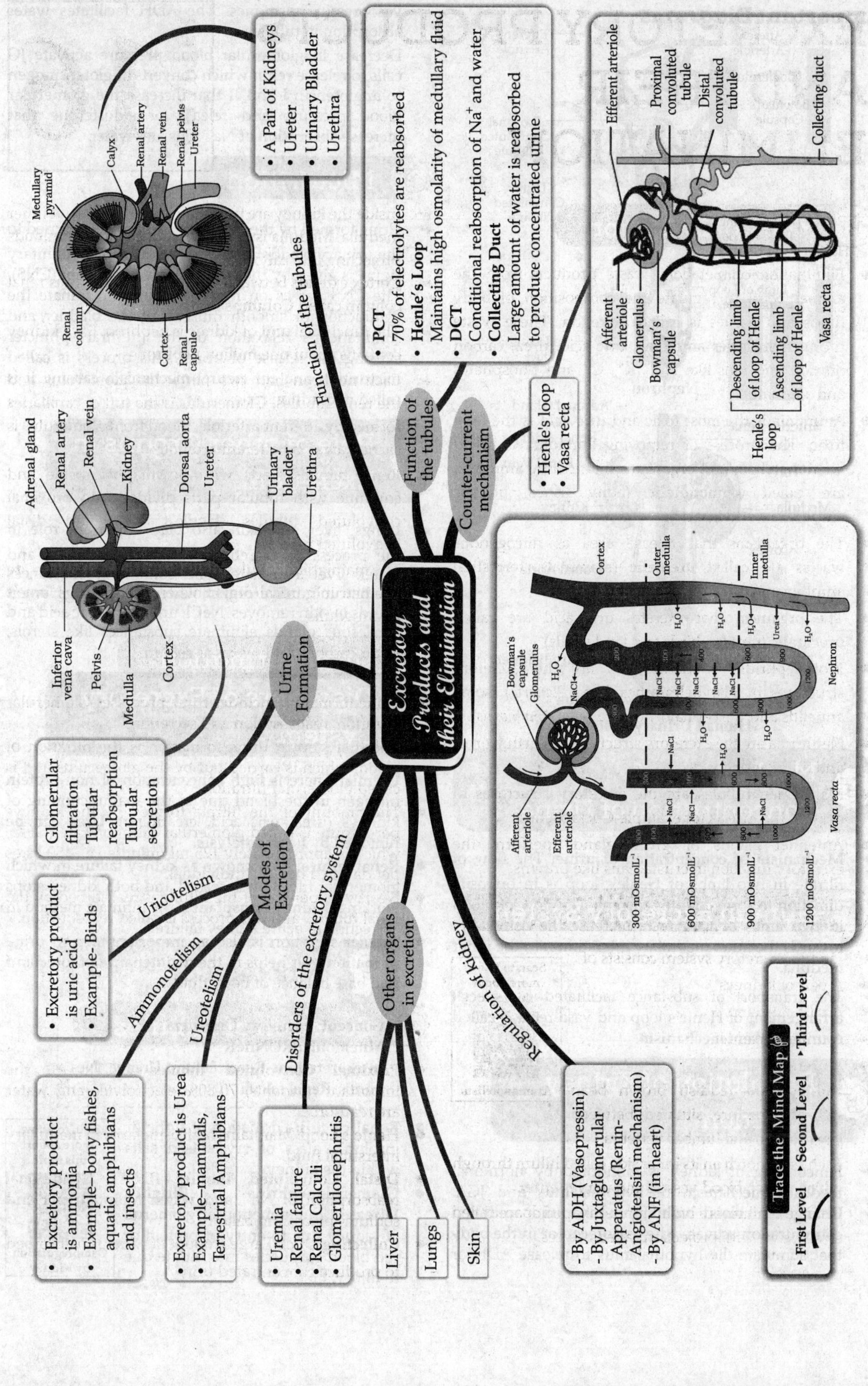
Excretory Products and their Elimination
Urine Formation
Glomerular filtration
Tubular reabsorption
Tubular secretion
Function of the tubules
• A Pair of Kidneys
• Ureter
• Urinary Bladder
• Urethra
Medullary pyramid
Calyx
Renal artery
Renal vein
Renal pelvis
Ureter
Renal column
Cortex
Renal capsule
Adrenal gland
Renal artery
Renal vein
Kidney
Dorsal aorta
Ureter
Urinary bladder
Urethra
Inferior vena cava
Pelvis
Medulla
Cortex
Function of the tubules
• PCT
70% of electrolytes are reabsorbed
• Henle's Loop
Maintains high osmolarity of medullary fluid
• DCT
Conditional reabsorption of Na+ and water
• Collecting Duct
Large amount of water is reabsorbed to produce concentrated urine
Counter-current mechanism
• Henle's loop
• Vasa recta
Afferent arteriole
Glomerulus
Bowman's capsule
Efferent arteriole
Proximal convoluted tubule
Distal convoluted tubule
Collecting duct
Descending limb of loop of Henle
Ascending limb of loop of Henle
Henle's loop
Vasa recta
Afferent arteriole
Efferent arteriole
Bowman's capsule
Glomerulus
Cortex
Outer medulla
Inner medulla
300 mOsmolL-1
600 mOsmolL-1
900 mOsmolL-1
1200 mOsmolL-1
NaCl
H2O
Urea
Vasa recta
Nephron
Modes of Excretion
Uricotelism
• Excretory product is uric acid
• Example- Birds
Ammonotelism
• Excretory product is ammonia
• Example–bony fishes, aquatic amphibians and insects
Ureotelism
• Excretory product is Urea
• Example–mammals, Terrestrial Amphibians
Disorders of the excretory system
• Uremia
• Renal failure
• Renal Calculi
• Glomerulonephritis
Other organs in excretion
Liver
Lungs
Skin
Regulation of kidney
- By ADH (Vasopressin)
- By Juxtaglomerular Apparatus (Renin-Angiotensin mechanism)
- By ANF (in heart)
Trace the Mind Map
First Level
Second Level
Third Level

Important Diagrams

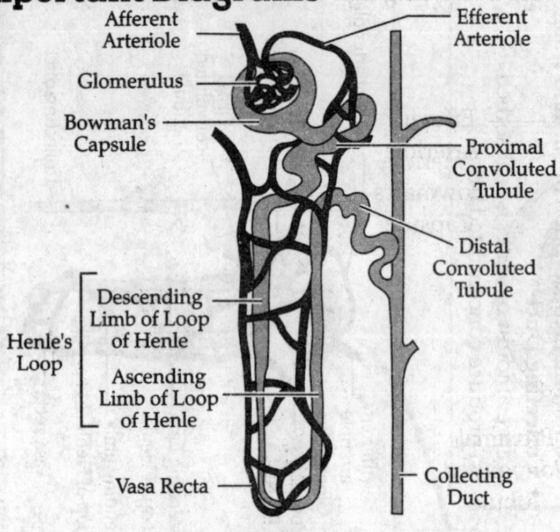

Nephron

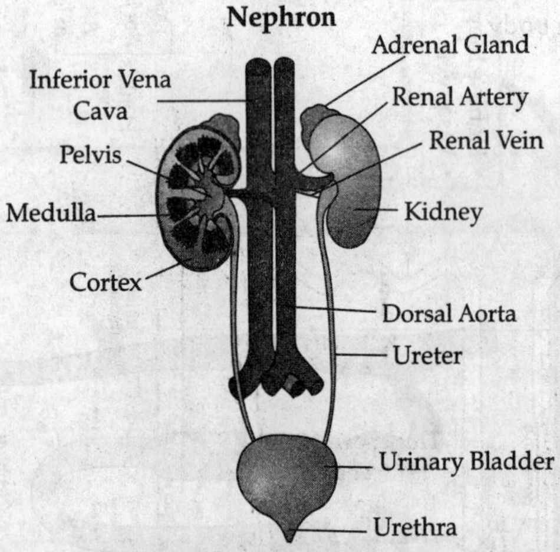

Human Urinary System

Mechanism of Concentration of Urine

- **Mechanism of concentration of urine:** The flow of filtrate in two limbs of Henle's loop is in opposite direction to form counter current. The flow of blood in two limbs of vasa recta increase the osmolarity towards the inner medullary interstitium in the inner medulla.
- The transport of substance facilitated by special arrangement of Henle's loop and vasa recta is called counter **current mechanism**.

Regulation of Kidney Function

- Functioning of kidney is monitored by hormonal feedback mechanism of hypothalamus and JGA. Change in blood volume, body fluid and ion concentration activates the osmoreceptor in the body that stimulate the hypothalamus to release ADH or vasopressin hormones. The ADH facilitates water absorption in tubules.
- Decrease in glomerular blood pressure activate JG cells to release renin which converts angiotensinogen to angiotensin I and II that increase the glomerular blood pressure and release of aldosterone that increase absorption of Na^+ ions and water.

Micturition

- Urine formed by the nephrons is ultimately carried to the urinary bladder where it is stored till a voluntary signal is given by the control Nervous system (CNS). The CNS passes on motor messages to initiate the contraction of smooth muscles of the bladder and simultaneous relaxation of the urethral sphincter causing the release of urine. This process is called micturition and the neural mechanism causing it is called micturition reflex.

Role of other Organs in Excretion

- Lungs, liver and skin also play important role in the process of excretion. Lungs remove CO_2 and water, liver eliminates bile containing substances like bilirubin biliverdin, cholesterol and drugs, sweat glands in skin removes, NaCl, urea and lactic acid and Sebaceous glands eliminate substances like sterols, hydrocarbons and waxes as sebum.

Disorders of Excretory System

- **Uremia:** There is high concentration of non-protein nitrogen in the blood due to the malfunctioning of kidneys (urea, uric acid, creatinine). **Urea can be removed by haemodialysis.**
- **Renal failure:** Also known as kidney failure in which glomerular filtration is ceased and both kidney stops working. **Kidney transplant** is the ultimate method in correction of acute kidney failure.

Mnemonics

Concept: Excretory Disorders
Mnemonic: RUNneR
Interpretation: Renal failure, Uremia, Nephritis, Renal calculi.

- **Renal calculi:** Formation of stone or insoluble mass of crystallised salts within the kidney.
- **Glomerulonephritis (Bright's Disease):** Inflammation of glomeruli of kidney due to entry of protein or red blood corpuscles into filtrate due to injury.

Scan to know more about this topic

Osmoregulation by Kidney

- **Haemodialysis:** In patients with uremia, urea is removed by haemodialysis. During the process, the blood drained from a convenient artery is pumped into a dialysing unit called **artificial kidney.**

Important Diagrams

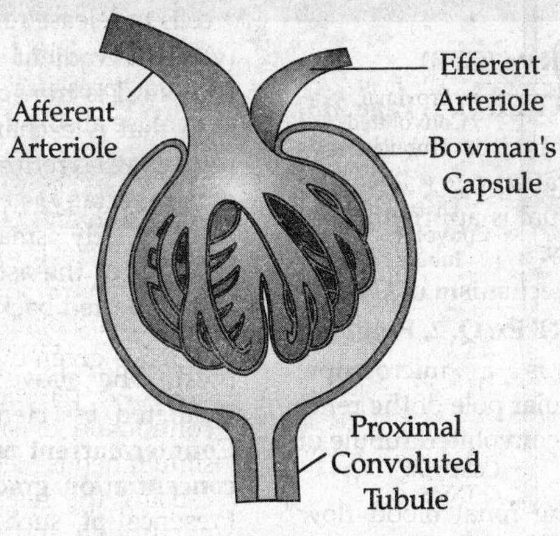

Malphigian body

Structure of renal corpuscle:

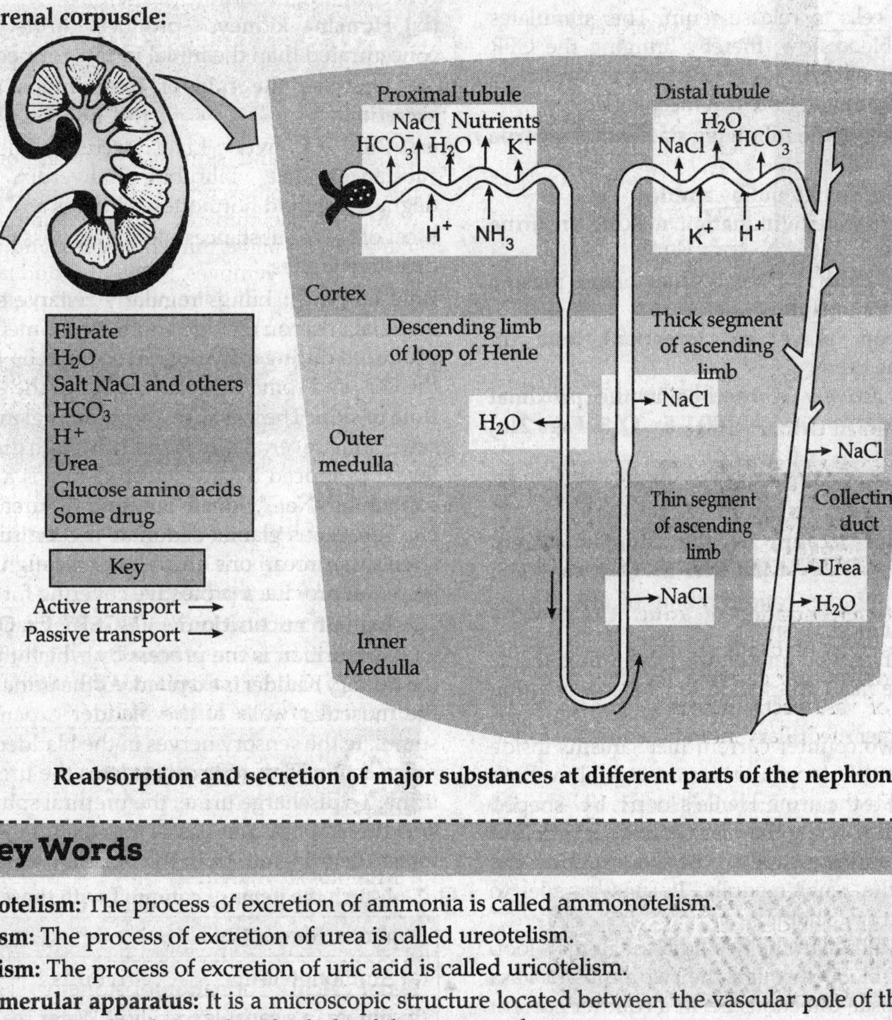

Reabsorption and secretion of major substances at different parts of the nephron

Key Words

- **Ammonotelism:** The process of excretion of ammonia is called ammonotelism.
- **Ureotelism:** The process of excretion of urea is called ureotelism.
- **Uricotelism:** The process of excretion of uric acid is called uricotelism.
- **Juxtaglomerular apparatus:** It is a microscopic structure located between the vascular pole of the renal corpuscle and the returning distal convoluted tubule of the same nephron.
- **Osmoregulation:** Osmoregulation is a homeostatic mechanism that regulates the optimum temperature of water and salts in the tissues and body fluids.
- **Osmolarity:** The total concentration of solutes in a solution.

NCERT CORNER

Q. 1. Define Glomerular Filtration Rate (GFR) **[NCERT Ex. Q. 1, Page 215]**

Ans. The amount of the filtrate formed by the kidneys per minute is called glomerular filtration rate (GFR). The value of GFR in a healthy individual is approximately 125 ml/minute i.e., 180 litres per day.

Q. 2. Explain the auto-regulatory mechanism of GFR. **[NCERT Ex. Q. 2, Page 215]**

Ans. Juxtaglomerular apparatus is a microscopic structure located between the vascular pole of the renal corpuscle and the returning distal convoluted tubule of the same nephron.

It plays a major role in regulating renal blood flow and glomerular filtration rate (GFR). When there is a fall in the glomerular filtration rate, it activates the juxtaglomerular cells to release renin. This stimulates the glomerular blood flow, thereby bringing the GFR back to normal. Renin brings the GFR back to normal by the activation of renin-angiotensin mechanism.

Q. 3. Indicate whether the following statements are true or false:

(i) Micturition is carried out by a reflex.

(ii) ADH helps in water elimination, making the urine hypotonic.

(iii) Protein-free fluid is filtered from blood plasma into the Bowman's capsule.

(iv) Henle's loop plays an important role in concentrating the urine.

(v) Glucose is actively reabsorbed in the proximal convoluted tubule. **[NCERT Ex. Q. 3, Page 215]**

Ans. (i) True **(ii)** False

(iii) True **(iv)** True

(v) True

Q. 4. Give a brief account on the counter current mechanism. **[NCERT Ex. Q. 4, Page 215]**

Ans. Mechanism of the concentration of the filtrate (Counter current mechanism):

(i) The counter current mechanism operating inside the kidney is the main adaptation for the conservation of water.

(ii) There are two counter current mechanisms inside the kidneys: Henle's loop and vasa recta. They both help to concentrate the urine. Henle's loop is a U-shaped part of the nephron, while the vasa recta are an efferent arteriole, which forms a capillary network around the tubules inside the renal medulla. It runs parallel to Henle's loop and is U-shaped.

(iii) The flow of filtrate in the two limbs of Henle's loop and the flow of blood through the two limbs of vasa recta are in opposite directions i.e. in a counter current pattern.

(iv) The proximity between the Henle's loop and vasa recta, as well as the counter current in them help to maintain an increasing osmolarity towards the inner medullary interstitium, i.e., from 300 $mOsmolL^{-1}$ in the cortex to about 1200 $mOsmolL^{-1}$ in the inner medulla.

(v) This gradient is mainly caused by NaCl and urea.

(vi) NaCl is transported by ascending limb of Henle's loop that is exchanged with descending limb of vasa recta. NaCl is returned to interstitium by ascending limb of vasa recta.

(vii) Similarly, small amount of urea enter the thin segment of the ascending limb of Henle's loop which is transported back to the interstitium by the collecting tubule.

(viii) The above described transport of substances facilitated by Henle's loop and vasa recta is called **Counter current mechanism.** This helps to maintain a **concentration gradient** in the medullary interstitium. Presence of such **interstitial gradient** helps in an easy passage of water from collecting tubule thereby concentrating the filtrate (urine).

(ix) Human kidneys produce urine four times concentrated than the initial filtrate formed.

Q. 5. Describe the role of liver, lungs and skin in excretion. **[NCERT Ex. Q. 5, Page 215]**

Ans. Role of liver: Liver secretes bile containing substances like bilirubin, biliverdin, cholesterol, degraded steroid hormones, vitamins and drugs.

Most of these substances ultimately pass out along with digestive wastes.

Role of lungs: Lungs regularly remove some volatile materials, carbon dioxide and water as metabolic wastes produced during oxidation of food in cells. Lung remove the CO_2 and some water as vapour in the expired air.

Role of skin: The sweat and sebaceous glands in the skin can eliminate certain substances through their secretions. Sweat produced by the sweat glands is a watery fluid containing NaCl, small amount of urea, lactic acid, etc. Sebaceous glands eliminate certain substances like sterols, hydrocarbons and waxes through sebum. This secretion provide a protective covering for the skin.

Q. 6. Explain micturition? **[NCERT Ex. Q. 6, Page 215]**

Ans. Micturition is the process by which the urine from the urinary bladder is excreted. As the urine accumulates, the muscular walls of the bladder expand. The walls stimulate the sensory nerves in the bladder, setting up a reflex action. This reflex stimulates the urge to pass out urine. To discharge urine, the urethral sphincter relaxes and the smooth muscles of the bladder contract. This forces the urine out from the bladder.

Q. 7. Match the items of column I with those of column II:

Column I	Column II
(a) Ammonotelism	(i) Birds
(b) Bowman's capsule	(ii) Water reabsorption
(c) Micturition	(iii) Bony fish
(d) Uricotelism	(iv) Urinary bladder
(d) ADH	(v) Renal tubule

[NCERT Ex. Q. 7, Page 215]

Ans.

Column I	Column II
(a) Ammonotelism	(iii) Bony fish
(b) Bowman's capsule	(v) Renal tubule
(c) Micturition	(iv) Urinary bladder
(d) Uricotelism	(i) Birds
(d) ADH	(ii) Water reabsorption

Q. 8. What is meant by the term osmoregulation?

[NCERT Ex. Q. 8, Page 216]

Ans. Osmoregulation is a process that regulates the body's salt and water concentration.

Q. 9. Terrestrial animals are generally either ureotelic or uricotelic, not ammonotelic, why ?

[NCERT Ex. Q. 9, Page 216]

Ans. It is because:

(i) Ammonia is highly toxic in nature. Therefore, it needs to be converted into a less toxic form such as urea or uric acid.

(ii) Terrestrial animals need to conserve water. Since ammonia is soluble in water, it cannot be eliminated continuously. Hence, it is converted into urea or uric acid. These forms are less toxic and also insoluble in water. This helps terrestrial animals conserve water.

Q.10. What is the significance of juxta glomerular apparatus (JGA) in kidney function?

[NCERT Ex. Q. 10, Page 216]

Ans. Significance of juxta glomerular apparatus:

(i) The aldosterone is a hormone secreted by the adrenal gland. It controls the level of sodium in the blood.

(ii) The reabsorption is controlled by a hormone renin produced in the kidneys. The function of the renin is the conversion of angiotensinogen into angiotensin II, which is produced in the liver.

(iii) This angiotensin stimulates the adrenal cortex to secrete aldosterone. Aldosterone induces the distal nephron to reabsorb more water and Na^+.

Q.11. Name the following:

(i) A chordate animal having flame cells as excretory structures.

(ii) Cortical portions projecting between the medullary pyramids in the human kidney.

(iii) A loop of capillary running parallel to the Henle's loop. **[NCERT Ex. Q. 11, Page 216]**

Ans. (i) *Amphioxus* (Lancelet)

(ii) Columns of Bertini

(iii) Vasa recta.

Q.12. Fill in the gaps:

(i) Ascending limb of Henle's loop is _______ to water whereas the descending limb is _______ to it.

(ii) Reabsorption of water from distal parts of the tubules is facilitated by hormone _______.

(iii) Dialysis fluid contain all the constituents as in plasma except _______.

(iv) A healthy adult human excretes (on an average) _______ gm of urea/day. **[NCERT Ex. Q. 12, Page 216]**

Ans. (i) impermeable, permeable.

(ii) vasopressin or ADH.

(iii) nitrogenous wastes.

(iv) 25 – 30

CHAPTER 17

LOCOMOTION AND MOVEMENT

- **Locomotion** is the voluntary movement of an individual from one place to another. Walking, running, climbing, swimming are the example of locomotory motion. All locomotion are movement but all movements are not locomotion.

Types of Movement

- Macrophages and leucocytes in blood exhibit **amoeboid movements**. Coordinated movements of cilia in trachea to remove dusts particles and passage of ova through fallopian tube are examples of **Ciliary movements.**
- **Flagellar movement** helps in the swimming of spermatozoa, maintenance of water current in the canal system of sponges and locomotion of Protozoans like *Euglena.*
- Movement of limbs, jaw, tongue needs **muscular movement.** Contractile property of muscles are used in movement in higher organism including human beings.

Scan to know more about this topic

Introduction and Movements in Invertebrates

Muscle

- **Muscles** are specialised tissues of mesodermal origin. They have property like excitability, contractility, extensibility and elasticity.
- Based on their location, three types of muscles are identified:

(a) Skeletal muscles: They are closely associated with skeletal components of the body and are involved in locomotory actions and changes in body posture. These muscles are striated muscles and voluntary in nature.

(b) Visceral muscles: They are located in the inner walls of hollow visceral organs of the body. They are non-striated muscles or smooth muscles and involuntary in nature.

(c) Cardiac muscles: They are the muscles of heart. They are striated and involuntary in nature.

- **Skeletal muscles** are made up of muscles bundles (fascicles), held together by collagenous connective tissue called fascia.
- Each muscle bundle contains a number of muscle fibres. Each muscle fiber is lined by plasma membrane called sarcolemma enclosing sarcoplasm. Partially arranged myofibrils are present in muscle bundle having alternate light and dark bands due to the presence of protein actin and myosin.
- Light bands contain actin and is called I-band (isotropic band) and the dark band contain myosin, and is called A-band (anisotropic band). Both bands are present parallel to each other in longitudinal fashion.
- In centre of each I-band is elastic fibre called 'Z' line. In the middle of A-band is thin fibrous 'M' line. The protein of myofibrils between two successive 'Z' lines is the functional unit of contraction called a **sarcomere.**
- At resting stage, thin filament overlaps the thick filament. The part of thick filament not overlapped is called 'H' zone.
- **Structure of contractile protein:** Each thin filament (actin) is made of two 'F' actins helically wounded to each other. Two filaments of other protein tropomyosin and troponin run parallel to each other. The thick filament consists mainly of myosin protein which contributes 55% of muscle protein by weight. Myosin is split by enzyme trypsin into two fragments called light meromyosin and heavy meromyosin. Each meromyosin has globular head with short arm and tails. Globular head has ATP binding sites.
- The mechanism of muscle contraction is explained by sliding filament theory in which thin filament slide over thick filament.
- Muscle contraction start with signal sent by CNS via motor neuron. Neural signal releases neurotransmitter (Acetylcholine) to generate action potential in the sarcolemma.
- **Red fibres** (aerobic muscles) contain myoglobin (a red coloured oxygen storing pigment) that has plenty of mitochondria to utilise large amount of oxygen stored in them. The muscle fibres containing less number of myoglobin are called **white fibres.**

Skeletal System

- Framework of bones and cartilage forms the skeletal system. In human beings, it consists of 206 bones and some cartilage.

Mnemonics

Concept: Bones of cranium

Mnemonic: Old People From Texas Eat Spiders

Interpretation: Occipital, Parietal, Frontal, Temporal, Ethmoid, Sphenoid

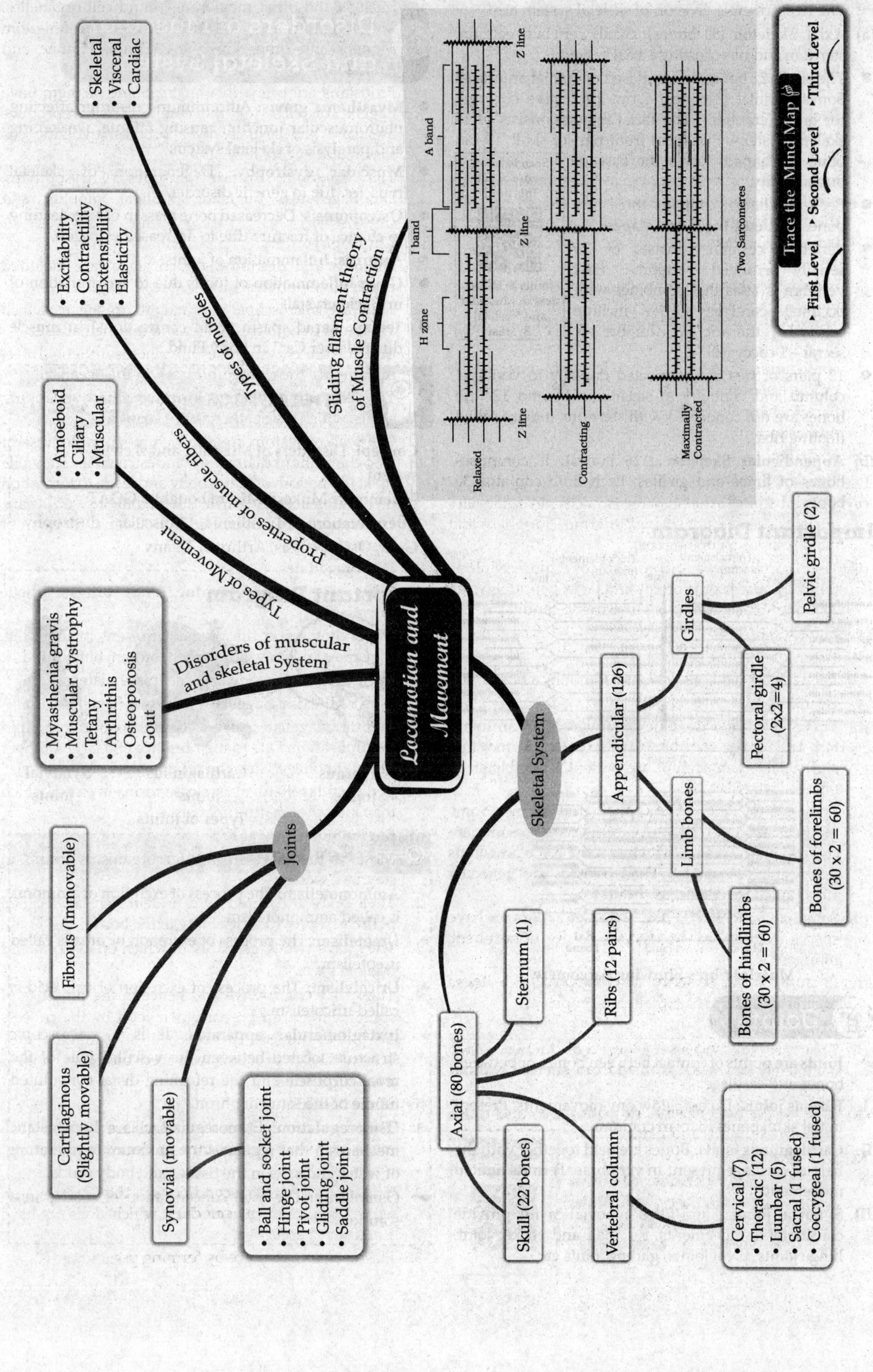
Trace the Mind Map
First Level
Second Level
Third Level
Locomotion and Movement
Types of Movement
Amoeboid
Ciliary
Muscular
Properties of muscle fibers
Excitability
Contractility
Extensibility
Elasticity
Types of muscles
Skeletal
Visceral
Cardiac
Sliding filament theory of Muscle Contraction
A band
I band
H zone
Z line
Relaxed
Contracting
Maximally Contracted
Two Sarcomeres
Disorders of muscular and skeletal System
Myasthenia gravis
Muscular dystrophy
Tetany
Arthrithis
Osteoporosis
Gout
Joints
Fibrous (Immovable)
Cartilaginous (Slightly movable)
Synovial (movable)
Ball and socket joint
Hinge joint
Pivot joint
Gliding joint
Saddle joint
Skeletal System
Axial (80 bones)
Skull (22 bones)
Sternum (1)
Ribs (12 pairs)
Vertebral column
Cervical (7)
Thoracic (12)
Lumbar (5)
Sacral (1 fused)
Coccygeal (1 fused)
Appendicular (126)
Girdles
Pectoral girdle (2x2=4)
Pelvic girdle (2)
Limb bones
Bones of forelimbs (30 x 2 = 60)
Bones of hindlimbs (30 x 2 = 60)

- The two principle division of skeletal system are:

(a) Axial Skeleton (80 bones): Skull, vertebral column, sternum and ribs constitute axial system.

- The skull (22 bones) is composed of cranial and facial bones. Cranial (8 bones) forms protective covering for brain (cranium). The facial region consists of 14 skeletal systems that form front part of skull. Hyoid bone (U-shaped) forms the base of buccal cavity.
- Each middle ear contains three tiny bones **Malleus, Incus** and **stapes.**
- Vertebral column consists of 26 serially arranged vertebrae. First vertebra is atlas that combines with occipital condyle. Other include cervical-7, thoracic -12, lumbar -5, sacral – 1 coccygeal -1.

Scan to know more about this topic

Joints & Disorders of Muscular and Skeletal System

- 12 pairs of ribs are connected dorsally to vertebral column and ventrally to sternum. 11th and 12th rib bones are not connected with sternum and are called floating ribs.

(b) Appendicular Skeleton (126 bones): It comprises bones of limbs and girdles. Each limb contains 30 bones.

Important Diagram

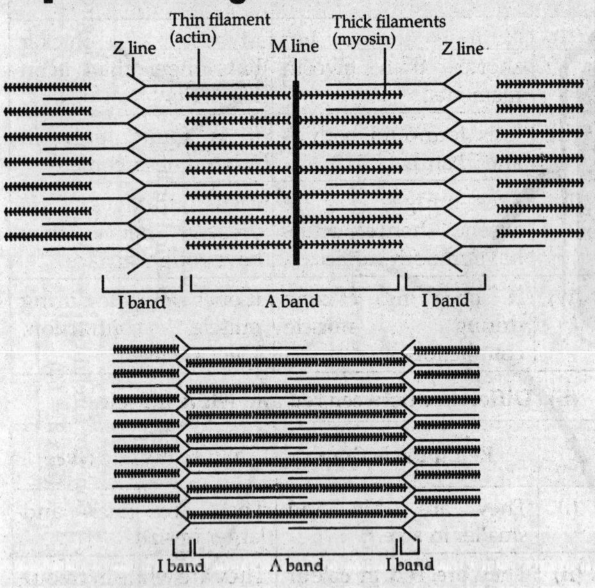

Muscles fibres Showing Sarcomere

Joints

- **Joints** are points of contact between bones, or between bones and cartilage.

I. Fibrous joints: Do not allow any movements. Present in flat skull bones to form cranium.

II. Cartilaginous joints: Bones are held together with the help of cartilage present in vertebrae. Permits limited movements.

III. Synovial joints: Fluid filled synovial cavity, provide considerable movements. *e.g.,* Ball and socket joint, hinge joints, pivot joints, gliding joints etc.

Disorders of Muscular and Skeletal System

- **Myasthenia gravis:** Auto immune disorder affecting neuromuscular junction causing fatigue, weakening and paralysis of skeletal system.
- **Muscular dystrophy:** Degeneration of skeletal muscles due to genetic disorder.
- **Osteoporosis:** Decreased bone mass in old age leading to chance of fracture due to decreased estrogen.
- **Arthritis:** Inflammation of joints.
- **Gout:** Inflammation of joints due to accumulation of uric acid crystals.
- **Tetany:** Rapid spasm (Wild contractions) in muscle due to lesser Ca^{2+} in body Fluid.

Mnemonics

Concept: Disorders of Muscular and skeletal system

Mnemonic: Mukesh Mishra bought a **GOAT**

Interpretation: Myasthenia, Muscular dystrophy Gout, Osteoporosis, Arthritis, Tetany

Important Diagram

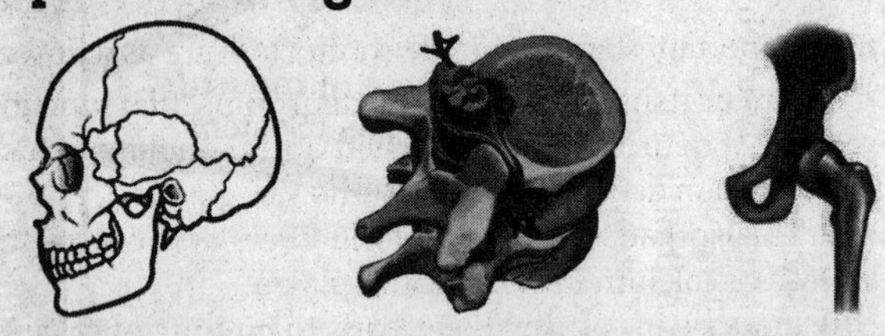

Types of Joints

Key Words

- **Ammonotelism:** The process of excretion of ammonia is called ammonotelism.
- **Ureotelism:** The process of excretion of urea is called ureotelism.
- **Uricotelism:** The process of excretion of uric acid is called uricotelism.
- **Juxtaglomerular apparatus:** It is a microscopic structure located between the vascular pole of the renal corpuscle and the returning distal convoluted tubule of the same nephron.
- **Osmoregulation:** Osmoregulation is a homeostatic mechanism that regulates the optimum temperature of water and salts in the tissues and body fluids.
- **Osmolarity:** The total concentration of solutes in a solution.

NCERT CORNER

Q. 1. Draw the diagram of a sarcomere of skeletal muscle showing different regions.
[NCERT Ex. Q. 1, Page 229]

Ans. Diagrammatic representation of a sarcomere:

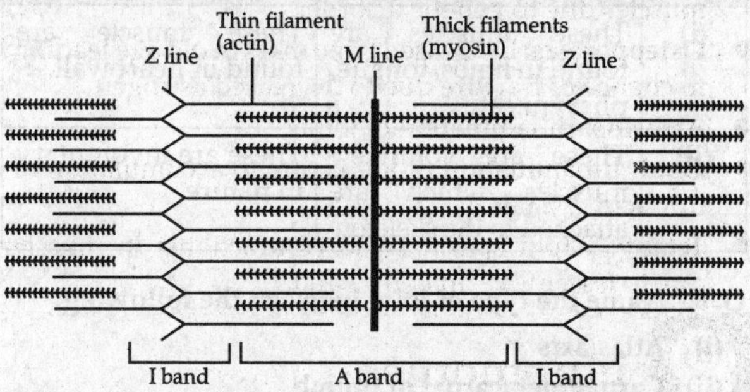

Q. 2. Define sliding filament theory of muscle contraction. **[NCERT Ex. Q. 2, Page 228]**

Ans. The sliding filament theory: It explains the process of muscle contraction during which the thin (actin) filaments slide over the thick (myosin) filaments, which shortens the myofibril.

Q. 3. Describe the important steps in muscle contraction.
[NCERT Ex. Q. 3, Page 228]

Ans. Important steps in muscle contraction are as follows:

(i) A neural signal reaching the neuromuscular junction releases a neurotransmitter called acetyl-choline, which generates an action potential in the sarcolemma.

(ii) This spreads through muscle fibers and causes the release of calcium ions into sarcoplasm.

(iii) Increase in calcium level leads to binding of calcium with a sub-unit of troponin on actin filaments. This removes the masking of active sites for myosin.

(iv) The myosin head now binds to the exposed active sites on actin to form a cross-bridge.

(v) This pulls the attached actin filaments towards the centre of A-band.

(vi) The Z-line attached to this actins are also pulled inwards, thereby causing the contraction of sarcomere.

(vii) During muscle shortening or muscle contraction, the I-bands get reduced whereas, the A-bands retain the same length.

(viii) The myosin, releasing ADP and Pi goes back to its relaxed state. A new ATP binds and cross-bridge is broken.

(ix) The ATP is again hydrolysed by the myosin head and the cycle of cross-bridge formation and breakage is repeated causing further sliding.

(x) The process continues till the calcium ions are pumped back to the sarcoplasmic cisternae, resulting in masking of actin filaments. This causes the return of Z-lines back to their original position i.e. relaxation.

Q. 4. Write true or false. If false change the statement so that it is true.

(i) Actin is present in thin filament

(ii) H-zone of striated muscle fibre represents both thick and thin filaments.

(iii) Human skeleton has 206 bones.

(iv) There are 11 pairs of ribs in man.

(v) Sternum is present on the ventral side of the body.
[NCERT Ex. Q. 4, Page 228]

Ans. (i) True

(ii) False.

Explanation: H-zone of striated muscle fiber is formed of only thick myosin filament.

(iii) True

(iv) False

Explanation: There are 12 pairs of ribs in man.

(v) True

Q. 5. Write the difference between:

(i) Actin and myosin

(ii) Red and white muscles

(iii) Pectoral and pelvic girdle
[NCERT Ex. Q. 5, Page 229]

Ans. (i) Difference between Actin and Myosin:

S. No.	Actin filaments	Myosin filaments
(i)	Actin is thinner but shorter than myosin filaments.	Myosin is thicker but longer than actin filaments
(ii)	It is found in both A and I bands	It is found only in A-band of sarcomere.
(iii)	Cross-bridges are absent, hence actins have smooth surface.	Cross bridges are present, hence they have rough surface.
(iv)	It slides into H-zone during muscle contraction	It does not slide during muscle contraction. They are fixed.

(ii) Difference between red and white muscles:

S. No.	Red muscle fibre	White muscle fibre
(i)	They are thin and smaller in size.	They are thick and larger in size.
(ii)	They are red in colour as they contain large amounts of myoglobin.	They are white in colour as they contain small amounts of myoglobin
(iii)	They contain numerous mitochondria.	They contain less number of mitochondria.
(iv)	They carry out slow and sustained contractions for a long period.	They carry out fast work for short duration.
(v)	They do not undergo fatigue.	They undergo early fatigue.
	Example: flight muscles of birds like kites, Extensor muscles of the back to maintain erect posture of the body.	**Example:** Muscles of the eyeball and flight muscles of birds like sparrow.

(iii) Difference between Pectoral and pelvic girdle:

S. No.	Pectoral girdle	Pelvic girdle
(i)	It is found in the shoulder region, hence also known as shoulder girdle.	It occurs in the hip region, hence also known as hip girdle.
(ii)	It is a skeletal support from where the forelimbs of vertebrates are attached.	It is a skeletal support from where the hind limbs of vertebrates are attached.
(iii)	It is composed of two bones namely, clavicle or collar bones and scapula or shoulder bone.	It is composed of three bones, upper ileum, inner pubic, and ischium.
(iv)	Each pectoral girdle has a glenoid cavity into which the head of humerus is articulated.	Each pelvic girdle has a deep depression called acetabulum to which the head of the femur is articulated.

Q. 6. Match Column I with Column II:

Column I	Column II
(i) Smooth muscle	(a) Myoglobin
(ii) Tropomyosin	(b) Thin filament
(iii) Red muscle	(c) Sutures
(iv) Skull	(d) Involuntary

[NCERT Ex. Q. 6, Page 229]

Ans.

Column I	Column II
(i) Smooth muscle	(d) Involuntary
(ii) Tropomyosin	(b) Thin filament
(iii) Red muscle	(a) Myoglobin
(iv) Skull	(c) Sutures

Q. 7. What are the different types of movements exhibited by the cells of human body? **[NCERT Ex. Q. 7, Page 229]**

Ans. Types of movement in human being are:

(i) Amoeboid movement: It is type of movement which occur with the help of pseudopodia formed by cytoplasmic streaming. **Examples:** Movement of leucocyte, macrophages and cytoskeleton elements in our body.

(ii) Ciliary movement: It is a type of movement which occurs with the help of cilia. This movement occurs in most of our internal tubular organs lined by the ciliated epithelium. **Examples:** Movement of cilia in trachea and movement of ova in the reproductive tract

(iii) Muscular movement: This movement occurs because of the contractile property of muscles. **Examples:** Movement of our jaws, limbs, tongue, etc.

Q. 8. How do you distinguish between a skeletal muscle and a cardiac muscle ? **[NCERT Ex. Q. 8, Page 229]**

Ans.

S.No.	Skeletal Muscle	Cardiac muscle
(i)	These muscles are found in limbs, tongue, pharynx, etc.	These muscle are found in heart wall.
(ii)	These are voluntary muscles which are attached to the skeleton	These are involuntary in nature.

Q. 9. Name the type of joint between the following:

(i) Atlas/axis
(ii) Carpal/metacarpal of thumb
(iii) Between phalanges
(iv) Femur/acetabulum
(v) Between cranial bones
(vi) Between pubic bones in the pelvic girdle

[NCERT Ex. Q. 9, Page 229]

Ans. (i) Atlas/axis- Pivot joint
(ii) Carpal/metacarpal of thumb-Saddle joint
(iii) Between phalanges- Hinge joint
(iv) Femur/acetabulum- Ball and Socket joint
(v) Between cranial bones- Fibrous joint
(vi) Between pubic bones in the pelvic girdle- Cartilaginous joint

Q. 10. Fill in the blank spaces:

(i) All mammals (except a few) have ______ cervical vertebra.
(ii) The number of phalanges in each limb of human is ______
(iii) Thin filament of myofibril contains 2 'F' actins and two other proteins namely______ and ______.
(iv) In a muscle fibre Ca^{++} is stored in______
(v) ______ and ______ pairs of ribs are called floating ribs.
(vi) The human cranium is made of______ bones.

[NCERT Ex. Q. 10, Page 229]

Ans. (i) All mammals (except a few) have seven cervical vertebra.
(ii) The number of phalanges in each limb of human is 14.
(iii) Thin filament of myofibril contains 2 'F' actins and two other proteins namely Troponin and tropomyosin.
(iv) In a muscle fibre Ca^{++} is stored in sarcoplasmic reticulum.
(v) 11th and 12th pairs of ribs are called floating ribs.
(vi) The human cranium is made of eight bones.

NEURAL CONTROL AND CO-ORDINATION

CHAPTER 18

Neural System

- **Coordination** is the process through which two of more organs interact and complement the function of each other.
- **Neural** system provides an organised network of point to point connection for quick coordination. The endocrine system provides chemical integration through hormones.
- **Neural system** of animals is composed of specialised cells called neuron, which can detect, receive and transmit different kinds of stimuli. In *Hydra* neural system is composed of network of neuron, in insects, it consists of brain and a number of ganglia and in vertebrates, it is highly developed neural system.

Human Neural System

- **Central nervous system** (CNS) includes brain and spinal cord. It is the site for information processing and control.
- **Peripheral nervous system** (PNS) includes all nerves associated with CNS.
- **Visceral nervous system** is the part of peripheral nervous system that comprises whole complex of nerves, fibres, ganglia and plexuses by which impulses travel from the CNS to the viscera and from viscera to the CNS.
- The nerve fibres of the PNS are of two types:
  - **Afferent fibres:** transmit impulses from tissue/organ to CNS.
  - **Efferent fibres:** transmit regulatory impulses from CNS to concerned peripheral organs.
- The PNS is divided into two divisions.

  Somatic neural system relay impulses from CNS to skeletal muscles. Autonomic neural system transmits impulses from CNS to involuntary system and smooth muscles. The autonomic neural system is further classified into sympathetic neural system and parasympathetic neural system.

Neuron as structural and Function Unit of Neural System

- Neuron is structural and functional unit of neural system. It is made up of three major parts: cell body, dendrite and axon.
- Cell body contains cytoplasm, cell organelles and Nissl's granules.
- Short fibres projecting out from cell body is called dendrites. The axon is long fibre having branched structure at the end that terminates into knob like structure called synaptic knob.
- **Based on number of axon and dendrites, neuron are of three types:**
  - **Multipolar:** One axon and two or more dendrite found in cerebral cortex.
  - **Bipolar:** One axon and one dendrite found in retina of eyes.
  - **Unipolar:** Cell body with one axon, only found in embryos.
- **There are two types of nerve fibres:**
  - **Myelinated nerve** fibres are enveloped with **Schwann cells** to form myelin sheath around the axon. The gap between two myelin sheaths is called **nodes of Ranvier.** Found in spinal and cranial nerves.
  - **Unmyelinated nerve** fibre is enclosed by **Schwann cells** that do not form myelin sheath around the axon. Found in autonomous and somatic neural system.

Generation and Conduction of Nerve Impulse

- Ions channels are present in neural membrane which is selectively permeable to different ions. When neuron is not conducting impulse (resting), axonal membrane is more permeable to K^+ ions and impermeable to Na^+ ions.
- Ionic gradient across the resting membrane is maintained by active transport of ions by sodium-potassium pump. This will develop positive charge outside the axonal membrane and negative charge on inner side.
- The electrical potential difference across the resting membrane is called **resting potential.**
- When stimulus is applied at site A, the membrane becomes permeable to Na^+ ions to make rapid influx of Na^+ ions. This creates outer surface negatively charged and inner membrane positively charged. This electrical potential difference across membrane is termed as a nerve impulse.

Central Neural System

- Brain is the central information processing unit of our body and act as command and control centre. Human brain is protected by skull (cranium) and cranial meninges consisting of three layered membrane outer dura mater, middle arachnoid and inner pia mater.
- Brain can be divided into 3 parts: forebrain, midbrain and hindbrain.
- **Forebrain** consists of cerebrum, thalamus and hypothalamus.

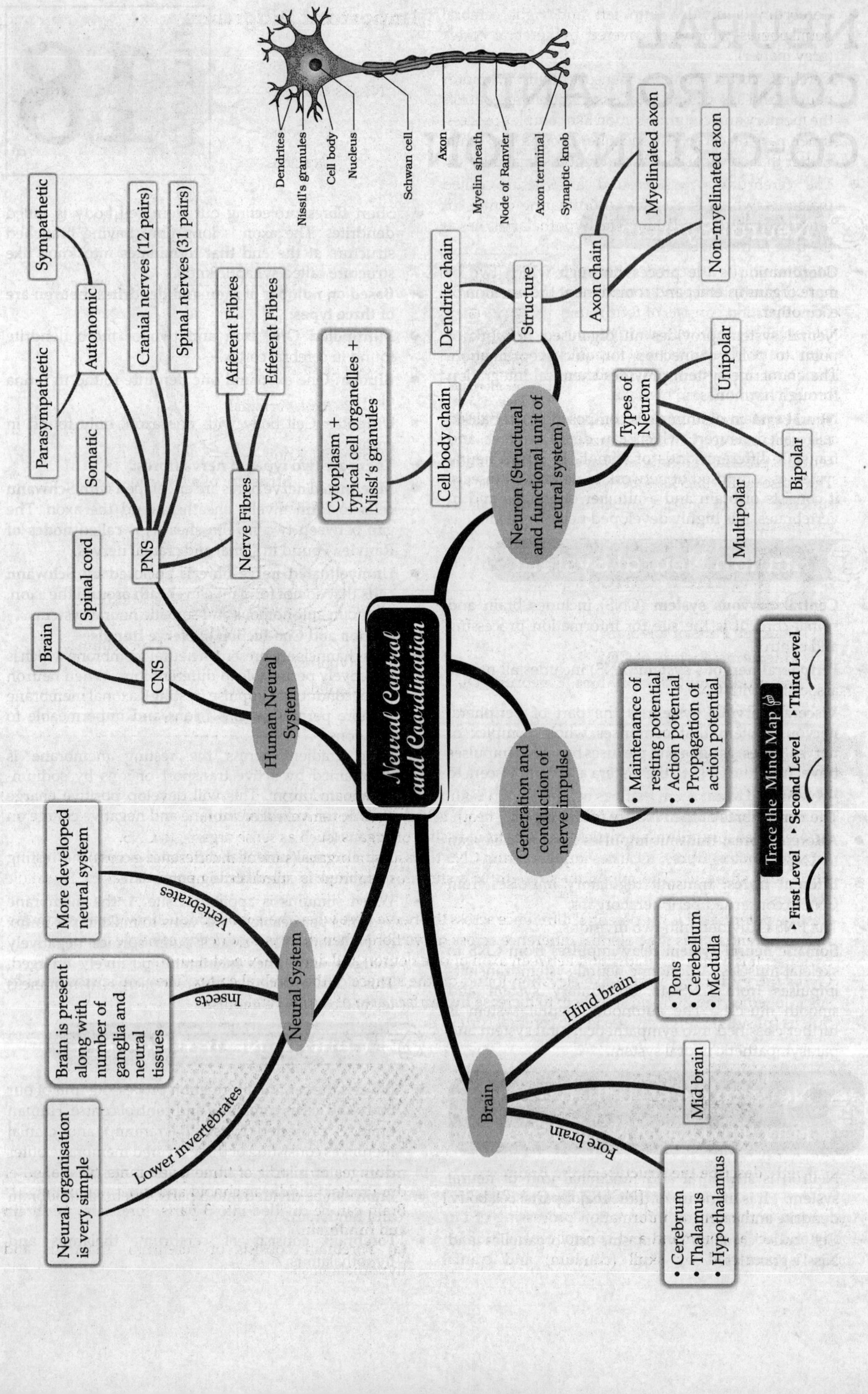
Neural Control and Coordination
Human Neural System
CNS
Brain
Spinal cord
PNS
Somatic
Autonomic
Parasympathetic
Sympathetic
Cranial nerves (12 pairs)
Spinal nerves (31 pairs)
Nerve Fibres
Afferent Fibres
Efferent Fibres
Neuron (Structural and functional unit of neural system)
Cell body chain
Cytoplasm + typical cell organelles + Nissl's granules
Structure
Dendrite chain
Axon chain
Myelinated axon
Non-myelinated axon
Types of Neuron
Unipolar
Bipolar
Multipolar
Dendrites
Nissl's granules
Cell body
Nucleus
Schwan cell
Axon
Myelin sheath
Node of Ranvier
Axon terminal
Synaptic knob
Generation and conduction of nerve impulse
• Maintenance of resting potential
• Action potential
• Propagation of action potential
Brain
Hind brain
• Pons
• Cerebellum
• Medulla
Mid brain
Fore brain
• Cerebrum
• Thalamus
• Hypothalamus
Neural System
Vertebrates
More developed neural system
Insects
Brain is present along with number of ganglia and neural tissues
Lower invertebrates
Neural organisation is very simple
Trace the Mind Map
• First Level
• Second Level
• Third Level

- Cerebrum is divided into left and right cerebral hemispheres which are covered by cerebral cortex (grey matter).
- Cerebral cortex contains sensory neuron, motor neuron and association area. Association area controls the memory and communication like complex process. Inner part of cerebral hemisphere forms the white matter that control sensory and motor signalling.
- The cerebrum wraps around a structure called thalamus, which is a major co-ordinating centre for sensory or motor signalling. The hypothalamus lies at the base of the thalamus.

➤ **Midbrain** is located between hypothalamus and pons of hindbrain. Dorsal portion consists of four round lobes called corpora quadrigemina. They are involved in relay of impulses back and forth between cerebrum, cerebellum, pons and medulla.

Scan to know more about this topic

Generation and Conduction of Nerve Impulse

➤ **Hind brain** consists of pons, medulla oblongata and cerebellum. Pneumatic centre is present in hindbrain that control inspiration. They also relay impulses between the medulla and superior part of brain. Cerebellum controls balance and posture.

Mnemonics

Concept: Parts of forebrain
Mnemonic: Factory of **CD**
Interpretation: Ol**F**actory lobe, **C**erebrum, **D**iencephalon

Important Diagrams

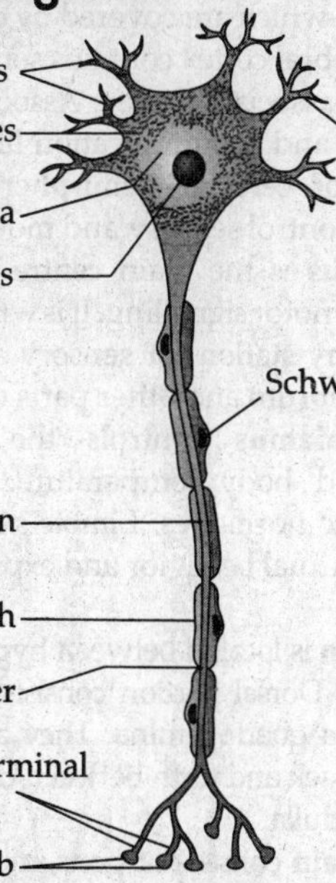

Structure of a Neuron

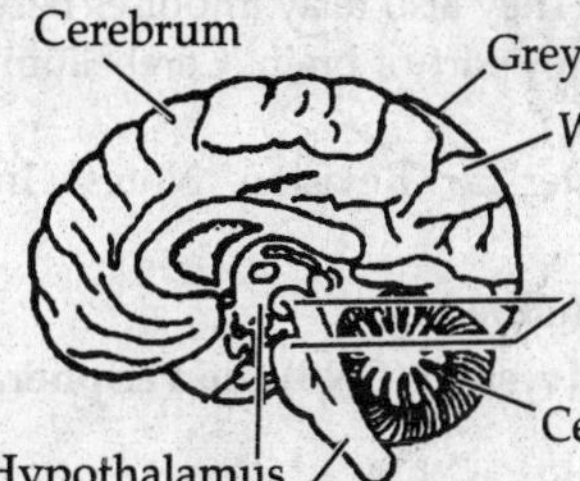

Structure of a Brain

Key Words

➤ **Myelinated axon:** Axon that has myelin sheath is known as myelinated axon
➤ **Non-myelinated axon:** Axon without myelin sheath is known as non-myelinated axon.
➤ **Afferent (sensory) fibres:** It carries impulses from tissues or organs (such as sense organs) to CNS.
➤ **Efferent (motor) fibres:** It carries impulses from CNS to tissues or organs (such as muscles and glands).
➤ **Threshold stimulus:** The minimum strength of a stimulus required to stimulate a neuron is called Threshold stimulus.
➤ **Resting potential:** It is the potential difference across the nerve fibre when there is no conduction of nerve impulse.
➤ **Action potential:** It is the potential difference across nerve fibre when there is conduction of nerve impulse.
➤ **Synapse:** It is a functional junction between axon of one neuron and dendrite of next neuron.
➤ **Gyrus (pl. gyri) :** It is a ridge-like elevation found on the surface of the cerebral cortex. They are surrounded by sulci. Together, the gyri and sulci help to increase the surface area of the cerebral cortex.
➤ **Sulcus (pl.sulci) :** It is a groove in the cerebral cortex.

NCERT CORNER

Q. 1. Briefly describe the structure of the Brain.
[NCERT Ex. Q. 1, Page 237]

Ans. Brain is the central information processing of our body and act as command and control centre. Human brain is protected by skull (cranium) and cranial meninges consisting of three layered membrane, outer dura mater, middle arachnoid and inner pia matter. Brain can be divided into 3 parts: **forebrain, midbrain and hindbrain.**

(a) Forebrain consists of cerebrum, thalamus and hypothalamus.

- **Cerebrum** is divided into left and right cerebral hemispheres which are covered by cerebral cortex (grey matter). Cerebral cortex contains sensory neuron, motor neuron and association area. Association area controls the memory and communication like complex process. Inner part of cerebral hemisphere forms the white matter that control sensory and motor signaling.
- **Thalamus** is the main centre of coordination for sensory and motor signalling. It is wrapped by cerebrum. It acts as relay station for sensory and motor impulses between cerebrum and other parts of the brain.
- **Hypothalamus** controls the urge for eating, drinking and body temperature. They also release hypothalamic hormones. Limbic system is involved in controlling sexual behavior and expression of emotional reactions.

(b) Midbrain is located between hypothalamus and pons of hindbrain. Dorsal portion consists of four round lobes called corpora quadrigemina. They are involved in relay of impulses back and forth between cerebrum, cerebellum, pons and medulla.

(c) Hind brain consists of pons, medulla oblongata and cerebellum. Pneumatic centre is present in hindbrain that control inspiration. They also relay impulses between the medulla and superior part of brain. Cerebellum controls balance and posture.

For Diagram: Refer to Revision Notes/ Important diagrams/ Fig 18.2

Q. 2. Compare the following:
(i) Central neural system (CNS) and Peripheral neural system (PNS)
(ii) Resting potential and action potential
[NCERT Ex. Q. 2, Page 237]

Ans. (i) Differences between Central neural system (CNS) and Peripheral neural system (PNS):

S. No.	Central neural system	Peripheral neural system
(i)	It lies in the centre of the body.	It lies in the periphery of the body.
(ii)	It includes brain and spinal cord.	It includes cranial and spinal nerves that connect central nervous system to different parts of the body.

(ii) Differences between resting potential and action potential:

S. No.	Resting potential	Action potential
(i)	It is the potential difference across the nerve fibre when there is no conduction of nerve impulse.	It is the potential difference across nerve fibre when there is conduction of nerve impulse.
(ii)	In resting potential the interior of the axon is electronegative and the exterior is electropositive.	In action potential the interior of axon is electropositive and the anterior is electronegative.

Q. 3. Explain the following processes:
(i) Polarisation of the membrane of a nerve fibre
(ii) Depolarisation of the membrane of a nerve fibre
(iii) Conduction of a nerve impulse along a nerve fibre
[NCERT Ex. Q. 3, Page 237]

Ans. (i) When a neuron is not conducting an impulse, i.e., resting, the axonal membrane is more permeable to K^+ and nearly impermeable to Na^+. Similarly, the membrane is impermeable to negatively charged proteins present in the axoplasm. Consequently, the axoplasm contains high concentration of K^+ and negatively charged proteins and low concentration of Na^+. In contrast, the fluid outside contains a low concentration of K^+, a high concentration of Na^+ and thus forms a concentration gradient. These ionic gradients across the resting membrane are maintained by the sodium-potassium pump. As a result, the outer surface of the axonal membrane possesses a positive charge while its inner surface becomes negatively charged and therefore is polarised.

(ii) Depolarisation of the membrane of a nerve fibre:

(a) Stimulation of an axon immediately enhances manifold its membrane permeability to Na^+. As a result, Na^+ ions diffuse across the membrane from the extracellular fluid (ECF) where their concentration is higher, to the interior of the fibre where the concentration is much lower. But the membrane permeability to K^+ starts rising somewhat later only, so there is simultaneous rise in the outward diffusion of K^+ from the cell interior having a higher K^+ concentration.

(b) These effects lower the overall cation concentration outside and enhance its concentration inside the membrane.

(c) The membrane is, thus deposited, with its interior becoming electropositive to the exterior.

(d) The Depolarisation spreads a local current. It induces nearby passive Na^+ channels to open and so as to depolarise the nearby site.

(e) Hence the initial Depolarisation passes outward over the membrane and spreads out in all directions from the site of stimulation.

(iii) Conduction of nerve impulse along a nerve fibre:

(a) It is a property of nerve fibre to become excited by a stimulus and then conduct that stimulus for the required and appropriate response.

(b) In conducting a stimulus, the nerve axon has to pass through resting phase to active phase and then the recovery phase.

Q. 4. Draw labelled diagrams of the following:
(i) Neuron (ii) Brain **[NCERT Ex. Q. 4, Page 238]**

Ans. (i) Structure of a neuron:

The nervous system is made up of highly specialised cells called as neurons. A neuron is composed of three main parts, namely cell body or cyton, dendrite and axon.

(i) Cyton: It contains a well defined nucleus, surrounded by granular cytoplasm called neuroplasm and all the cell organelles along with, Nissl's granules. Only centrosome is absent because nerve cells have lost the ability to divide.

(ii) Dendrites: These are branched cytoplasmic projections of cyton known as the dendrons which receives nerve impulses.

(iii) Axon: It is a very long process and projects from a part of cyton axon hillock. The lower end of the axon is branched and each branch terminates as a bulb like structures called nerve endings which have swollen synaptic knobs. There knobs possess synaptic vesicles, which store neurotransmitters. The axons transmit nerve impulses away from the cell body to a synapse or to a neuromuscular junction. **3+2**

For diagram: Refer to Revision Notes/ Important diagrams Fig 18.1

(ii) Structure of a brain:

Refer to NCERT Corner/Q.1

Q. 5. Write short notes on the following:

(i) Neural coordination **(ii) Forebrain**
(iii) Midbrain **(iv) Hindbrain**
(v) Synapse **[NCERT Ex. Q. 5, Page 238]**

Ans. (i) Neural coordination: The neural system provides rapid coordination among the organs of the body. This coordination is in the form of electric impulses and is quick and short lived.

All the physiological processes in the body are closely linked and dependent upon each other. For example, during exercise, our body requires more oxygen and food. Hence, the breathing rate increases automatically and the heart beats faster. This leads to a faster supply of oxygenated blood to the muscles. Moreover, the cellular functions require regulation continuously. These functions are carried out by the hormones.

Hence, the neural system works with the endocrine system to communicate, integrate and coordinate the functions of various organs and systems in our body and helps the body to respond to the external stimuli.

(ii) Forebrain (Prosencephalon): Refer to NCERT corner. Q.1.

(iii) Mid Brain (Mesencephalon): Refer to NCERT corner Q.1.

(iv) Hind brain Refer to NCERT Corner Q.1.

(v) Synapse: It is a junction between the axon terminal of one neuron and the dendrite of next neuron. It is separated by a small gap known as synaptic cleft. There are two types of synapses:

(a) Electrical synapse

(b) Chemical synapse

In electrical synapses, the pre and post synaptic neurons lie in close proximity to each other. Hence, the impulse can move directly from one neuron to another across the synapse. This represents a faster method of impulse transmission.

In chemical synapses, the pre and post-synaptic neurons are not in close proximity. They are separated by a synaptic cleft. The transmission of nerve impulses is carried out by chemicals such as neurotransmitters.

Q. 6. Give a brief account of mechanism of synaptic transmission. **[NCERT Ex. Q. 6, Page 238]**

Ans. Synaptic transmission can be of two types:

Electrical synaptic transmission: At electrical synapses, the membranes of pre- and post- synaptic neurons are in very close proximity. Electrical current can flow directly from one neuron into the other across these synapses. Transmission of an impulse is very similar to impulse conduction along a single axon.

Chemical synaptic transmission: The membranes of the pre- and post-synaptic neurons are separated by a fluid-filled space called synaptic cleft. Neurotransmitters are involved in the transmission of impulses. When an impulse (action potential) arrives at the axon terminal, it stimulates the movement of the synaptic vesicles towards the membrane where they fuse with the plasma membrane and release their neurotransmitters in the synaptic cleft. The released neurotransmitters bind to their specific receptors, present on the post-synaptic membrane. This binding opens ion-channels allowing the entry of ions which can generate a new potential in the post-synaptic neuron.

Q. 7. Explain the role of Na^+ in the generation of action potential. **[NCERT Ex. Q. 7, Page 238]**

Ans. Role of Na^+ in the generation of action potential:

(a) Stimulation of an axon enhances its membrane permeability to Na^+.

(b) As a result, Na^+ ions diffuse across the membrane from the extracellular fluid (ECF) where their concentration is higher, to the interior of the fibre where the concentration is much lower.

(c) The membrane permeability to K^+ start rising somewhat later only. So there is simultaneous rise in the outward diffusion of K^+ from the cell interior having a higher K^+ concentration.

(d) These effects lower the overall cation concentration outside and enhance that inside the membrane.

(e) The membrane is, thus deposited, with its interior becoming electropositive to the exterior.

(f) The Depolarisation spreads producing a local current. It induces nearby passive Na^+ channels to open and so to depolarise the nearby site.

(g) Hence, the initial depolarisation passes outward over the membrane and spread out in all directions from the site of stimulation.

Q. 8. Differentiate between:

(a) Myelinated and non-myelinated axons

(b) Dendrites and axons

(c) Thalamus and Hypothalamus

(d) Cerebrum and Cerebellum

[NCERT Ex. Q. 8, Page 238]

Ans. (a) Differences between myelinated and non-myelinated axons:

S.No.	Myelinated axon	Non-myelinated axon
(i)	These axons are generally found in spinal and cranial nerves.	These are commonly found in autonomous and somatic neural systems.
(ii)	The myelinated nerves fibers are enveloped with schwann cells.	Non-myelinated nerve fibers are not enclosed by a schwann cells.
(iii)	They forms a myelin sheath around the axon.	They do not form a myelin sheath around the axon.

(b) Differences between dendrites and axons:

S.No.	Dendrites	Axon
(i)	Dendrites are the short fibres which branch repeatedly.	Axons are long fibres, the distal end of which is branched.
(ii)	Nissl's granules are present.	Nissl's granules are absent.
(iii)	These fibres transmit impulses towards the cell body.	The axons transmit nerve impulses away from the cells body to a synapse or to a neuro-muscular junction.

(c) Differences between Thalamus and hypothalamus:

S.No.	Thalamus	Hypothalamus
(i)	It lies below the cerebrum.	It lies at the base of thalamus.
(ii)	It is the major coordinating centre for sensory and motor signaling.	It contain many centres to control body temperature, eating and drinking.
(iii)	It relays sensory impulse and does not secrete any hormone.	It contains many group of neuro secretory cells that produce hypothalamic hormones.

(d) Differences between cerebellum and cerebrum:

S.No.	Cerebellum	Cerebrum
(i)	It forms a major part of hind brain.	It is the part of forebrain consisting of grey matter and white matter.
(ii)	It maintains equilibrium, and maintenance of posture.	It controls sight, hearing, taste and higher mental abilities and voluntary control.

Q. 9. Answer the following:

(a) Which part of the human brain is the most developed?

(b) Which part of our central neural system acts as a master clock? **[NCERT Ex. Q. 9, Page 238]**

Ans. (a) Cerebrum of the forebrain

(b) Hypothalamus

Q.10. Distinguish between:

(i) Afferent neurons and efferent neurons

(ii) Impulse conduction in a myelinated nerve fibre and unmyelinated nerve fibre

(iii) Cranial nerves and spinal nerves. **[NCERT Ex. Q. 10, Page 238]**

Ans. (i)

S. No.	Afferent neuron	Efferent neuron
(i)	They conduct impulses from the receptors to the CNS.	They conduct impulses from CNS to the effectors.
(ii)	They are sensory in nature.	They are motor in nature.

(ii)

Impulse conduction in a myelinated nerve fibre	Impulse conduction in an non-myelinated nerve fibre
(i) In a myelinated nerve fibre, the action potential is conducted from one node to another.	In a non-myelinated nerve fibre, the action potential is not conducted from node to node. It is carried along the whole length of the nerve fibre.
(ii) The conduction of impulses is faster.	The conduction of impulses is slower.

(iii)

S.No.	Cranial nerves	Spinal nerves
(i)	Cranial nerves arises from different parts of the brain.	A pair of spinal nerves arises from each segment of the spinal cord.
(ii)	There are 12 pairs of cranial nerves present in man.	There are 31 pairs of spinal nerves present in man.
(iii)	Cranial nerves are sensory motor and mixed.	All spinal nerves are mixed nerves.

□□

CHEMICAL CO-ORDINATION AND INTEGRATION

CHAPTER 19

Endocrine Glands and Hormones

- In animals, control and coordination is performed by neural system and endocrine system jointly. As the nerve fibres do not innervate all cells of the body, the endocrine or hormonal system is required to coordinate the functions.

Endocrine Glands

Scan to know more about this topic

Endocrine Glands Hormone

- Endocrine glands have no ducts and their secretion get absorbed into the immediate surrounding blood circulation to reach the specific organs to initiate a particular metabolic change.
- The endocrine glands secrete and chemicals called **hormones**. Hormones are non-nutrient chemicals which act as intercellular messengers and are produced in trace amount.

Human Endocrine System

- The endocrine glands and hormone producing tissues/cells are located in different parts of the body.
- Gastrointestinal tract, kidney, liver and heart also produce small quantity of hormones to control and coordinate the function of respective organs.
- **Hypothalamus** contains several groups of neurosecretory cells called nuclei which produce hormones. These hormones control and regulate the synthesis and secretion of pituitary hormones.
- The hormones released from hypothalamus reaches to pituitary gland through portal circulatory system and regulate the function of anterior pituitary. The posterior pituitary is under direct control of hypothalamus.
- **Pituitary Gland** is located in a body cavity called sella turcica and is attached to the hypothalamus by a stalk. Pituitary is divided into adenohypophysis and neurohypophysis. Adenohypophysis consists of two parts: pars distalis or anterior pituitary secreting growth hormone (GH), prolactin (PRL), thyroid stimulating hormone (TSH), adrenocorticotrophic hormone (ACTH), luteinising hormone (LH) and follicle stimulating hormone (FSH) and pars intermedia secreting melanocyte stimulating hormone (MSH).

- Neurohypophysis (pars nervosa) known as posterior pituitary releases two hormones: oxytocin and vasopressin.
- Over secretion of GH (growth hormone) causes overgrowth of the body leading to gigantism and low secretion causes stunted growth called dwarfism.
- **Prolactin** stimulates growth of mammary gland, and secretion of milk.
- TSH stimulates and regulates thyroid hormone secretion from the thyroid gland.
- **LH and FSH** stimulates gonadal activity. In male, **LH** stimulates synthesis and secretion of androgen hormone from testis. In female, LH induce ovulation of fully mature ovum from ovary.
- **Oxytocin** helps in contraction of uterus during child birth and milk ejection from mammary glands.
- **Vasopressin** stimulates absorption of water and electrolyte in kidney. Vasopressin is also known as **Anti-diuretic hormone (ADH).** Deficiency of ADH leads to diabetes insipidus.

Mnemonics

Concept: Endocrine glands
Mnemonic: Please Pickup That APPle
Interpretation: Pituitary, Prolactin, Thyroid, Adrenal, Parathyroid, Pancreas.

- **Pineal gland:** It is located on dorsal side of forebrain and releases melatonin hormone that help in the regulation of 24-hour rhythm of body like sleep—wake cycle and body temperature.
- **Thyroid gland:** Composed of two lobes on either side of trachea connected by isthmus. Iodine is essential for synthesis of thyroid hormones. Deficiency of iodine leads to hyperthyroidism (Goitre).
- **Exophthalmic goitre** is a form of hypothyroidism. It is characterised by enlargement of thyroid gland. It is also known as Grave's disease.
- During pregnancy, hypothyroidism may cause stunted growth of baby and mental retardation.
- **Parathyroid gland:** It is located on the back side of thyroid gland, secretes peptide hormone called parathyroid hormone (PTH). PTH regulates the circulating level of calcium ions. It also helps in reabsorption of calcium from renal tubules and digestive tracts.
- **Adrenal gland:** It is located on anterior part of each kidney, composed of two types of tissues: central adrenal medulla and outside adrenal cortex. **Adrenal medulla** secretes adrenaline and nor-adrenaline hormone, together called emergency hormone. **Adrenal cortex** secretes many hormones together

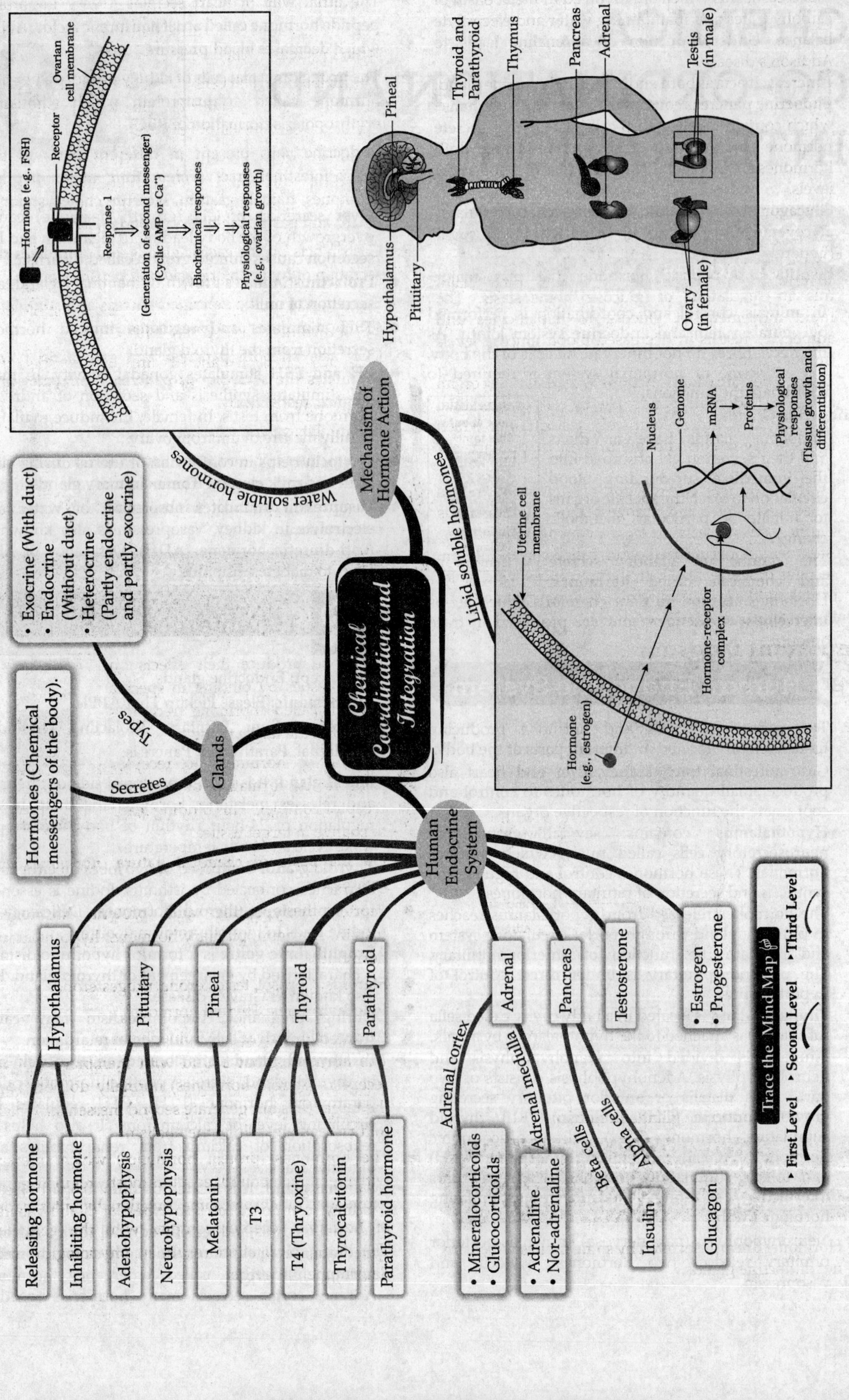
Chemical Coordination and Integration
Glands
Secretes
Hormones (Chemical messengers of the body).
Types
• Exocrine (With duct)
• Endocrine (Without duct)
• Heterocrine (Partly endocrine and partly exocrine)
Mechanism of Hormone Action
Water soluble hormones
Hormone (e.g., FSH)
Receptor
Ovarian cell membrane
Response 1
(Generation of second messenger) (Cyclic AMP or Ca++)
Biochemical responses
Physiological responses (e.g., ovarian growth)
Lipid soluble hormones
Hormone (e.g., estrogen)
Hormone-receptor complex
Uterine cell membrane
Nucleus
Genome
mRNA
Proteins
Physiological responses (Tissue growth and differentiation)
Hypothalamus
Pituitary
Pineal
Thyroid and Parathyroid
Thymus
Pancreas
Adrenal
Testis (in male)
Ovary (in female)
Human Endocrine System
Hypothalamus
Releasing hormone
Inhibiting hormone
Pituitary
Adenohypophysis
Neurohypophysis
Pineal
Melatonin
Thyroid
T3
T4 (Thryoxine)
Thyrocalcitonin
Parathyroid
Parathyroid hormone
Adrenal
Adrenal cortex
• Mineralocorticoids
• Glucocorticoids
Adrenal medulla
• Adrenaline
• Nor-adrenaline
Pancreas
Beta cells
Insulin
Alpha cells
Glucagon
Testosterone
• Estrogen
• Progesterone
Trace the Mind Map
First Level
Second Level
Third Level

called corticoids which are involved in metabolism of carbohydrates and maintaining water and electrolyte balance. Underproduction of adrenaline leads to Addison's disease.

- **Pancreas:** It acts as both endocrine and exocrine gland. **Endocrine pancreas** consists of **"Islets of Langerhans"** which contain α-cells and β-cells. The α-cells secrete hormone glucagon and β-cells secrete insulin. Both hormones are involved in maintenance of blood sugar levels.
- **Glucagon** is a peptide hormone that stimulates glycogenolysis resulting in increased blood sugar (hyperglycemia).
- **Insulin** is a peptide hormone that play major role in regulation of glucose homeostasis. The rapid movement of glucose to hepatocytes and adipocytes results in decreased blood glucose levels (hypoglycemia).
- **Testis:** It perform dual functions as a primary sex organ as well as endocrine glands. Leydig cells or interstitial cells produce androgen mainly **testosterone** which regulate regulation and maturation of primary sex organs.
- **Ovary:** Produces two groups of steroid hormones called estrogen and progesterone. **Estrogen** is synthesised and secreted by growing ovarian follicles. After ovulation, **ruptured** ovum called corpus luteum, secretes progesterone. Estrogen produces wide range of actions like growth of female secondary sex organs. **Progesterone** regulates pregnancy.

Important Diagram

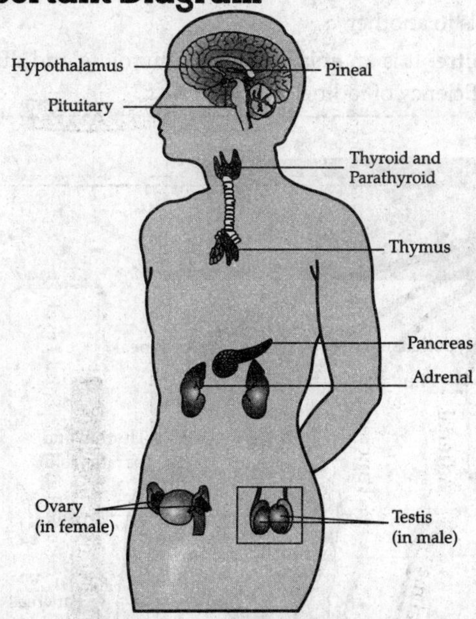

Endocrine glands in human

Hormones of Heart, Kidney and Gastrointestinal Tract

- Hormones are also secreted by some tissues which are not endocrine glands.
- The atrial wall of heart secretes a very important peptide hormone called atrial natriuretic factor (ANF), which decreases blood pressure.
- The juxtaglomerular cells of kidney produce a peptide hormone called erythroprotein which stimulates erythropoiesis (formation of RBC).
- Endocrine cells present in different parts of the gastro-intestinal tract secrete four major peptide hormones, namely gastrim, secretin, cholecystokinin (CCK) and gastric inhibitory peptide (GIP).
- Gastrin acts on the gastric glands and stimulates the secretion of hydrochloric acid and pepsinogen.
- Secretin acts on the exocrine pancreas and stimulates secretion of water and biocarbonate ions.
- CCK acts on both pancreas and gall bladder and stimulates the secretion of pancreatic enzymes and bile juice, respectively.
- GIP inhibits gastric secretion and motility.
- Several other non-endocrine tissues secrete hormones called growth factors. These factors are essential for normal growth of tissues and their repairing/ regeneration.

Mechanism of Hormone Action

- Hormone produce their effects on target tissues by binding to specific protein called hormone receptors located in the target tissue.
- Binding of hormones to receptor leads to the formation of hormone receptor complex. This binding leads to change in target tissue.

Scan to know more about this topic

Mechanism of Action: Steroid hormone

On the basis of chemical nature, hormones are grouped as:

- **Peptide, polypeptide and protein hormones:** Insulin, glucagon, pituitary hormone, hypothalamus hormones.
- **Steroids:** Cortisol, testosterone, progesterone.
- **Iodothyronines:** Thyroid hormones.
- **Amino acid derivatives:** Epinephrine.
- The hormones that bound with membrane bound receptors (steroid hormones) normally do not enter the target cells but generate second messenger which in turn regulate cellular metabolism.
- The hormones (protein hormones) which interact with membrane bound receptors mostly regulate gene expression or chromosome function by interaction of hormone receptor complex with the genome. The biochemical effect results in physiological and developmental effects.

Hypo and Hyper activity of hormones.

- Deficiency of hormones leads to hypoactivity of the hormones.
- Excess secretion of the hormones increases hormones action which is called hyperactivity of the hormones.
- Hypoactivity or hyperactivity of the hormones can cause disorders.
- **Pituitary dwarfism** is caused by the deficiency of growth hormone (GH) from childhood. It is characterised by small but proportionate body and sexual maturity. **Acromegaly** is caused by excess of growth hormone from early age. It is characterised by disproportionate increase in size of bones of face, hands and feet.
- **Cretinism** is caused by deficiency of thyroid hormone in infants. It is characterised by slow body growth and mental development with reduced metabolic rate.
- **Goitre** is caused by deficiency of iodine in diet because iodine is needed for the synthesis of thyroxine. It causes thyroid enlargement.
- **Exophthalmic goitre** is a thyroid enlargement (goitre) in which the thyroid secretes excessive amount of thyroid hormone. It is characterised by exophthalmia, i.e., protrusion of eye balls, loss of weight, rapid heart beat, nervousness and restlessness.
- **Diabetes mellitus** is caused by the failure of the beta-cells in the islet of langerhans situated in the pancreas to produce adequate amount of insulin. Some of the glucose is excreted in the urine. This causes excess thirst and the person becomes very weak.
- **Addision's disease** is caused by the deficiency of mineralocorticoids and glucocorticoids. Its symptoms include low blood sugar, low plasma Na^+, high K^+ plasma, nausea, vomiting, diarrhoea, etc.

Important Diagram

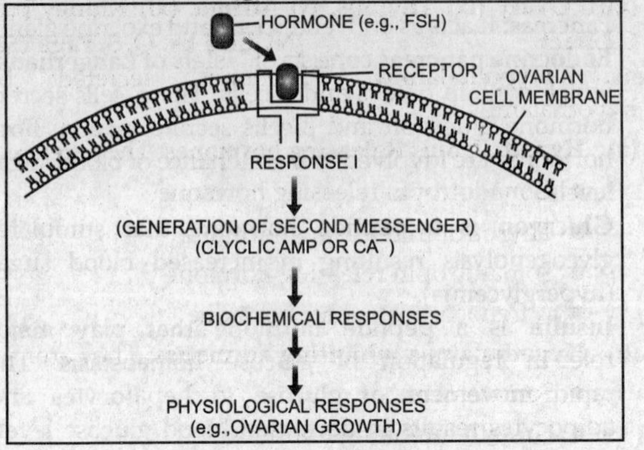

Mechanism of hormone action

Key Words

- **Exocrine glands:** These are glands that release their secretions with the help of ducts at specific site.
- **Endocrine glands:** These are glands that pour their secretions directly into the blood.
- **Heterocrine glands:** The glands that are partly exocrine with duct and partly endocrine without duct is known as heterocrine glands.
- **Hormones:** Hormones are chemical messengers of the body that transfers information from one set of cells to another.
- **Goitre:** It is an enlargement of thyroid gland due to deficiency of iodine.

NCERT CORNER

Q. 1. Define the following:

(i) Exocrine gland

(ii) Endocrine gland

(iii) Hormone **[NCERT Ex. Q. 1, Page 251]**

Ans. (i) Exocrine gland: Glands that release their secretions with the help of ducts at specific site are known as exocrine gland.

(ii) Endocrine gland: Glands that pour their secretions directly into the blood are called endocrine glands.

(iii) Hormone: Hormones are chemical messengers of the body that transfers information from one set of cells to another.

Q. 2. Diagrammatically indicate the location of the various endocrine glands in our body. **[NCERT Ex. Q. 2, Page 251]**

Ans.

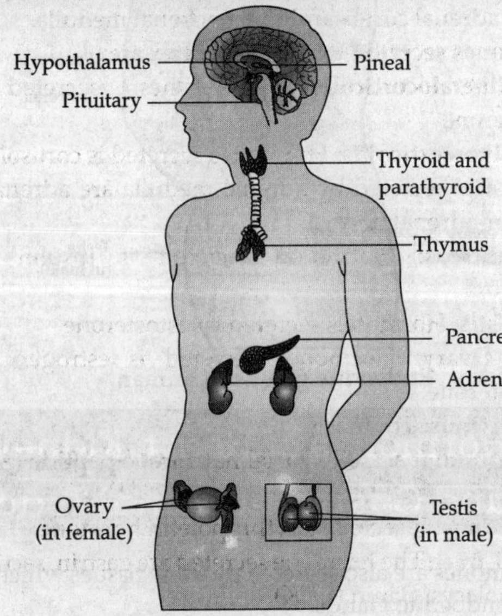

Q. 3. List the hormones secreted by the following:

(i) Hypothalamus (ii) Pituitary (iii) Thyroid (iv) Parathyroid (v) Adrenal (vi) Pancreas (vii) Testis (viii) Ovary (ix) Thymus, (x) Atrium, (xi) Kidney (xii) GI Tract [NCERT Ex. Q. 3, Page 251]

Ans. (i) Hypothalamus: Hormones secreted by hypothalamus are:

(a) Hypothalamus Releasing hormones: They are:

- Gonadotropin releasing hormone
- Thyrotropin releasing hormone
- Somatotropin releasing hormone
- Adrenocorticotrophic hormone

(b) Hypothalamus inhibiting hormones: They are:

- Somatostatin
- Growth inhibiting hormone
- Melanocyte inhibiting hormone

(ii) Pituitary: Pituitary gland comprises two components: Adenohypophysis and neurohypophysis.

Hormones secreted by anterior lobe (a adenohypophysis) are:

(a) Growth hormone

(b) Prolactin

(c) Thyroid stimulating hormone

(d) Adrenocorticotrophic hormone

(e) Luteinising hormone

(f) Follicle stimulating hormone

(g) Melanocyte stimulating hormone

Hormones secreted by posterior pituitary (neurohypophysis) are:

(a) Oxytocin

(b) Vasopressin

(iii) Thyroid: Thyroid gland secretes three hormones: Thyroxin, triiodothyronin and calcitonin.

(iv) Parathyroid: It secretes a hormone called parathyroid hormone.

(v) Adrenal: Adrenal gland is divided into two parts: Outer adrenal cortex and inner adrenal medulla.

Hormones secreted by adrenal cortex are:

(a) Mineralocorticoids: Hormones secreted is aldosterone.

(b) Glucocorticoids: Hormones secreted is cortisol.

Hormones secreted by adrenal medulla are adrenaline and nor-adrenalin.

(vi) Pancreas: Hormones secreted is insulin and glucagon.

(vii) Testis: Hormones secreted is testosterone.

(viii) Ovary: Hormones secreted is estrogen and progesterone.

(xi) Thymus: Thymosin

(x) Atrium: It secretes Atrial natriuretic peptide (ANP) hormone.

(xi) Kidney: It secretes erythropoietin hormone.

(xii) GI Tract: The hormone secreted are gastrin, secretin, and cholecystokinin (CCK).

Q. 4. Fill in the blanks:

Hormones	**Target gland**
(i) Hypothalamic hormones	....
(ii) Thyrotrophin (TSH)	....
(iii) Corticotrophin (ACTH)	....
(iv) Gonadotrophins (LH, FSH)	....
(v) Melanotrophin (MSH)	....

[NCERT Ex. Q. 4, Page 251]

Ans.

Hormones	**Target gland**
(i) Hypothalamic hormones	Pituitary
(ii) Thyrotrophin (TSH)	Thyroid
(iii) Corticotrophin (ACTH)	Adrenal
(iv) Gonadotrophins (LH, FSH)	Ovary, Testis
(v) Melanotrophin (MSH)	Melanocyte

Q. 5. Write short notes on the functions of the following hormones:

(i) Parathyroid hormone (PTH)

(ii) Thyroid hormones

(iii) Androgens

(iv) Estrogens

(v) Insulin and Glucagon [NCERT Ex. Q. 5, Page 251]

Ans. (i) Parathyroid hormone (PTH):

(a) Parathyroid hormone (PTH) increase the Ca^{2+} levels in the blood.

(b) PTH acts on bones and stimulates the process of bone resorption (dissolution/ demineralisation).

(c) PTH also stimulates reabsorption of Ca^{2+} by the renal tubules and increases Ca^{2+} absorption from the digested food.

(d) PTH is a hypercalcemic hormone, i.e., it increases the blood Ca^{2+} level in body.

(ii) Thyroid hormones: Refer Topic 1/SAQ-II/Q-4.

(iii) Androgens:

(a) Androgens regulate the development, maturation and functions of the male accessory sex organs like epididymis, vas deferens, seminal vesicles, prostate gland, urethra etc.

(b) These hormones stimulate muscular growth, growth of facial and axillary hair, aggressiveness, low pitch of voice etc.

(c) Androgens play major stimulatory role in the process of spermatogenesis (formation of spermatozoa).

(d) Androgens act on the central neural system and influence the male sexual behavior (libido).

(e) These hormones produce anabolic (synthetic) effects on protein and carbohydrate metabolism.

(iv) Estrogens:

(a) Estrogens produce wide range of actions such as stimulation of growth and activities of female secondary sex organs, development of growing ovarian follicles, appearance of female secondary sex characters (e.g., high pitch of voice, etc.), and mammary gland development.

(b) Estrogens also regulate female sexual behaviour.

(v) Insulin:

(a) Insulin is a peptide hormone, which plays a major role in the regulation of glucose homeostasis.

(b) Insulin acts mainly on hepatocytes and adipocytes (cells of adipose tissue), and enhances cellular glucose uptake and utilisation.

(c) Insulin also stimulates conversion of glucose to glycogen (glycogenesis) in the target cells.

Glucagon:

(a) Glucagon is a peptide hormone, and plays an important role in maintaining the normal blood glucose levels.

(b) Glucagon acts mainly on the liver cells (hepatocytes) and stimulates glycogenolysis resulting in an increased blood sugar (hyperglycemia).

(c) In addition, this hormone stimulates the process of gluconeogenesis which also contributes to hyperglycemia.

(d) Glucagon reduces the cellular glucose uptake and utilisation. Thus, glucagon is hyperglycemic hormone.

Q. 6. Give example(s) of:
(i) Hyperglycemic hormone and hypoglycemic hormone
(ii) Hypercalcemic hormone
(iii) Gonadotrophic hormones
(iv) Progestational hormone
(v) Androgens and estrogens
[NCERT Ex. Q. 6, Page 251]

Ans. (i) Glucagon and Insulin
(ii) PTH
(iii) LH and FSH (Luteinising hormone and Follicle stimulating hormone.
(iv) Progesterone.
(v) Testosterone and estradiol

Q. 7. Which hormonal deficiency is responsible for the following?
(i) Diabetes mellitus (ii) Goitre (iii) Cretinism
[NCERT Ex. Q. 7, Page 251]

Ans. (i) Diabetes mellitus: It is caused due to the deficiency of hormone called insulin.
(ii) Goitre: It is caused due to deficiency of thyroxine hormone.
(iii) Cretinism: It is caused due to deficiency of thyroid hormone.

Q. 8. Briefly mention the mechanism of action of FSH.
[NCERT Ex. Q. 8, Page 251]

Ans. Mechanism of action of FSH:
(i) Follicle stimulating hormone (FSH), secreted by the pars distalis region of the anterior pituitary regulates the development, growth, and reproductive processes of the human body. In the ovary, FSH stimulates the growth and maturation of ovarian follicle. As the follicle grows and matures, it releases an inhibitory hormone known as inhibin that ends the process of FSH production.
(ii) Action of FSH: Follicle stimulating hormone produces its effect by binding to its specific receptors present on the ovarian cell membrane.
(iii) Binding of FSH hormone to its receptor leads to the formation of hormone receptor complex. The formation of this complex leads to biochemical changes in the ovarian follicle, present in the ovary. The ovarian follicles mature and release a mature ovum in the fallopian tube for fertilisation.

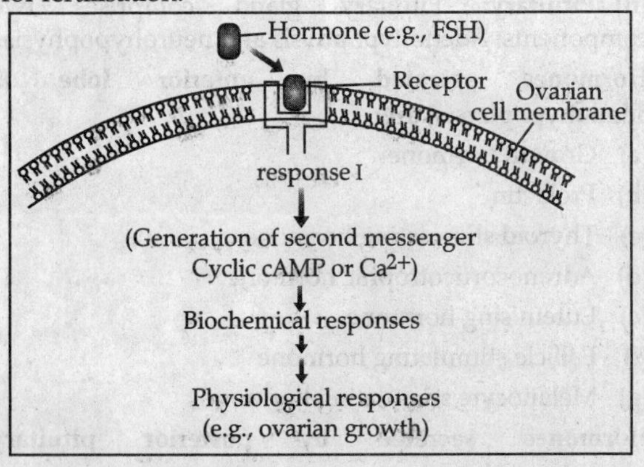

Q. 9. Match the following:

Column I	Column II
(i) T_4	(a) Hypothalamus
(ii) PTH	(b) Thyroid
(iii) GnRH	(c) Pituitary
(iv) LH	(d) Parathyroid

[NCERT Ex. Q. 9, Page 251]

Ans.

Column I	Column II
(i) T_4	(b) Thyroid
(ii) PTH	(d) Parathyroid
(iii) GnRH	(a) Hypothalamus
(iv) LH	(c) Pituitary

□□